Biology of Plants
Laboratory Exercises

Sixth Edition

Biology of Plants
Laboratory Exercises

Henry L. Dean

Robert W. Schuhmacher

Book Team

Editor
Kevin Kane
Developmental Editor
Mary J. Porter
Production Editor
Diane S. Clemens
Designer
Jeanne M. Rhomberg
Photo Research Editor
Carol M. Smith
Permissions Editor
Mavis M. Oeth
Product Manager
Matt Shaughnessy

wcb group

Wm. C. Brown
Chairman of the Board
Mark C. Falb
President and Chief Executive Officer

wcb

**Wm. C. Brown Publishers,
College Division**

G. Franklin Lewis
Executive Vice-President, General Manager

George Wm. Bergquist
Editor in Chief

John Stout
Executive Editor

Beverly Kolz
Director of Production

Chris C. Guzzardo
Vice-President, Director of Sales and Marketing

Bob McLaughlin
National Sales Manager

Julie A. Kennedy
Production Editorial Manager

Marilyn A. Phelps
Manager of Design

Faye M. Schilling
Photo Research Manager

Cover photograph © Pete Krumhardt

Copyright © 1987 by Wm. C. Brown Publishers.
All rights reserved

ISBN 0-697-00644-1

Printed in the United States of America
10 9 8 7 6 5 4 3

Contents

Appendixes

Keys

This laboratory manual is intended for use in basic college botany courses that emphasize the organized study of living plants. It may be used unchanged in a wide variety of teaching situations and may be easily adapted to particular academic schedules by rearranging, combining, or omitting certain exercises. This manual is designed for use by students who have had little or no formal training in botany and for courses that carry no prerequisite.

This manual begins with three exercises that concern (1) the plant as a whole, (2) modifications and identification of common (tree) leaves, and (3) photographs and diagrams of modern microscopes now used in botanical laboratories. The exercises proceed to a detailed (often microscopic) study of plant parts beginning with the plant cell and continuing with leaves, stems, roots, flowers, fruits, seeds, seedlings, and then to some introductory embryology.

The cell division study has been moved to follow the plant cell exercise since these topics are often linked in textbooks and frequently studied together. A study of meiosis, as it is seen in the generation of microspores in the anther, has been included with cell division but has been cross referenced to the exercise on the flower, for those who would rather study it at that time. Each exercise is designed to be a complete, independent investigation so that it may be used at the place in a course where it best satisfies local needs.

Five exercises are devoted entirely to plant physiology. This beginning study concerns the flowering seed plants (monocots and dicots), which are the most economically important, common, widespread, and are the best known. Exercises in the second half of this manual treat (in phylogenetic order) bacteria, algae, fungi, lichens, bryophytes, lower vascular plants, ferns, and gymnosperms. This manual concludes with one exercise on plant ecology and a new exercise on Mendelian inheritance.

Five appendixes are included at the end of this manual to provide the instructor with information on various procedures and sources of laboratory materials. A glossary and complete index are also provided.

Each exercise begins with a simplified listing of the plant materials, equipment, and reagents needed for that particular exercise. These supplies are commonly available in most college and university storerooms. Almost every exercise is accompanied by one or more illustrations. Five new photos have been added and four figures,

in three worksheets, have been modified for clarity and accuracy. Fourteen worksheets have a total of fifty-two new individual figures and fourteen new figures have been added to the text. Drawings are completely labeled, except for those that are to be labeled by the student. Worksheets appear at the end of each exercise, along with study questions designed to aid the student.

In this edition, terminology and nomenclature have been updated throughout, and the five-kingdom system of classification is now used. Many diagrams were shifted to worksheets so that students could demonstrate their ability to correlate their observations with the diagrams by labeling the appropriate structures. Exercises 36 and 37 have been combined (now exercise 36) and rewritten, with genetics problems added. New materials to clarify life cycles have also been added to the appropriate exercises. Mitosis and meiosis have been combined into a single exercise. Also, the glossary has been expanded.

The exercise on plant ecology is especially timely in view of the many environmental-impact studies prepared for projected construction and conservation projects. This exercise provides basic work on conventional plant ecology, suggested material for many class projects, and specific readings and proposed topics for classroom seminars covering a wide range of subjects. This exercise can easily provide enough material for a teacher in practically any location to conduct several weeks' work on interesting and varied ecological subjects. Teachers may also introduce a statistical approach to this work, but the basic thrust of this exercise is toward living plants and animals in relation to their environment.

No particular textbook is recommended for use with this manual. However, a table is provided at the beginning of the manual that correlates specific pages and chapters of seven popular textbooks with each of the exercises. Although prepared originally for use with the lecture-laboratory type of instruction, this manual has been employed successfully with a variety of teaching methods. One method is to employ this manual as a central "core" of tested laboratory procedures around which imaginative instructors can build a variety of their own individualized laboratory programs.

The use of living plants in the laboratory is recommended throughout, except when prepared slides are used or preserved materials are needed because living plants are out of season or otherwise unavailable (algae, fungi, ferns, and all living leaves are not easily accessible to everyone). All plants used are common, well-known forms that are easily obtained. No rare, exotic, or hard-to-find forms are included.

Teachers may wish to augment this manual with spring and fall field trips, photographic displays, motion pictures (especially time-lapse), in-depth discussions, classroom seminars, use of overhead projectors, 35 mm slides, video and audio tapes, library or other literature reports, and any other activity that capitalizes on the outstanding botanical features of their own community. The use of local floras during spring and fall terms is strongly recommended, especially in view of the need to know plant names in connection with modern ecological developments. Other useful supplements may be found in the growing number of ready-made laboratory kits or modules (see appendix E).

The authors are grateful to, and wish to thank, those users of previous editions and other persons who were kind enough to make practical suggestions for improving the present edition. Reviewers offering suggestions and criticisms for up-dating and improving this edition include: Edward Cawley, Loras College; William R. Gordon, Howard University; James E. Marler, Louisiana State University–Alexandria; Harvey A. Miller, University of Central Florida–Orlando; Muriel E. Poston, Howard University; and Janet Winstead, James Madison University. Numerous changes, omissions, and additions have been made following these suggestions. We sincerely thank Joan Cox and Dr. Nancy Brotzman for their work on the original drawings and diagrams in this manual. Many of the new drawings in this edition were prepared by R. W. Schuhmacher. It is also a pleasure to express our appreciation for the many courtesies of the personnel and the excellent publishing craftsmanship of Wm. C. Brown Company, Publishers, especially Mary Porter, whose patience and encouragement sparked this revision and Diane Clemens who guided its production. Comments and suggestions for future editions will be gratefully received.

H. L. Dean
R. W. Schuhmacher

General Directions
for Laboratory Work

1. *Equipment* to be purchased by the student:
   a. This laboratory manual
   b. 3H drawing pencil
   c. Drawing paper and notepaper
   d. Six-inch millimeter ruler
   e. Beveled-edge eraser, not art gum
   f. Single-edged razor blades
   g. Scalpel (useful but not required)
   h. Box of colored pencils, not wax crayons
   i. Forceps with fine curved points (useful but not required)
   j. Small, lint-free hand towels or similar polishing cloths
2. *Equipment* furnished by the department:
   a. Compound microscope
   b. Slides and cover glasses
   c. Two dissecting (teasing) needles
   d. One Syracuse watch glass
   e. One medicine dropper
   f. An envelope containing lens paper and filter paper
   g. A small hand lens
   h. Assorted glassware
   i. Glass and rubber tubing
   j. Chemicals and reagents
   k. Various special equipment
3. *Laboratory Study*
   The laboratory provides an opportunity to study plants at close range and examine the various structures, processes, and relationships that are characteristic of plant life. Whenever possible, living plants will be supplied for study. Laboratory study will not be confined strictly to indoor work; field trips and the observation of plants in their natural environment will be included. Botany may be studied anywhere that plants are found, and the concept of a laboratory should be expanded to include this broader viewpoint. Critically observe all plants and plant parts supplied for study. Personal observations should provide the answers to most questions that arise concerning the material. Learn to think independently. The laboratory instructor will offer helpful suggestions but will not be regarded as a source of ready answers to all questions. The entire laboratory program is designed so that a student can spend a minimum of time in recording observations, therefore having more time to study the plant itself. Students are required to perform all assigned laboratory work in the laboratory or in the field.

Do not interfere with the work of others. Work *independently,* except when cooperation with classmates is suggested. Careful study, observations, comparisons, and measurements should always precede the making of notes or work with drawings.

A written answer is not ordinarily required in the exercises in which questions are asked concerning material under observation. These questions are inserted to point out certain particulars and will usually be answered by a study of the material at hand. In most instances, it will be sufficient to have the question answered clearly in your own mind.

Students are required to fill in the tables or worksheets and add labels when necessary to the drawings accompanying the exercises.

Emphasis in the laboratory is placed on knowledge of the plant itself, not on study of the drawings. A reliable means of measuring a student's firsthand knowledge of plants is necessary for this program. Consequently, most laboratory examinations will be of a direct, practical nature.

Introduction

Botany: A Biological Science

Biologists study living organisms; botanists study plants. It was logical, when schemes of classification were being developed, that the largest and most encompassing category be called a kingdom. All living things were grouped either within the animal kingdom or within the plant kingdom. If the subject of study was mobile and ate another organism it was an animal and if it did not move or eat it must therefore be a plant—a plant was anything that was not an animal.

As long as external form and gross internal anatomy were the major criteria of classification, this grouping held up rather well. During this century, however, the means for comparing and examining organisms have improved tremendously. Better light microscopes, electron microscopes, and biochemical techniques that tell us the molecular and genetic structure of cells have provided information that has fundamentally altered our concepts of the basic types of life on our earth.

The light microscope enabled the discovery of hundreds of species of unicellular organisms, some of which had characteristics of both plants and animals. While botanists lumped these simple organisms into a category called Cellulares within the plant kingdom, zoologists (Hogg and Haeckel 1860) proposed a third kingdom, Protista, that would include algae, fungi, and sponges. Careful study of cell structure brought forth the proposal that all procaryotic (cells without nuclei) organisms be placed in the Kingdom Monera (Copeland 1938). Examination of differences in nutrition, and of unicellular versus tissue level of organization, led to the proposal of the five kingdom system (R. H. Whittaker 1969). In it all multicellular organisms belong to one of three kingdoms based on the mode of nutrition. **Animalia** are motile and ingest solid food. **Fungi** are nonmotile and absorb food in solution. **Plantae** are nonmotile and carry out photosynthesis. By these criteria vascular plants, bryophytes, and multicellular algae (reds, greens, and browns) are plants. Unicellular eukaryotes (golden, fire, and euglenoid algae and protozoa) remain in the **Protista**. The bacteria and the blue-green algae also remain in the **Monera.**

Some biologists (L. Margulis, P. Raven) have moved the multicellular algae out of the plant kingdom and placed them with the unicellular protists in an alternative five-kingdom classification. Recent biochemical studies in procaryotes have shown that there are significant differences in ribosomal RNA, cell wall, and lipid membrane composition that justify separating Monera into **Eubacteria** and **Archaebacteria.** It has already been proposed that the Archaebacteria be placed in a separate kingdom. For the present, the five-kingdom view of the world seems to reflect natural relationships and provides a convenient framework for a study of life.

By modern standards, a botanist studies more than what are classified as plants today. Inheriting the traditions of the two-kingdom view, a botanist still studies all living organisms that are not animals; but it is the green vascular plant, which dominates the land areas of the world, that is the prime focus of a botanist's study. Fossil evidence indicates that life has existed on earth for over three billion years and of all the more than two billion species of organisms now living on this planet, [none] could live for long without the photosynthetic ability of the plants. Some of the following characteristics identify an organism as a vascular plant:

1. Photosynthesis: ability to manufacture food (glucose) from raw materials (CO_2 and H_2O).
2. Chlorophyll (green pigment).
3. Thick, rigid, cellulose cell walls that may be impregnated with lignin, suberin, etc.
4. Ability for continued indeterminate growth. Growth in length by apical meristems in stem and root tips; in thickness, by vascular cambium.
5. Life span indefinite (bristlecone pine 4,600 years old). Death usually due to external causes.
6. Synthesizes amino acids. Synthesizes vitamins or their precursors. Manufactures and stores starch.
7. Mechanical support furnished largely by woody tissues (xylem). High turgor of cells prevents wilting in herbaceous plant.
8. No locomotion: remains fixed in one spot throughout life.
9. Usually responds slowly to stimuli; no definite nervous system.
10. Simple circulatory system; no pumping heart.
11. No specialized systems for digestion, respiration, and excretion. Slow rate of respiration.
12. Typical parts are roots, stems, leaves, flowers, fruits, seeds, etc.
13. Vegetative reproduction common.
14. Woody plant consists largely of dead cells: wood (xylem), cork, fibers, etc.

Correlation Chart for Use with Textbooks

Biology of Plants: Laboratory Exercises Dean/ Schuhmacher wcb (1987)	The Botanical World Northington/ Goodin Times/Mosby (1984)	Botany: An Introduction to Plant Biology Nadakavukaren/ McCracken West (1985)	Biology of Plants, 4th ed. Raven/Evert/ Curtis Worth (1986)	Botany Ray/Steeves Saunders (1983)	Botany: A Brief Introduction to Plant Biology, 2nd ed. Rost, et al Wiley (1984)	Botany: An Introduction to Plant Biology, 6th ed. Weiring/ Stocking/ Barbour Wiley (1982)	Botany, 2nd ed. Jensen/ Salisbury Wadsworth (1984)
Exercise 1 The Plant as a Whole	Chapter 4 Pages 89–109	Chapter 1 Pages 4–8	Chapter 1 Pages 5–7	Chapter 3 Pages 33–43	Chapter 4 Pages 43–45	Chapter 3 Pages 27–30	
Exercise 2 Modifications of Leaves	Chapter 4 Pages 103–9	Chapter 8 Pages 143–52	Chapter 22 Pages 423–25	Chapter 3 Pages 45–47	Chapter 5 Pages 67–69, 74–75	Chapter 10 Pages 179–82, 191–98	Chapter 12 Pages 215–25
Exercise 3 The Compound Microscope							
Exercise 4 The Living Plant Cell	Chapter 6 Pages 171–86	Chapter 2 Pages 9–33	Chapter 2 Pages 13–36	Chapter 4 Pages 57–76	Chapter 3 Pages 19–33	Chapter 4 Pages 33–58	Chapter 3 Pages 42–52
Exercise 5 Cell Division: Mitosis Meiosis	Chapter 7 Pages 200–206	Chapter 4 Pages 61–73	Chapter 2 Pages 36–44	Chapter 4 Pages 76–80 Chapter 16 Page 273	Chapter 3 Pages 34–41	Chapter 6 Pages 93–101	Chapter 7 Pages 114–30
Exercise 6 The Microscopic Structure of Leaves	Chapter 7 Pages 214, 218–20	Chapter 8 Pages 152–64	Chapter 22 Pages 425–37	Chapter 8 Pages 135–43	Chapter 5 Pages 69–74	Chapter 10 Pages 183–91	Chapter 12 Pages 218–25
Exercise 7 The Formation of Food in Leaves: Starch	Chapter 10 Pages 302–15	Chapter 9 Pages 167–84	Chapter 7 Pages 95–112	Chapter 7 Pages 119–33	Chapter 8 Pages 103–11	Chapter 13 Pages 233–52	Chapter 5 Pages 74–95
Exercise 8 Respiration	Chapter 10 Pages 319–30	Chapter 10 Pages 187–201	Chapter 6 Pages 82–94	Chapter 6 Pages 103–17	Chapter 2 Pages 3–17	Chapter 14 Pages 255–67	Chapter 6 Pages 97–112
Exercise 9 Transpiration	Chapter 9 Pages 280–85	Chapter 11 Page 213	Chapter 27 Pages 541–58	Chapter 1 Pages 13–14 Chapter 9 Pages 147–58	Chapter 7 Pages 89–102	Chapter 12 Pages 215–24	Chapter 15 Pages 269–89
Exercise 10 Features of Herbaceous Stems	Chapter 4 Pages 95–103 Chapter 7 Page 216	Chapter 6 Pages 91–100	Chapter 22 Pages 413–23	Chapter 10 Pages 161–63 Chapter 12 Pages 197–204	Chapter 4 Pages 43–53	Chapter 7 Pages 132–34	Chapter 12 Pages 201–14
Exercise 11 Features of Woody Dicotyledonous Stems	Chapter 8 Pages 227–40	Chapter 6 Pages 100–103	Chapter 23 Pages 446–70	Chapter 13 Pages 219–25	Chapter 4 Pages 54–60	Chapter 7 Pages 112–32 Chapter 8 Pages 137–56	Chapter 13 Pages 226–42
Exercise 12 Structure of Coniferous Wood: Pine	Chapter 8 Pages 232–37	Chapter 6 Pages 106–7	Chapter 23 Pages 459–61	Chapter 13 Pages 225–29	Chapter 19 Page 308	Chapter 8 Pages 142–43	Chapter 13 Pages 238–40
Exercise 13 Structure of Angiosperm (Dicot) Wood	Chapter 8 Pages 221–31	Chapter 6 Pages 104–6	Chapter 23 Pages 463–70	Chapter 13 Pages 225–34	Chapter 4 Pages 55–58	Chapter 8 Pages 137–56	Chapter 13 Pages 240–42
Exercise 14 Monocotyledonous Stems	Chapter 7 Page 217	Chapter 6 Page 95	Chapter 22 Pages 418–21	Chapter 10 Pages 161–62 Chapter 13 Pages 234–36	Chapter 4 Pages 61–63	Chapter 7 Pages 132–34	Chapter 12
Exercise 15 Modified Stems	Chapter 4 Pages 98–102	Chapter 6 Pages 107–10	Chapter 22 Pages 443–44 Chapter 28 Page 570	Chapter 3 Pages 46–50	Chapter 4 Pages 63–65	Chapter 8 Pages 152–54	Chapter 12 Pages 210–15
Exercise 16 Roots of Plants	Chapter 4 Pages 89–95 Chapter 7 Page 217	Chapter 7 Pages 117–41	Chapter 21 Pages 400–12	Chapter 11 Pages 179–82 Chapter 12 Pages 204–7	Chapter 6 Pages 79–88	Chapter 9 Pages 159–75	Chapter 11 Pages 186–200

Correlation Chart for Use with Textbooks *Continued*

Biology of Plants: Laboratory Exercises Dean/ Schuhmacher wcb (1987)	The Botanical World Northington/ Goodin Times/Mosby (1984)	Botany: An Introduction to Plant Biology Nadakavukaren/ McCracken West (1985)	Biology of Plants, 4th ed. Raven/Evert/ Curtis Worth (1986)	Botany Ray/Steeves Saunders (1983)	Botany: A Brief Introduction to Plant Biology, 2nd ed. Rost, et al Wiley (1984)	Botany: An Introduction to Plant Biology, 6th ed. Weiring/ Stocking/ Barbour Wiley (1982)	Botany, 2nd ed. Jensen/ Salisbury Wadsworth (1984)
Exercise 17 Diffusion and Osmosis	Chapter 9 Pages 272–79	Chapter 11 Pages 205–8	Chapter 4 Pages 58–67	Chapter 9 Pages 143–45 Chapter 11 Pages 187–89	Chapter 7 Pages 89–94	Chapter 5 Pages 74–78	Chapter 4 Pages 60–73
Exercise 18 Growth Movements	Chapter 11 Pages 356–62	Chapter 12 Pages 222–42	Chapter 25 Pages 493–512	Chapter 12 Pages 206–16 Chapter 14 Pages 239–56	Chapter 9 Pages 114–29	Chapter 20 Pages 394–417	Chapters 16, 17 Pages 291–346
Exercise 19 The Flower	Chapter 5 Pages 117–27	Chapter 20 Pages 401–20	Chapter 18 Pages 353–69 Chapter 22 Pages 437–40 Chapter 29 Pages 590–611	Chapter 16 Pages 271–90 Chapter 31 Pages 617–27	Chapter 12 Pages 173–88	Chapter 15 Pages 269–300 Chapter 30 Pages 623–41	Chapter 27 Pages 529–61
Exercise 20 Fruits and Seeds	Chapter 5 Pages 128–36	Chapter 21 Pages 427–33	Chapter 29 Pages 611–16	Chapter 17 Pages 297–303	Chapter 13 Pages 195–204 Chapter 20 Pages 319–42	Chapter 16 Pages 303–21	Chapter 27 Pages 529–61
Exercise 21 Seed Germination and Seedling Development	Chapter 5 Pages 137–44	Chapter 21 Pages 433–42	Chapter 19 Pages 373–83	Chapter 17 Pages 293–96, 303–9	Chapter 13 Pages 189–92	Chapter 16 Pages 321–25	
Exercise 22 The Procaryotes: Bacteria and Blue-Green Algae (Cyanophyta)	Chapter 14 Pages 440–42, 446–54	Chapter 15 Pages 284–98	Chapter 11 Pages 165–85	Chapter 22 Pages 401–23 Chapter 25 Pages 493–99	Chapter 16 Page 253	Chapter 21 Pages 420–38	Chapter 20 Pages 393–413
Exercise 23 Green Algae (Chlorophyta)	Chapter 15 Pages 476–81	Chapter 17 Pages 324–41	Chapter 15 Pages 263–78	Chapter 23 Pages 425–46	Chapter 16 Pages 253–55, 258–60	Chapter 23 Pages 477–82	Chapter 23 Pages 467–76
Exercise 24 Plankton: Diatoms and Dinoflagellates	Chapter 15 Pages 456–58	Chapter 17 Pages 341–45	Chapter 14 Pages 241–50	Chapter 23 Pages 447–51	Chapter 16 Pages 239–55	Chapter 23 Pages 461–63	Chapter 21 Pages 414–32
Exercise 25 Brown Algae (Phaeophyta) and Red Algae (Rhodophyta)	Chapter 15 Pages 481–83	Chapter 17 Pages 345–49	Chapter 15 Pages 251–62	Chapter 23 Pages 451–57	Chapter 16 Pages 253–66	Chapter 23 Pages 475–77, 471–73	Chapter 23 Pages 458–67
Exercise 26 Slime Molds (Myxomycota)	Chapter 15 Pages 475–76	Chapter 16 Pages 302–6	Chapter 14 Pages 239–40	Chapter 24 Pages 478–80	Chapter 15 Pages 220–21	Chapter 25 Pages 500–502	Chapter 21 Pages 426–31
Exercise 27 The Lower Fungi (Algalike Fungi)	Chapter 15 Pages 459–63	Chapter 16 Pages 306–9	Chapter 14 Pages 231–36 Chapter 13 Pages 239–40	Chapter 24 Pages 462–65	Chapter 15 Pages 221–26	Chapter 25 Pages 499–508	Chapter 22 Pages 433–43
Exercise 28 Ascus-bearing Fungi (Ascomycota)	Chapter 15 Pages 463–66	Chapter 16 Pages 308–10	Chapter 13 Pages 203–11	Chapter 24 Pages 466–72	Chapter 15 Pages 226–31	Chapter 26 Pages 515–25	Chapter 22 Pages 443–46
Exercise 29 Lichens	Chapter 15 Pages 474–75	Chapter 16 Pages 317–19	Chapter 13 Pages 211–15	Chapter 25 Pages 483–89	Chapter 15 Pages 237–38	Chapter 26 Pages 544–47	Chapter 22 Pages 455–56
Exercise 30 Basidium – bearing Fungi (Basidiomycota)	Chapter 15 Pages 466–71	Chapter 16 Pages 310–16	Chapter 13 Pages 215–27	Chapter 24 Pages 472–78 Chapter 26 Pages 515–17	Chapter 15 Pages 231–36	Chapter 26 Pages 526–38	Chapter 22 Pages 446–54

Correlation Chart for Use with Textbooks *Continued*

Biology of Plants: Laboratory Exercises Dean/ Schuhmacher wcb (1987)	The Botanical World Northington/ Goodin Times/Mosby (1984)	Botany: An Introduction to Plant Biology Nadakavukaren/ McCracken West (1985)	Biology of Plants, 4th ed. Raven/Evert/ Curtis Worth (1986)	Botany Ray/Steeves Saunders (1983)	Botany: A Brief Introduction to Plant Biology, 2nd ed. Rost, et al Wiley (1984)	Botany: An Introduction to Plant Biology, 6th ed. Weiring/ Stocking/ Barbour Wiley (1982)	Botany, 2nd ed. Jensen/ Salisbury Wadsworth (1984)
Exercise 31 Liverworts and Mosses (Bryophyta)	Chapter 15 Pages 483–88	Chapter 18 Pages 352–62	Chapter 16 Pages 280–99	Chapter 27 Pages 529–45	Chapter 17 Pages 267–80	Chapter 27 Pages 551–70	Chapter 24 Pages 493–500
Exercise 32 Club Mosses and Horsetails	Chapter 16 Pages 495–503	Chapter 18 Pages 362–68	Chapter 17 Pages 300–320	Chapter 28 Pages 547–73	Chapter 18 Pages 281–94	Chapter 28 Pages 573–84	Chapter 25 Pages 501–8
Exercise 33 Ferns (Pteridophyta)	Chapter 16 Pages 503–7	Chapter 18 Pages 369–78	Chapter 17 Pages 321–30	Chapter 29 Pages 575–91	Chapter 18 Pages 295–301	Chapter 28 Pages 584–93	Chapter 25 Pages 508–17
Exercise 34 The Pine and Other Gymniosperms	Chapter 16 Pages 508–20	Chapter 19 Pages 382–99	Chapter 18 Pages 332–53	Chapter 30 Pages 593–613	Chapter 19 Pages 303–18	Chapter 29 Pages 599–612	Chapter 26 Pages 518–81
Exercise 35 Plant Ecology	Chapter 2 Pages 517–88	Chapter 24 Pages 487–508	Chapters 31, 32 Pages 651–96	Chapters 33, 34 Pages 665–707 Chapter 19 Pages 333–57	Chapter 10 Pages 131–53	Chapter 18 Pages 347–71	Chapters 29–31 Pages 599–684
Exercise 36 Inheritance in Plants	Chapter 7 Pages 187–200	Chapter 13 Pages 250–66 Chapter 22 Pages 44–61	Chapters 8, 9 Pages 115–47	Chapter 18 Pages 311–31	Chapter 11 Pages 155–71	Chapter 17 Pages 327–43	Chapters 8, 9 Pages 131–61

The Plant as a Whole

Plant Materials

The materials needed for this exercise are dwarf (bush) bean, buckwheat, corn about 20 inches tall, monocot flowers as available (see p. 3). Alternate or optional plants include dodder, Spanish moss, duckweed, prickly pear, bluegrass (with roots), grape, knotweed, *Pelargonium, Zebrina,* morning glory, asparagus, carrot, dandelion, mullein, and insectivorous plants. Also needed are leaf skeletons.

Equipment

A hand lens 10x, and a metric ruler are needed.

Introduction

Seed plants dominate the modern landscape. They include not only the cone-bearing trees such as the pines, firs, spruces, and *Sequoia* but also the everpresent, fruit-bearing, flowering plants, which are the best known, the most common, the most diversified, and the most numerous of seed plants. They are widely distributed throughout the world and are the plants humans depend upon for food, many building and industrial materials, fibers, fuel, and drugs. Although flowering plants were first classified according to their growth form as trees (woody stems) or as herbs (no woody stems) or according to their use as sources of food, medicine, fiber, or decoration, by the 1700s they were classified by the characteristics of their fruits and seeds. The flowering plants were divided into the Dicots and the Monocots. Each seed contains an embryo plant that has at least one specialized leaf, or cotyledon, modified for food storage or absorption. The number of seed leaves is a reliable characteristic in distinguishing one plant from another, but since it is within the seed and not readily visible, other characteristics are used as well.

1. The Dicotyledoneae (dicots) are characterized by having two cotyledons (seed leaves) on the embryo, flower parts mostly in fours or fives, a cambium with the vascular bundles forming a circle around the central pith, both woody and herbaceous forms, and leaves mostly with net veins. The Dicots are a much larger group than the Monocots, and common examples include most trees and shrubs, beans, potatoes, snapdragons, lilacs, flax, chrysanthemums, tobacco, sunflowers, daisies, and many others.

2. The Monocotyledoneae (monocots) are characterized by having one cotyledon on the embryo, flower parts mostly in threes, no cambium, and the vascular bundles are mostly scattered throughout the stem (in the pith or ground tissue). Practically all are herbaceous forms with leaves, mostly parallel veined. Common examples include corn, bamboo and all other grasses, sedges, rushes, cattails, iris, lilies, orchids, *Tradescantia,* and many others.

The Plant as a Whole

Examine a mature, living buckwheat (fig. 1.1) or alternate plant grown singly in a small (7.6–10.3 cm) flowerpot.

A typical seed plant (either dicot or monocot) is composed of a number of interrelated parts, each having different structures and functions but each part contributing to the unity of the plant as a whole.

The principal parts of a seed plant are leaves, stems, roots, flowers, fruits, and seeds. The leaf, stem, and root are vegetative parts (nonfruiting) concerned with the growth, nutrition, and development of a plant and are called organs because each is composed of one or more tissues such as epidermis, cortex, xylem, and phloem. Flowers, fruits, and seeds are concerned with reproduction (seed formation) and are composed of one or more different organs such as petals, pistils, anthers, and ovules.

The Leaf

A complete leaf consists of a broad flattened *blade* (lamina), a slender stalk (*petiole*), and a pair of leaflike (usually) *stipules* at the junction of the petiole with the stem. Stipules are typically expanded leaflike structures (see fig. 2.1B), but with buckwheat (fig. 1.1) they are membranous and form a sheath (*ocrea*) around the stem at the node. Ocreae are characteristic of the Polygonaceae, the buckwheat family of plants. Some leaves do not have stipules. Typical stipules and their modifications will be studied later.

An axillary bud occurs at the junction of the petiole and the stem (in the leaf axil, see fig. 2.1A). Everything from the axillary bud outward is called a leaf regardless of its shape, size, lobing, or division into separate leaflets as in compound leaves.

Figure 1.1 A typical seed plant, buckwheat (*Fagopyrum esculentum*)

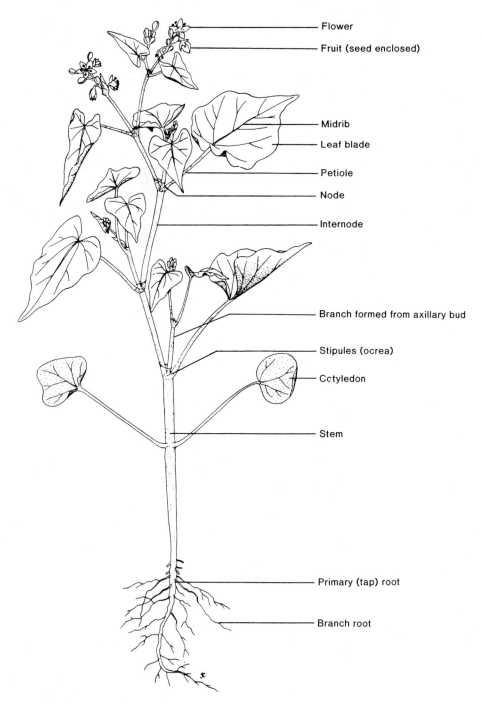

Flower
Fruit (seed enclosed)
Midrib
Leaf blade
Petiole
Node
Internode
Branch formed from axillary bud
Stipules (ocrea)
Cotyledon
Stem
Primary (tap) root
Branch root

Note the veins in the blade of the leaf. What is the general arrangement of the larger (major) veins? Are both surfaces of the leaf alike? A central midrib passes longitudinally through the leaf blade from the petiole junction to the leaf tip. Major veins extend laterally from each side of a midrib to the leaf margin and a fine network of smaller minor veins occurs in the tissues between major veins. Small areas ("islands") of green leaf tissue enclosed by minor veins are vein islets.

The distance from a minor vein ending in a vein islet to the nearest vein, or from a minor vein across a vein islet to another minor vein, is the intervascular interval of a leaf. Veins are the vascular (supporting and conducting) tissues of a leaf.

The color of the leaf is due to the green pigment, *chlorophyll,* contained in tiny corpuscular bodies, the *chloroplasts.* Chlorophyll and chloroplasts will be studied later.

With a hand lens (see p. 4 and fig. 1.2) examine mounted leaf skeletons of elm and other leaves. Note the pattern of *minor veins,* the area of *vein islets,* and the *intervascular intervals.* Compare a leaf skeleton with a living green leaf. Review functions of the major and minor veins.

Leaf skeletons may be obtained from novelty or department stores, floral display counters, and decorator supply houses under the trade name of Angel Feathers. For methods of making leaf skeletons by chemical action, see *Turtox News* 11:41–42, 1933; by bacterial action, the *American Journal of Botany* 35:719–22, 1948.

The Stem

Note the regions of the stem to which the leaves are attached. These prominent joints from which the leaves arise are the *nodes.* The stem length between any two nodes is the *internode.* How many nodes and internodes are there on one plant? Are the internodes of uniform length? Note color, length, and thickness of the stem. Look down on the plant from the top. Are the leaves arranged in a definite pattern? Are they opposite or do they alternate with each other? Does the stem branch? If so, at what points do branches occur? Is the stem straight or zigzag in appearance?

The pair of rounded, fleshy, leaflike structures attached by long slender petioles to the lower part of the stem are the *cotyledons.* Do the cotyledons persist? What value are they to the plant? Is buckwheat a dicotyledon? Internal structures will be studied in detail in later labs. The permanent tissues are produced by continually embryonic regions called meristems. If you cut the stem with a razor blade and examine it with the hand lens you will see the vascular bundles.

A vascular bundle is composed of xylem (conducts water upward and provides mechanical support) and phloem (conducts food materials downward). A cambium layer may lie between the xylem and phloem. Terminal meristems (apical meristems) are found at the stem apex (stem tip) and root apex (root tip). Division of cells in these three regions enable a plant to grow in length and increase in thickness.

Conducting tissues of a vascular bundle provide a continuous channel from root tip to stem tip; and water, an essential raw material of photosynthesis, moves upward through the xylem to the leaves. The second essential raw material, carbon dioxide, diffuses into leaves from the atmosphere.

The Root

Remove the plant from the soil, taking care not to break the roots. What is the extent of the root system? How much of the plant is underground? Is there a central tap (primary) root? Are there secondary roots, tertiary roots? Is there any regularity in the branching of the smaller roots?

Flower, Fruit, and Seed

Flowers and fruits are often present on the same plant. The buckwheat fruit is a three-sided, hard-walled, single-seeded fruit called an **achene.** The food-storage tissue around the embryo in the seed, the **endosperm,** is starchy.

Buckwheat is an *annual* plant, one which completes its growth, produces seeds, and dies within one growing season. A *biennial* requires two seasons to complete this cycle. A *perennial* plant is one that continues to live and grow for an indefinite number of years.

Many seed plants grow larger, live longer, and are different in other respects from buckwheat; nevertheless, in its general features buckwheat may be considered as typical for the seed plants as a group.

Referring to the previous description of terms, study the labelled drawing (fig. 1.1) of a buckwheat plant.

A. A Typical Dicotyledonous Seed Plant: Dwarf (Bush) Bean *(Phaseolus vulgaris)*

Examine a living dwarf (bush) bean plant 50 to 60 days old, grown in a 7.6–10.3-cm pot. Although the bean has the same number and kind of interrelated parts as the buckwheat, it nevertheless differs in a number of significant ways. For example, in the bean: (1) the lower leaves on the stem (not cotyledons) are simple, cordate, and are oppositely placed; (2) all other and higher leaves are alternate and compound with three leaflets each; (3) the small green stipules are short, pointed, sessile, and recurved; (4) the fruit is a pod (legume) containing several seeds; (5) the flower (usually not present on a 50-day-old plant) is characteristic of the pea family (Leguminosae); and (6) each leaflet of the compound leaves has reduced stipules and a pulvinus at its base.

Study the bean plant carefully, noting any other observable differences or similarities between it and buckwheat. Compare with figure 1.1, or, better still, the living buckwheat plant itself.

Make an accurate sketch of the bean plant similar in size and style to the drawing of a buckwheat plant (fig. 1.1). Label all parts.

B. Typical Monocotyledonous Seed Plants

Examine a corn (*Zea mays*) plant 20 inches (50.8 cm) tall (or a mature grass plant) that has been carefully removed from the soil and the roots washed free from soil particles.

The Leaf

The leaf is long and relatively narrow with a strong flexible midrib. It has major veins paralleling the midrib and tapers to a sharp point. A clasping leaf base or sheath encloses the stem for some distance downward and arises from a hard swollen node. The leaves are alternate.

The Roots

The many roots are long, cylindrical, and practically the same diameter throughout. They form a fibrous (diffuse) root system.

Flower, Fruit, and Seed

Typical monocot flowers are easier to study in plants other than grasses. Use the larger flowers of *Zebrina, Tradescantia, Iris, Gladiolus,* Tulip, *Amaryllis, Crocus, Yucca, Narcissus,* Hyacinth, or others as available.

Examine a flower and determine the number of petals, sepals (may be the same color and texture as petals), stamens, and stigmas (may be three-parted). Cut a cross section of the ovary and determine the number of cavities it contains. Note the many small white ovules attached to the placental regions. The ovary ripens into a fruit; the ovules develop into seeds.

Special option: for the best example of a monocot flower and rapid growth, obtain a giant Dutch Amaryllis "bulb" and follow the enclosed directions for starting growth. Leaves and one or more flower stalks will emerge and grow rapidly to develop in five or six weeks into a cluster of large flowers.

Note: To obtain giant Dutch Amaryllis bulbs write Brecks, 6523 North Galena Road, Peoria, Illinois, 61632, or get them from better seed and garden catalogs or from an up-to-date local florist or commercial greenhouse. These bulbs usually must be ordered during the early fall months.

Make an accurate sketch of a monocot plant or its parts as directed by your instructor.

C. Alternate or Optional Plants

If time permits, a number of the following seed plants may be studied: dodder, Spanish moss, duckweed, prickly pear (or other cactus types), bluegrass, grape, morning glory, insectivorous plants, asparagus, carrot, dandelion, and mullein. Identify the principal organs of these plants. Are they always alike?

Tabulate any modifications found and illustrate with neat sketches.

D. Use of the Hand Lens

1. The lens, eye, and object to be examined must be brought into the correct working distances and then held rigidly in this relationship.
2. The object must be well lighted. Keep clear of shadows from hat brims, fingers, and other persons.
3. Grasp object with thumb and finger of one hand (unless obviously too large for this procedure), and the lens with thumb and finger of the other hand. Clench the other fingers to get them out of the way and place hands together in a manner similar to that shown in figure 1.2.

Figure 1.2 Use of hand lens

4. Raise hands so that base of thumb carrying the lens rests firmly against the cheekbone, bringing the lens about the same distance and position from the eye as with spectacles.
5. Focus by moving object toward or away from the lens. If the object examined is too large to focus in this manner, move the lens toward or away from the object until sharp focus is obtained.

Reference

Headstrom, Richard. *Adventures with a Hand Lens.* New York: Dover Publications, 1976.

Questions

1. What are the principal parts of a typical seed plant?
2. Explain how each part appears structurally adapted for the function *(s)* it performs?
3. What is a node? an internode?
4. What are the functions of veins in a leaf?
5. How are leaf skeletons made in nature? in the laboratory?
6. What is the importance of the vein islets in a green leaf?
7. What is an annual plant? a biennial? a perennial?
8. What are the parts of a complete leaf?
9. What is a cotyledon?
10. State briefly how other seed plants studied differ from buckwheat.
11. Why are these highly modified forms still considered to be seed plants?
12. What is the economic importance of buckwheat? bean? corn?

2 Modifications of Leaves

Plant Materials

The student will need leaves of cottonwood, rose, maple, elm, horse chestnut, hickory, black locust, sweet pea, bean, *Smilax,* and *Catalpa,* as well as a whole *Mimosa* plant. Also needed are leaves for identification and comparison—consult the leaf key at the end of this exercise for the names of those leaves to be collected.

Introduction

To discuss plants intelligently, it is first necessary to know their proper names. Plants are known by scientific names throughout the world, and because these names are usually in Latin or Greek (languages that do not change), people of all nationalities know what plant is indicated when they read its scientific name. Plants are grouped into a series of well-defined categories, but for the present study it is necessary to know only that the scientific name of a plant consists essentially of two parts: the *genus* (generic name) and the *species* (specific name). All roses, for instance, belong to the genus *Rosa* (the ancient Latin name for rose), but each different kind or species of rose would, in addition, have a specific name setting it apart from all other roses. For example, the complete scientific name for the cinnamon rose would be *Rosa cinnamomea* L. The L refers to Linnaeus, a Swedish botanist of the eighteenth century who first applied the specific name *cinnamomea* to this particular rose. The science devoted to the systematic classification and naming of plants is called plant taxonomy.

Students usually know from their background of everyday knowledge that all plants are not alike and that the leaves of these plants differ from one another. Because each plant always bears the same kind of leaves, it is possible to identify many of them by means of their leaf characteristics alone. To do this successfully, students must learn fundamental facts about the different kinds of leaves, their parts, special structures, and some of the more commonly occurring modifications.

The purpose of this exercise is to demonstrate some of the typical features and modifications of leaves and to provide enough practical working knowledge to begin the identification of common trees by means of their leaf characteristics. The leaf key (p. 9) enables students to learn the generic name only.

A. Simple and Compound Leaves

Examine a cottonwood or similar type of leaf. This is a *simple leaf.* Where does it break naturally from the stem? When a leaf breaks from the stem naturally, the separation occurs at this place because of the formation of the abscission layer. Compare it with the leaf of a rose, locust, or box elder. This is a *compound leaf.* The units of a compound leaf are called *leaflets.* Does an abscission layer form where the stalk (petiolule) of each leaflet joins the *rachis* of a compound leaf? Describe the ways in which students can distinguish between simple and compound leaves. Study material provided; then, study the parts of the simple and compound leaves shown in figure 2.1. Label the parts of the leaf.

B. Palmate and Pinnate Arrangement

Note the arrangement of large veins in a maple leaf; in an elm leaf. The maple is *palmately* veined; the elm *pinnately* veined. The Gingko leaf is dichotomously veined and grasses have leaves with parallel veins. The vein patterns may also be expressed in the lobing of the leaf (maple and sycamore, palmately lobed) or in the arrangement of compound leaves (horse chestnut, palmately compound; hickory or locust, pinnately compound). See figures 2.2 and 2.3. Label the parts of the leaves in figure 2.2.

C. Surface

Hairy plant surfaces are described as *pubescent;* rough, sandpaperlike surfaces as *scabrous;* smooth, hairless surfaces as *glabrous.* There are numerous other precise terms descriptive of surface, but these will be sufficient for present purposes.

D. Special Structures

Examine leaves of peas or vetch. Note that the tips are modified into *tendrils.* Compare with the leaves of *Smilax* and black locust. The tendrils of *Smilax* leaves and the sharp spines at the petiole base of black locust leaves are modified stipules. Compare with the leaflike stipules of a rose leaf; a willow leaf. Examine the leaves of a beanplant, sensitive plant, or black locust and note the cylindrical, swollen structure at the base of the petiole. This is the

Figure 2.1 *A*, simple leaf: poplar; and *B*, compound leaf: rose

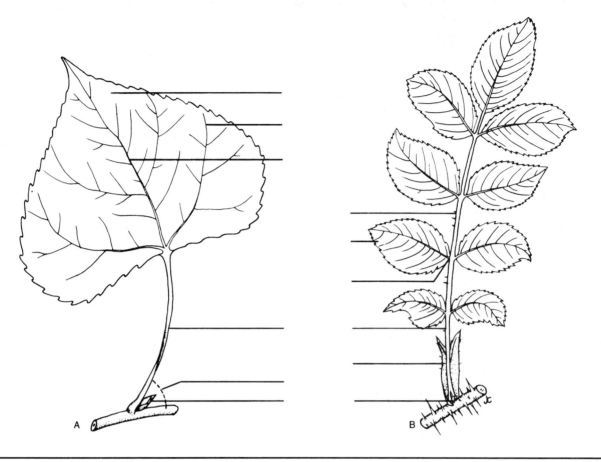

Figure 2.2 Vein patterns in simple leaves: *A*, oak; *B*, maple; *C*, gingko

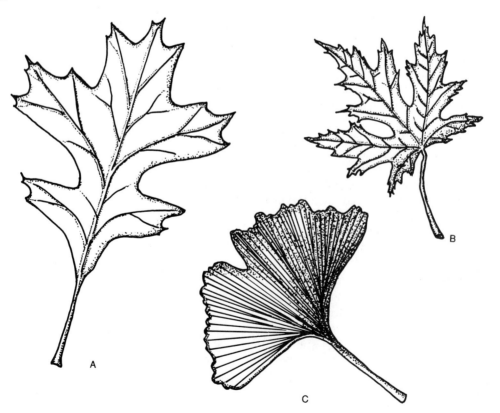

pulvinus (plural, *pulvini*) which causes the leaf to move, producing the "sleep movements" of leaflets, and even the drooping of entire leaves.

A leaf mosaic is formed when leaves move to arrange themselves so that a maximum amount of each leaf surface is exposed to the prevailing light, which gives the appearance of their being fitted together side-by-side in an orderly manner (resembling stones in a mosaic). Good examples are maple, beech, and Boston ivy. There are other special structures of leaves, but they will not be studied in this exercise.

E. Comparison of Leaf Types

Study a series of different leaves, referring to the preceding material and the accompanying page of drawings (fig. 2.3). Record neatly in worksheet 2.1 the following particulars: (1) name of plant; (2) simple or compound leaf (palmately or pinnately compound); (3) leaves alternate (spiral), opposite, or whorled; (4) general shape of leaf (of leaflets, if a leaf is compound); (5) shape of base; (6) shape of apex; (7) kind of margin; (8) type of venation; (9) stipules (present or absent; modifications); (10) surface; and (11) pulvinus (present or absent).

F. Identification of Trees by Their Leaves

Following the preceding outline for description, and using the accompanying leaf key (p. 9) or a local key for your area, determine the genera of the tree leaves furnished. Return all plant material in good condition to the proper pile on the supply tables. This leaf key may be used outdoors if conditions permit.

G. Field Work

A short field trip may be made to study trees in their natural habitat. For field use, take notes and make charts as suggested by the instructor. Hand these in before leaving the grounds.

H. Personal Observations

Observe the trees growing on the campus, city streets, parks, estates, lawns, and woodlots. How many trees can you identify? You should be able to recognize at sight the most common trees of your locality.

Questions

1. How can one distinguish between simple and compound leaves?
2. What are the parts of a compound leaf?
3. Suggest how a pinnately compound leaf might have evolved from a pinnately lobed leaf.
4. What are stipules?
5. In what way, if any, are stipules useful to the plant?
6. List modifications of stipules that occur in different leaves.
7. What is the difference between palmate and pinnate venation?
8. What is the position on the stem of leaves arranged alternately (spirally)? opposite? whorled?
9. What is a pulvinus? What is its function?
10. Explain the formation and function of the abscission layer. What does the word abscission mean?
11. At what time of the year does the abscission layer usually form?
12. Name and diagram the four common types of venation in leaves and give an example of a plant in which each type occurs.
13. What is plant taxonomy?

Figure 2.3 Leaf modifications

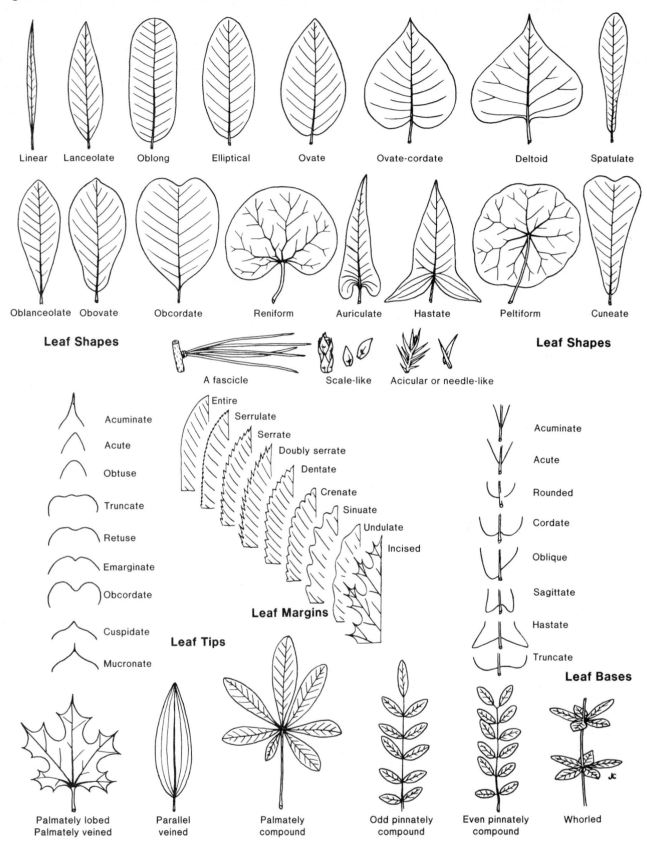

Linear   Lanceolate   Oblong   Elliptical   Ovate   Ovate-cordate   Deltoid   Spatulate

Oblanceolate   Obovate   Obcordate   Reniform   Auriculate   Hastate   Peltiform   Cuneate

Leaf Shapes

A fascicle   Scale-like   Acicular or needle-like

Leaf Shapes

Acuminate
Acute
Obtuse
Truncate
Retuse
Emarginate
Obcordate
Cuspidate
Mucronate

Leaf Tips

Entire
Serrulate
Serrate
Doubly serrate
Dentate
Crenate
Sinuate
Undulate
Incised

Leaf Margins

Acuminate
Acute
Rounded
Cordate
Oblique
Sagittate
Hastate
Truncate

Leaf Bases

Palmately lobed
Palmately veined

Parallel
veined

Palmately
compound

Odd pinnately
compound

Even pinnately
compound

Whorled

Leaf Key to the Genera of Common Trees

By Dr. H. D. Harrington

Note: Shrubs and cultivated forms are not included in this key.

1. Leaves needlelike, scalelike, or narrowly flattened, less than 3 mm wide **2**
   2. Leaves scalelike or narrowly triangular **3**
      3. Twigs flattened; fruit a small tan cone **Arbor Vitae (Thuja)**
      3. Twigs not flattened; fruit blue and berrylike **Red Cedar (Juniperus)**
   2. Leaves needlelike or narrow and flattened **4**
      4. Leaves solitary or in a group of five or less, rather stiff and some remaining on the twig in winter **5**
         5. Leaves solitary, not in groups **6**
            6. Leaves somewhat four-sided in cross section, not flattened **Spruce (Picea)**
            6. Leaves flattened **7**
               7. Leaves under 13 mm long; short stalked; a row of shorter leaves, whitened side up, usually present at top of twig **Hemlock (Tsuga)**
               7. Leaves over 13 mm long, not at all stalked, no such row of leaves present **Fir (Abies)**
         5. Leaves in groups of two to five **Pine (Pinus)**
      4. Leaves on older twigs, in tufts; many in a group, flexible and falling in winter **Larch, Tamarack (Larix)**
1. Leaves broad, more than 3 mm wide **8**
   8. Leaves opposite or whorled (cyclic) **9**
      9. Leaves simple **10**
         10. Leaves definitely lobed **Maple (Acer)**
         10. Leaves not lobed or rarely slightly so **11**
            11. Leaf edges toothed; two leaves at a node **Black Haw (Viburnum)**
            11. Leaf edges not toothed; usually over two leaves at a node (whorled) **Catalpa (Catalpa)**
      9. Leaves compound **12**
         12. Leaves pinnately compound **13**
            13. Petiole bases of opposite leaves almost meeting around the twig; leaves often somewhat lobed **Box Elder (Acer)**
            13. Petiole bases widely separate; leaflets never lobed **Ash (Fraxinus)**
         12. Leaves palmately compound **Buckeye, Horse Chestnut (Aesculus)**
   8. Leaves alternate (spiral) **14**
      14. Leaves simple **15**
15. Leaves shaped like an open folding fan, all veins small, dichotomously branching (fig. 2.2C) **Ginkgo (Ginkgo)**
15. Leaves not fan shaped, some of the veins larger **16**
   16. Leaf margins neither lobed nor toothed **17**
      17. Leaves bristle tipped; some of the leaves crowded out near end of twig **Shingle Oak (Quercus)**
      17. Leaves not bristle tipped; leaves not crowded out near end of twig **18**
         18. Leaves two ranked (arranged along the twig in two rows), no thorns **19**
            19. Leaves heart shaped at base **Red Bud (Cercis)**
            19. Leaves not heart shaped at base **Beech (Fagus)**
         18. Leaves more than two ranked (arranged along the twig in more than two rows) **20**
            20. Leaves with a coating of small silvery scales on underside at least; no milky juice in leaf **Russian Olive (Eleagnus)**
            20. Leaves without such silvery scales; milky juice usually present in leaf **Osage Orange (Maclura)**
   16. Leaf margins either lobed or toothed **21**
      21. Petiole strongly flattened from side **Cottonwood, Aspen (Populus)**
      21. Petiole not flattened from sides **22**
         22. Leaves two ranked, arranged along the twig in two rows (avoid twigs that are twisted or have closely crowded leaf scars) **23**
            23. Leaves palmately veined, two or more large veins arising together from near the base of the leaf blade **24**
               24. Leaves with sharp pointed lobes **Sycamore (Platanus)**
               24. Leaves either without lobes or with rounded lobes **25**
                  25. Sides of leaf about even at base; petiole often with milky sap; some of the leaves usually lobed **Mulberry (Morus)**
                  25. Sides of leaf very uneven at base; petiole without milky sap; leaves never lobed **26**
                     26. Leaves much longer than broad; pith usually with small crosswalls at nodes **Hackberry (Celtis)**
                     26. Leaves about as broad as long; pith without crosswalls **Basswood (Tilia)**

23. Leaves pinnately veined, only one main vein from near leaf base **27**

27. Margin doubly serrate (teeth of unequal size, the larger teeth often with toothed edges) **28**

    28. Bark of older branches in papery layers; widest part of leaf usually below the middle **Birch *(Betula)***

    28. Bark of older branches not in papery layers; widest part of leaf usually at middle **29**

        29. Sides of leaf uneven at base, leaf dark green and rather rough above; bark of older trunks ridged **Elm *(Ulmus)***

        29. Sides of leaf about even at base; leaf light green above; bark not ridged **30**

            30. Bark brownish, in scalelike plates; fruit hoplike **Hop Hornbeam *(Ostrya)***

            30. Bark gray, smooth; fruit with a three-lobed bract **Blue Beech *(Carpinus)***

27. Margin of leaf not doubly serrate (teeth of about equal size) **31**

    31. Teeth far apart, less than six to 2.5 cm of margin **32**

        32. Leaves 15 to 20 cm long; buds short; bark dark and ridged **Chestnut *(Castanea)***

        32. Leaves 7.5 to 12.7 cm long; buds long and narrow; bark gray and smooth **Beech *(Fagus)***

    31. Teeth closer, more than six to 2.5 cm of margin **33**

        33. Leaves dark green above, never heart-shaped at base but usually uneven; buds short and blunt; bark of trunk dark and ridged **Elm *(Ulmus)***

        33. Leaves light green above, often heart-shaped at base but not uneven, buds long and pointed; bark gray and smooth **Serviceberry, Juneberry *(Amelanchier)***

22. Leaves more than two ranked on the twig **34**

  34. Leaves somewhat square shaped, end of leaf without a distinct tip **Tulip Tree *(Liriodendron)***

  34. Leaves not square shaped, end of leaf with a rounded or sharp tip **35**

    35. One bud scale covering entire bud; leaves usually over three times longer than broad **Willow *(Salix)***

    35. More than one bud scale visible; leaves usually less than three times longer than broad **36**

        36. End of young twigs wooly, hairy **37**

            37. Leaves palmately veined, more than one large vein from near the base; pith rather five pointed in cross section **White Poplar *(Populus)***

            37. Leaves pinnately veined, only one large vein from near the base of the leaf; pith not five pointed in cross section **Wild Crab Apple *(Pyrus)***

        36. End of young twigs hairless or almost so, never wooly, hairy **38**

            38. Branches and twigs with smooth thorns; fruit applelike with a bony core **Red Haw, Hawthorn *(Crataegus)***

            38. Branches and twigs very rarely with thorns, thorns if present rough and ending short twigs; fruit various; if applelike, without a bony core **39**

                39. Leaves lobed, usually crowded out near end of twig; fruit, an acorn **Oak *(Quercus)***

                39. Leaves not lobed, not tending to crowd out near end of twig; fruit not an acorn **40**

            40. Teeth of leaf edges not crowded, less than six to 2.5 cm of margin; leaf about 15 to 20 cm long **Chestnut *(Castanea)***

            40. Teeth more than six to 2.5 cm of margin; leaf less than 15 cm long **41**

                41. Petiole top or base of leaf blade bearing raised darkened glands; bark of twigs rather bitter tasting; fruit a drupe, one seeded **Plum, Cherry *(Prunus)***

                41. No such glands present; bark not bitter; fruit a pome, pearlike or small and applelike **42**

                    42. Leaves rather glossy above, never heart-shaped at base; twigs usually olive green in color; a cultivated fruit tree **Pear *(Pyrus)***

                    42. Leaves not at all glossy above, some usually heart-shaped at base; twigs gray brown to reddish; not a fruit tree **Serviceberry, Juneberry *(Amelanchier)***

14. Leaves compound **43**

  43. Pith of older twigs with cross partitions separating cavities (fig. 2.4A) **Butternut, Black Walnut *(Juglans)***

  43. Pith of older twigs continuous (fig. 2.4B) **44**

    44. Leaflets sharply and definitely toothed **45**

        45. About eleven to seventeen leaflets to a leaf; pith roundish in cross section (fig. 2.4D) **Mountain Ash *(Pyrus)***

        45. About five to nine leaflets to a leaf; pith five pointed in cross section (fig. 2.4C) **Hickory *(Carya)***

    44. Leaflets not toothed or only slightly so **46**

        46. Pith of older twigs white, thorns or spines usually present **47**

            47. Leaflets even numbered; one thorn at a node **Honey Locust *(Gleditsia)***

            47. Leaflets odd numbered; two stipular thorns at a node **Black Locust *(Robinia)***

        46. Pith of older twigs reddish to brown; no spines or thorns present **48**

            48. Pith of older twigs brown; leaflets usually more than 7.6 cm long **Tree-of-Heaven *(Ailanthus)***

            48. Pith of older twigs reddish; leaflets less than 7.6 cm long **Kentucky Coffee Tree *(Gymnocladus)***

Figure 2.4 Pith characteristics

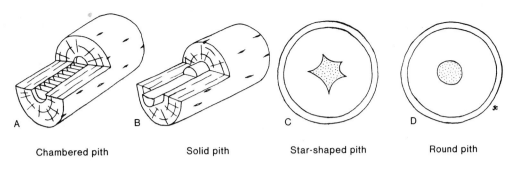

Chambered pith   Solid pith   Star-shaped pith   Round pith

Name _____

Comparison of Leaf Types

1. Name of plant	2. Simple or comp.	3. Alt., opp. or whorled	4. Shape	5. Base	6. Apex	7. Margin	8. Venation	9. Stipules pres. or abs. type	10. Other features

Exercise 3

The Compound Microscope

Plant and Other Materials

Materials needed are living algae; *Spirogyra, Protococcus, Cladophora, Rhizoclonium, Anabaena, Oscillatoria,* diatoms, etc.; hair from student's head or beard, or from a cat, dog, sheep (wool), rabbit, or other animal; cotton and other fibers are also recommended.

Equipment

Recommended are a compound microscope, microscope instruction booklets; polarizing, ultraviolet, phase, electron and scanning electron microscopes as available; transparent celluloid metric ruler, blank slides, cover glasses, fine-pointed curved forceps; prepared slides of crossed silk (different colored) fibers, fine print pasted on a slide; lens paper; teasing needles; stage micrometer, and an eyepiece micrometer.

Reagents

Balsam and xylene are needed.

Introduction

Many plant parts, cells, and even entire plants are too small to be seen with the unaided eye or a hand lens. Ordinarily, a compound microscope is used to observe clearly minute details of these plant structures. The compound microscope is essentially a system of highly corrected lenses arranged to give sharp, clear, highly magnified images of very minute objects.

The common laboratory instrument is called a light microscope because ordinary light rays from a window or electric bulb supply illumination. Other kinds use ultraviolet light (UV microscope) or polarized light (polarizing microscope).

The phase microscope enhances contrast of essentially colorless objects by creating phase differences in light waves.

The electron microscope uses a beam of electrons instead of light rays. Your instructor will explain the operation and use of these instruments, and will demonstrate those which may be available.

Parts

Examine figure 3.1 and worksheet 3.1. Note what is meant by the arm and the base. Carefully remove the microscope from its place of storage by taking it firmly by the arm with one hand and supporting it at the base with the other. Place it on the desk with the arm toward you. With the aid of figure 3.1 and worksheet 3.1 identify its main features as follows:

1. The V-shaped base, which rests firmly in place
2. The pillar, which supports the movable parts
3. The inclination joint for tilting the microscope if present
4. The stage clips for holding the slide in place
5. The arm, which is used in handling the instrument and which also supports the optical mechanism
6. The fine-adjustment knob
7. The coarse-adjustment knob
8. The draw tube
9. The eyepiece, or ocular
10. The body tube
11. The revolving nosepiece, which holds the objectives
12. The 4 mm h.p. objective, longer and with smaller lenses for greater magnification
13. The 16 mm low-power objective, shorter and with larger lenses for low magnification
14. The stage with an opening in the center over which is placed the slide bearing the object to be studied
15. The Abbe condenser, a lens in the center of the stage for concentrating the light; some models do not have a condenser
16. The substage iris diaphragm, which controls the opening in the substage and thereby regulates the amount or the intensity of the light; newer models may have a 5 aperture disc diaphragm instead of an iris diaphragm
17. The mirror fork for holding the mirror and providing a double hinge or substage illuminator
18. The double-faced mirror for reflecting the light through the object and the lenses of the microscope to the eye or light switch

Figure 3.1 Light pathway and named parts of figure 3.3 (has mirror illumination) (Courtesy of Bausch and Lomb Optical Company)

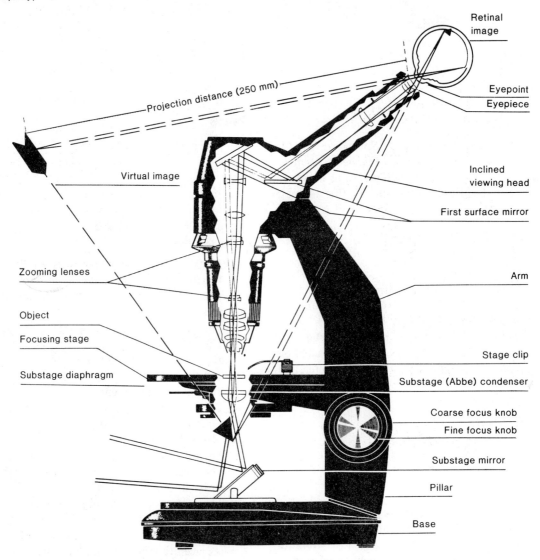

Uses

The outstanding purpose of the microscope is to magnify the image of objects and thereby enable one to study the detailed structure of minute objects or organisms that are invisible or poorly seen with the naked eye. This magnification depends on the lenses of the ocular and of the objectives, particularly the objectives. The lenses commonly used in introductory biological courses are the 5×, 7.5× and 10× oculars and the 16-mm and 4-mm objectives that magnify 10× and 43×, respectively.

When we speak of the 10× ocular, we mean that it magnifies the original object ten times in diameter. On the other hand, when we speak of the 16-mm objective, we do not mean that it magnifies sixteen times, but we are referring to the focal length of the objective lens. This is always somewhat greater than the actual working distance between the end of the lens and the slide.

The distance between the points of insertion of the ocular and the objective into the body tube of the microscope is called the tube length. The short standard tube length (160 mm) is usually used (see fig. 3.2). On newer microscopes the tube length is fixed. With the tube length set at 160 mm the magnifications obtained with the different combinations of lenses are as follows:

Objective	Working distance	Ocular	Magnification
16 mm (10×)	4–8 mm	5×	50 diameters
16 mm (10×)	4–8 mm	7.5×	75 diameters
16 mm (10×)	4–8 mm	10×	100 diameters
4 mm (43×)	.2–.6 mm	5×	215 diameters
4 mm (43×)	.2–.6 mm	7.5×	322.5 diameters
4 mm (43×)	.2–.6 mm	10×	430 diameters
1.8 mm (97×) (oil immersion)	.11–.16 mm	10×	970 diameters

Figure 3.2 A zoom compound microscope with built-in illuminator and inclined eyepiece (Courtesy of Bausch and Lomb Optical Company)

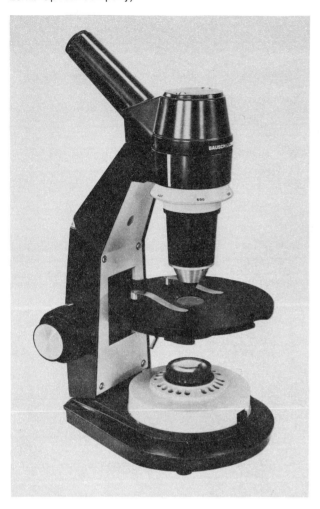

Many microscopes used in botany teaching laboratories today have fixed 10× oculars and 4×, 10×, and 43× objectives. All other parts of the microscope are accessory to the main purpose of magnification by the lenses.

Illumination

Arrangements for microscope illumination vary widely in different laboratories, and many newer student microscopes feature built-in illumination (figs. 3.2, 3.3, and 3.4). Your laboratory instructor will instruct you on the use of the facilities provided.

Since you are going to use the iris diaphragm a great deal in regulating the light, it is necessary that you acquaint yourself with its construction and operation. Take the microscope by the arm, and allowing it to rest on the table, carefully tip it over on its side so that you can see the iris diaphragm directly above the mirror. Find the iris diaphragm lever and slowly move it back and forth so you can see how the overlapping leaves of the diaphragm operate in controlling the amount of light reflected by the

mirror. Determine the direction of the lever movement when increasing or decreasing the amount of light. In models with a disc diaphragm, note which direction to turn the disc when regulating the light.

Focusing

To focus a microscope means to adjust the relation of the lenses to the object so that a clear image of the object may be seen through the ocular. The image of the object cannot be seen unless the objective is at the proper distance from it; in other words, unless it is in focus. Locate again the milled coarse-adjustment knob. Turn it a bit toward you counterclockwise and note that the movement raises the tube. Then turn it the same distance away from you clockwise and note that the tube moves downward. Never allow the objectives to touch the condenser or the slide that may be on the stage. This may damage the lens, the slide, or both. Practice the operation of the coarse adjustment back and forth, then do likewise with the fine adjustment, which will cause a barely perceptible up-and-down movement of the tube.

Practical Exercise in the Manipulation of the Microscope and Slide

1. Place the microscope directly in front of you. The tube length has been set at 160 mm. Do not attempt to change it.
2. Turn the low-power objective until it clicks in place directly over the center of the opening in the middle of the stage. Look to one side of the objective and with the coarse adjustment lower the objective down to within 1 cm of the stage.
3. Open the iris diaphragm, or use a large aperture in disc diaphragm.
4. Adjust the light as instructed.
5. A practice slide bearing an ordinary slide label with the words *Biology of Plants* in small print has been prepared by clearing the paper in xylene, mounting it in balsam, and covering it with a cover glass. (Other small printed matter would do as well.) Fine print may be pasted directly on a slide and used dry for observation. Place the slide in the center of the stage so the word *Biology* will be directly under the objective and directly over the condenser. Rays of light may be seen passing through it. Again look from one side and lower the objective close to the cover glass of the slide (about 3 mm). Now look through the ocular and with the coarse adjustment slowly focus up until some of the letters of the word *Biology* are clearly in view. Focus carefully, and if necessary, regulate the mirror and diaphragm for better light. If no object appears, make sure the word *Biology* is exactly in position as directed and repeat the process.

Figure 3.3 Dissecting microscope (stereomicroscope) (Courtesy of Reichert Scientific Instruments)

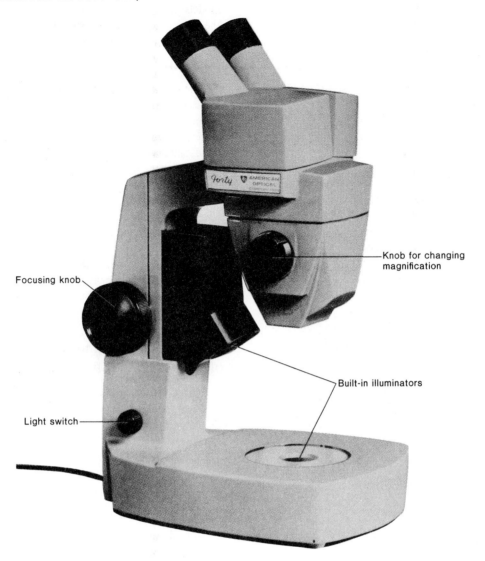

Knob for changing magnification

Focusing knob

Built-in illuminators

Light switch

6. Now slowly move the slide and examine all of the letters of the word *Biology*. Note that the letters and the entire word are reversed and upside down. Focus on the letter *y* and move the slide toward the right. In what direction do the letters move in the microscopic field of vision? Move the slide toward the left and note the result. This is because the image in the eyepiece, or ocular, is reversed in position from that of the object. Find the dot of the letter *i*. How many times in diameter is the dot magnified? Move the slide so that the dot will be exactly in the center of the field for examination under high power.

7. Turn on the high-power objective, regulate the light, and carefully focus with the fine adjustment. The dot may not be exactly in the center under high power; it is more apt to be a little off center. Microscopes differ a little in this respect. Center

the dot while you have it under high power and then turn on low power to determine how far off-center the object is in your particular microscope. This is important and should aid you in all your future microscope work. With high power again, note the size of the dot. What is its magnification in diameters now? Practice shifting from low power to high and back again. Note that only a small amount of manipulation with the fine adjustment is necessary to bring the object again into proper focus whenever the objective is swung into position. The objectives have been carefully adjusted to the nosepiece so that they are *parfocal*. Such an adjustment is a decided advantage to the student, and to retain this precision and efficiency, the objectives must not be loosened or unscrewed.

8. When looking into the microscope, keep both eyes open; the one not in use will soon ignore its field of vision. To avoid fatigue, it is well to alternate the eyes at work. In doing this, however, it must be remembered that the two eyes are not always the same, and while the object is perfectly clear to one eye, it may be slightly out of focus for the other. Do not try to focus with your eyes but use the fine adjustment. Ordinarily, use your left eye for the microscopic work and keep the right eye free for drawing and other work.

9. In starting a microscopic study, always examine the slide or object under low power first. Get a good general idea of it and then, if necessary, bring the specific part to be studied into the center of the field for further examination with high power. (It is not always necessary or desirable to use high power.) With the use of low power a relatively larger part of the object or area on the slide is visible. With high power only a small part of the object or area is visible but, of course, highly magnified so it can be examined in greater detail.

10. It is much more difficult to locate an object with high power than it is with low. In this connection (while you have the practice slide) move the slide from its present position, and then with high power, try to locate the dot of the letter *i*.

11. To accurately measure microscopic objects, ruled micrometer discs are placed in the ocular of the microscope; however, these micrometer discs are not usually available for individual use in elementary classes. For this reason other means of estimating the size of small objects may be used. Ordinary millimeter cross-section paper is soaked in xylene, a drop of balsam is added and covered with a cover glass. Observe under low power and measure the diameter of the low-power field by counting the millimeters shown on the paper. This gives a rough approximation of the diameter of the low-power field. Repeat for high power. Which has the larger field of view? A clear or transparent celluloid ruler marked off in millimeters may be used for the same purpose.

The size of objects under the microscope may be estimated by comparing the object with the diameter of the field; for example, one-half the field, one-eighth, and so forth. If a millimeter contains 1,000 micrometers (μm), what is the estimated diameter of the dot over the letter *i* in the word *Biology*? Would you use low or high power for this estimation? Look through the demonstration microscope fitted with a micrometer disc; your instructor will explain how this disc is calibrated and some of its practical uses in microscopy.

You have the diameter of the field of view under the microscope. The area of a circle is determined by applying the formula πr^2. What is the area of the low-power field? the high-power field?

The Zoom Microscope

The zoom microscope (figs. 3.1 and 3.2) has continuously variable magnifications ranging from 100× to 500× (some to 400×). With the zoom microscope one simply focuses at first on an object with the zooming ring usually set at the lowest magnification (100×). Thereafter, to change magnification one turns the zooming ring to any point between 100× and 500× where the object appears at its best. Focus is usually sharp, but if not, a small adjustment with the focusing knob will correct it.

Examine a prepared slide of crossed silk fibers that have been dyed different colors. By focusing with the fine adjustment, attempt to determine the relative levels of these fibers. Call the instructor for verification.

Practice mounting various types of fibers, algae, and hairs in water and examine them under the microscope. Spread the material in a drop of water so it is not bunched or matted and place a clean cover glass on it. Touch the water drop with the edge of the cover glass first and lower gently so air bubbles will be driven out; this is a *water mount*. Do not allow water to get on top of the cover glass. The material is now ready for examination.

The Binocular Dissecting Microscope (Stereomicroscope)

The binocular (two inclined eyepieces) dissecting microscope (fig. 3.3) is used in biological work for low magnification (under 100×) studies of entire small animals, insects, flowers, seeds, leaves, or any object requiring low magnification to make details more apparent. Because the image is seen in three dimensions, this instrument is called a stereomicroscope. The image is also seen right side up and is not reversed. Specimens may be studied dry and without previous preparation. Similarly, small fish (guppies) and other aquatic organisms may be studied under water in a petri dish placed on the stage.

Methods of illumination vary and your instructor will explain this and other operational details of the instrument used.

Zoom models are also available.

Carefully study the books of instructions giving a detailed description of the various microscopes and their parts. Never forget that a microscope is a precision-made instrument and requires careful use and intelligent handling for it to function properly. There can be no acceptable excuse for careless and rough handling of a microscope. The instructor will discuss the microscope and give detailed directions for its use.

Questions

1. What are the parts of a microscope? Name the function of each part. Label the parts shown in worksheet 3.1.

2. What approximate magnifications can be obtained with this instrument?

3. Why must objects ordinarily be transparent for examination under the microscope?

4. What is a water mount?

5. Why must an object be surrounded by water or another suitable medium for examination under the microscope?

6. Of what advantage is it to know the diameter of the field of view (l.p. and h.p.) of the microscope?

7. How are accurate measurements made of microscopic objects?

8. What does it mean when a lens is corrected for spherical and chromatic aberrations?

9. What is the electron microscope? What magnifications are possible with this instrument?

10. Compare the light, UV, polarizing, and phase microscopes with an electron microscope.

Name _____

Figure 3.4 Light pathway and parts of figure 3.2 (Courtesy of Reichert Scientific Instruments)

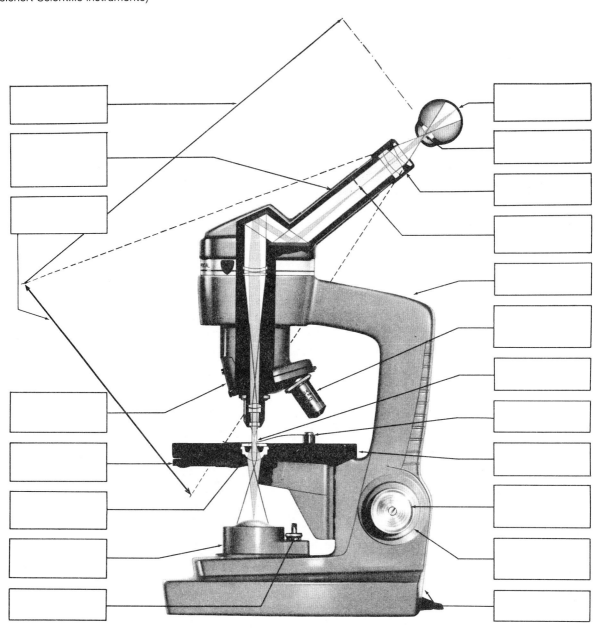

Exercise 4 — The Living Plant Cell

Plant Materials

The materials required are onion bulbs, *Elodea* shoots, and *Tradescantia* flowers.

Equipment

Required equipment includes a compound microscope, blank slides and cover glasses, metric ruler, dissecting needles, fine-pointed curved forceps and electron micrographs of common plant organelles. Also consult the Ledbetter and Porter reference, which contains EM micrographs of plant material only.

Reagents

The reagents needed are neutral red, 1% solution, iodine potassium iodide solution (diluted to a light amber color), and dilute glycerine.

Introduction

All plant parts are usually made up of microscopic protoplasmic units called cells. Plant cells vary greatly in shape, size, and contents, but they must nevertheless be regarded as fundamental, structural, and dynamic units of a plant. Because cells are considered to be basic units of all organisms, it is necessary to know fundamental details of their structures and functions in order to understand how these organisms live, grow, and reproduce.

Beginning students seldom see an electron microscope (EM) (fig. 4.1), but some knowledge of the results obtained by it should be included in any modern consideration of cells. Photographs (electron micrographs) secured using an electron microscope are more commonly and easily studied than are the actual images projected on the viewing screen of this instrument. Thus, every student may become well informed in the developments of electron microscopy without learning to operate the complex microscope itself.

Electron micrographs show fine, highly magnified details of cell ultrastructure, but they are flat and have no depth of field. The scanning electron microscope (SEM), however, produces micrographs especially noted for their exceptionally great depth of field and fine detail of external features.

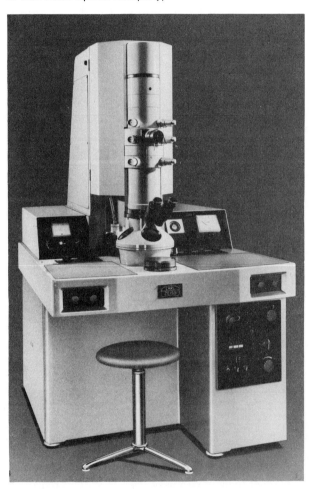

Figure 4.1 A transmission electron microscope (Courtesy of Carl Zeiss Optical Company)

A plant cell is a microscopic unit of living protoplasm, the *protoplast,* and is composed of a nucleus, cytoplasm, and various inclusions completely enclosed on all sides by nonliving cellulose walls secreted by the protoplast. The outermost very thin layer of the protoplast appressed to the cell wall is the *plasma membrane.* A similar outer limiting membrane of each vacuole is the *tonoplast.* An intercellular layer, the *middle lamella* (commonly of calcium pectate), occurs between all inner adjoining cell wall surfaces, cementing them firmly together (see fig. 4.4 and worksheet 4.1).

Figure 4.2 A parenchyma cell of *Begonia* petiole

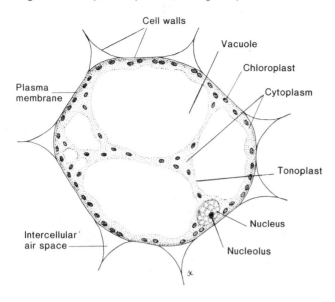

A group of cells of similar origin and function is called a *tissue;* for example, the epidermis.

To determine the relationship of the above structures in a single cell, study the labeled diagram (fig. 4.2) showing a parenchyma cell section of a living *Begonia* petiole.

Plant cells are variously modified for different functions, but in the present exercise only a few representative examples of living plant cells can be studied. The biological study devoted entirely to cells is known as cell biology, or cytology.

A. Study of a Plant Cell

Mount a small piece of skin (epidermis) from the inner side of an onion scale in a drop of water, add cover glass, and examine under the microscope, first using l.p., then h.p. Make certain the outer surface of the epidermis is uppermost in the mount. Why? The cell walls should be easily seen, but it may be necessary to regulate the light by means of the iris diaphragm in order to clearly see the cytoplasm and nucleus. Identify cell walls, cytoplasm, vacuoles and nucleus (plural, nuclei).

In order to make details of the cell contents more visible, mount another piece of onion scale epidermis in a 0.1% solution of neutral red. The stain should accumulate in the protoplasm, leaving the cell walls clear white. Compare this mount with that of the unstained epidermis. State advantages of each preparation.

B. Cells of the Leaf
of a Water Plant: *Elodea*

Mount a leaf of *Elodea* in water on a slide, selecting a young leaf from near the tip of the shoot. Take care that the leaf is mounted so its top side is uppermost in the mount. Examine, using l.p., making sure to focus sharply on the surface of the leaf. Note the shape of the cells and their arrangement with reference to each other. What is the character of the leaf margin? Note the spur cells protruding stiffly from the leaf margin.

C. Detailed Structure of a Single Cell

Find a cell suitable for detailed study and adjust carefully under h.p. until the side and end walls are exactly in focus. Determine the length and breadth of the selected cell by comparing its dimensions with the diameter of the field.

Cell Wall How does the cell wall's thickness compare with the diameter of the cell? Is it of uniform thickness on all sides? Is the wall between two cells homogeneous or is there a line of division visible in the center, the middle lamella? It may be necessary to reduce the light coming through the microscope to see this. It will appear much sharper in killed and fixed stained cells used in later exercises.

Cytoplasm Focusing carefully, note the transparent, slightly refractive, granular-appearing substance lining the inside walls of the cell. Is this the only place it may be seen? When looking at the cell through the microscope, why is the cytoplasm more readily seen at the sides than on the top or bottom of the cell?

Note any movement (streaming) of the cytoplasm. In what direction does it stream, clockwise or counterclockwise?

Nucleus Embedded in the cytoplasm and often appressed to the sidewall will be found a rounded or somewhat flattened body, the nucleus. How many nuclei are in each cell? Are the contents homogeneous or not? Is the nucleus really embedded in the cytoplasm? What are the functions of the nucleus? Nucleus and cytoplasm together form the *protoplasm* or living cell material (i.e., the protoplast).

Note: The nuclei in many cells are not easily seen unless stained. Adding a weak iodine solution to the mount kills the cells and often makes the nuclei more visible. The leaf may also be mounted in 0.1% solution of neutral red to stain protoplasmic structures.

Vacuole The inside of the cell is occupied by the cell sap (water and substances in solution) forming one or more vacuoles.

Chloroplasts Note that the green color is not diffused generally throughout the cell, but is borne in definite corpuscular bodies, the chloroplasts. Count the number of chloroplasts in one cell. What is their shape? their average size? Are they restricted to the cytoplasm, to the vacuole, or do they occur in both? Can details of their structure be determined?

Identify all the parts described, then label the detailed drawing of a cell from an *Elodea* leaf (worksheet 4.1). Indicate by small arrows the direction of cytoplasmic streaming. Carefully color the chloroplasts green.

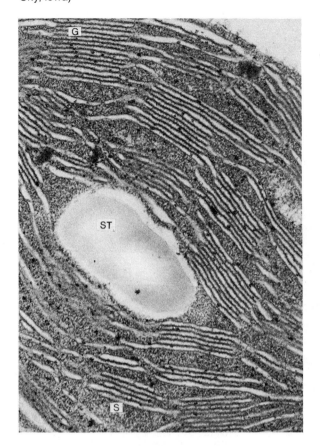

D. Photosynthetic Area of Chloroplasts

The chloroplasts in an *Elodea* leaf are approximately 4.5 μm in diameter. A number (about 50) of smaller, denser, green bodies called *grana* (singular, *granum*) are dispersed in the colorless matrix *(stroma)* of each chloroplast. Electron micrographs reveal that grana (fig. 4.3) are short, cylindrical structures composed of thin, parallel laminations (thylakoids) piled on top of one another (similar to a stack of pancakes). Layers of chlorophyll one molecule thick alternate with and occur between the thylakoids. The most important chemical reaction in the world from an economic and survival standpoint (food and oxygen supply) is carried out in these monomolecular layers of chlorophyll because they are the actual site of the light reaction of *photosynthesis*.

E. Electron Microscopy of Organelles

Study the micrograph of a plant cell (fig. 4.4) showing common *organelles* at a magnification obtained by an electron microscope. Compare with the drawing (worksheet 4.1) and living cell of *Elodea* as shown by a light microscope. Explain in detail the advantages of an electron microscope, as compared with a light microscope, in the study of cell organelles.

Carefully study the various books, articles, or reprints on demonstration showing electron micrographs of common organelles and learn to recognize them at sight. State how the ultrastructure of various organelles may be correlated with their function(s) as now understood. Is molecular biology related to this topic?

F. Optional

Using fine-pointed forceps, carefully remove a stamen hair from a flower of *Tradescantia*. Place in a drop of water or dilute glycerin solution and gently add a cover glass. How many cells are in this hair? Focus carefully on the cytoplasm. Is streaming of the cytoplasm apparent? In what direction does it stream, clockwise or counterclockwise? Is a nucleus visible in the cell? Are chloroplasts present?

Make a detailed drawing (about 6 cm long) of a cell from the stamen hair of *Tradescantia*. Label all parts and indicate the direction of cytoplasmic streaming by means of small arrows.

Examine any other cells provided from prepared slides or by following the directions of your laboratory instructor. Make a drawing of each cell studied and label all parts.

References

Ledbetter, M. C., and Porter, K. R. 1970. *Introduction to the fine structure of plant cells.* New York: Springer-Verlag.

Lott, J. N. A. 1976. *A scanning electron microscope study of green plants.* St. Louis: C. V. Mosby.

Questions

1. Name the parts of a typical green-plant cell, giving the functions of each.
2. If the cell walls were removed, would the remaining protoplasmic content still be considered a cell? How would cell shape change?
3. What is the protoplast?
4. Do the chloroplasts float or swim in the cytoplasm?
5. What do the vacuoles contain?
6. How do plant cells differ from animal cells?
7. What is a chloroplast?
8. What is the middle lamella?
9. Does cytoplasmic streaming serve any useful function in the plant?
10. Does cytoplasmic streaming occur in plant cells other than those of *Elodea*?
11. What is the importance of chlorophyll surface in relation to photosynthesis?
12. How does this reaction (photosynthesis) affect the daily life of humans?

Figure 4.4 Cross section through leaf mesophyll cells of a
garden bean seedling seen with the aid of an electron
microscope (Courtesy Jean Whatley)

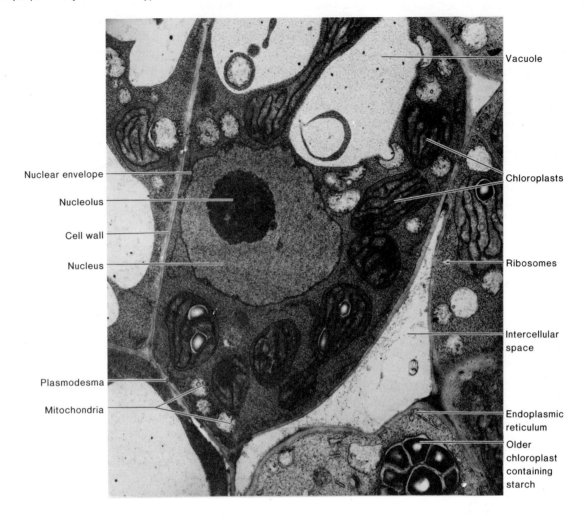

Vacuole

Nuclear envelope

Nucleolus

Cell wall

Nucleus

Chloroplasts

Ribosomes

Intercellular
space

Plasmodesma

Mitochondria

Endoplasmic
reticulum

Older
chloroplast
containing
starch

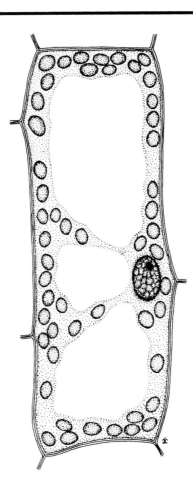

5

Cell Division: Mitosis, Meiosis

Plant Materials

Materials required are prepared slides of onion root longitudinal sections stained to show mitosis and prepared slides of onion mitosis squash preparation Feulgen stained for DNA. Slides can also be made using lily (*Lilium*), hyacinth, spiderwort, *Trillium* or *Podophyllum*. Also needed are prepared slides of cross sections of lily ovary to show the stages of meiosis from the megasporocyte to migrating haploid nuclei and cross sections of lily anthers to show meiosis and the development of the microspore.

Equipment

A compound microscope; colored modeling clay or colored pipe cleaners.

Introduction

Not until a cell has stored enough food for energy and building materials and replicated its nuclear material will it divide. The pattern of division depends on the type of cell. In procaryotic cells, the whole cell pinches in two; a process called fission. In many eukaryotic protists, the nucleus seems to divide by fission followed by a splitting of the cytoplasm. In the multicellular plants, division is most abundant in the meristematic regions, the root and stem tips, the vascular and cork cambiums, and in organs in the early stages of growth. Two parts of typical cell division are generally recognized: (1) *mitosis,* or karyokinesis, the actual division of the nucleus into two daughter nuclei and (2) *cytokinesis,* the separation of the cell into two units by the formation of a new cell wall between the two daughter nuclei. Sometimes you may see the whole process of cell division called mitosis. In the land plants, a special type of nuclear division called *meiosis* takes place just prior to the formation of spores. In animals and fungi, meiosis takes place at other stages in the life cycle.

Mitosis is a smoothly continuous process in which each stage (phase) merges gradually into another. The phases of mitosis usually named and illustrated are purely terms of convenience in description, and must not be considered to occur as sharply distinct stages. Undoubtedly, the most significant event of mitosis is molecular; for instance, the precise doubling of the DNA in the genes and chromosomes during interphase in order that an exact replication of this genetic material may later appear in each daughter cell nucleus.

The time required for mitosis varies greatly with the plant and the conditions to which it may be exposed; however, in an onion root tip at 30°C it may be completed in approximately ninety minutes. Because mitosis is quite involved, only the essentials of this process will be considered in this exercise. Consult your textbook and the references for additional material in cell biology.

A. An Undifferentiated (Metabolic) Cell

Slides with stained sections of the root tips of onion, corn, hyacinth, *Trillium,* or spiderwort will be provided. Examine the cells just in back of the root cap. What is the general shape of the cells in this region? What differences exist between the cells with respect to size and shape? with respect to the nuclei? What is the character of the cell wall?

Find a cell a short distance back of the growing point in which the contents are relatively homogeneous. What is the relative size and shape of the nucleus? Note the *nucleolus* (plural, *nucleoli*). Is there more than one? Describe the appearance of the cytoplasm. Are there any vacuoles visible?

Interphase (worksheet 5.1A). During interphase the nucleus of an undifferentiated (nondividing) cell undergoes great metabolic activity in preparation for division. All proteins and other materials necessary for mitosis are accumulated or synthesized during this period. Following approximately the first one-third to one-half of interphase time, the synthesis of deoxyribonucleic acid (DNA) begins, and when interphase ends, the DNA content of the nucleus has exactly doubled. Long, slender, chromatin threads corresponding to the diploid number of chromosomes (16 in onion) are dispersed as a faintly staining network within the karyolymph (nuclear sap). A complete longitudinal splitting or doubling of each strand to produce a chromosome composed of two halves, each called a chromatid, accompanies the doubling of the DNA originally present in each thread. Deeply staining nucleoli (1 to 4 in onion) are prominent during interphase.

At least two important events occur during interphase: (1) the emerging chromatin threads become longitudinally doubled or split, but do not separate; (2) the DNA content of the nucleus, and hence specifically the genetic material (genes) of the chromosomes, is exactly doubled at the same time.

B. The Dividing Nucleus (Mitosis)

Prophase (worksheet 5.1B and C). Prophase begins when the long, thin, longitudinally doubled chromatin threads of the interphase nucleus first become clearly visible (more stainable). Shortening and thickening of the chromatin threads and their enclosing matrix terminate with the formation of a definite number (16 in onion) of typical chromosomes.

Premetaphase (worksheet 5.1D). Nucleoli disappear during premetaphase and the nuclear membrane breaks down into endoplasmic reticulum. Freely migrating chromosomes move toward the central region (equator) of the newly forming mitotic spindle.

Metaphase (worksheet 5.1E and F). Metaphase is attained when the centromeres, or kinetochores (points of attachment for spindle fibers), become arranged in a line parallel to the equatorial plate of a cell. The chromosome arms, however, may extend in any direction. Spindle fibers, some connected to centromeres (chromosomal or traction fibers) and some free (continuous fibers), make up the mitotic spindle with the fibers converging toward the cell poles.

Anaphase (worksheet 5.1G and H). Anaphase begins when the centromeres divide, allowing the two chromatids of a metaphase chromosome to separate and move diametrically away from each other. Each such chromatid (now called a chromosome) has a spindle fiber attached to its daughter centromere. These tractile fibers shorten until the chromosomes reach opposite poles, where they aggregate into a progressively tighter group as anaphase ends.

Telophase (worksheet 5.1I, J, and K). Telophase begins when the poleward movement of the daughter chromosomes stops, and they begin to organize themselves into a compact group. The events of telophase are essentially those of prophase in reverse, with the tight coils of each chromosome relaxing into slender threads that become progressively longer, thinner, and more transparent until they finally attain the diffuse condition characteristic of interphase. The nucleoli reappear, and the nuclear membrane is reconstituted from the endoplasmic reticulum. *Cytokinesis* begins while the nuclei are reorganizing themselves. Thickenings, or vesicles apparently derived from the dictyosomes (Golgi apparatus), appear in a line on the spindle fibers along the equatorial plane of a cell. These fuse to form a cell plate, or primary wall, which develops laterally outward from the center to meet and join the surrounding walls, thus forming two daughter cells (worksheet 5.1L) as telophase ends. Each new daughter cell has exactly the same number and kinds of chromosomes and the same amount of DNA as the parent cell.

Study the selected phases of mitosis shown (worksheet 5.1A–L) on the accompanying plate of photographs and label the different structures identified.

C. Meiosis, Microsporogenesis

The anthers of a flower develop masses of diploid pollen mother cells (microsporocytes), which undergo meiosis to form *quartets (tetrads)* of microspores, each containing the haploid number of chromosomes.

Note: The diploid (or sporophytic) number of chromosomes for most species of lily is twenty-four; the haploid (or gametophytic) number is twelve. Chromosome numbers should be carefully noted for each stage or nucleus described in all portions of this exercise that follow.

Carefully study (worksheet 5.2A–J) showing a series of stages of meiosis in lily *(Lilium)* anthers. Examine slides (first l.p., then h.p.) showing sections of lily anthers, or (preferably) acetocarmine, or other squash preparations of dividing microsporocytes showing similar stages. Identify each stage shown by the drawings.

The meiotic prophase is a long, complex process, and only certain features of it can be studied in this exercise. At the beginning of prophase, long, slender chromosomal threads (the *chromonemata*) appear in the nucleus of a microspore mother cell. They are present in the diploid number, and each represents a chromosome. Small, clearly defined lumps (*chromomeres*) occur on each thread. This is the *leptotene* stage (worksheet 5.2B).

The leptotene threads pair side by side throughout their full length. Each chromosomal thread pairs precisely with its homologue, chromomere for chromomere. The paired threads enter into very intimate contact, but do not actually fuse. This exact longitudinal pairing is called *synapsis*. When synaptic pairing is complete, the nucleus is in the *zygotene* stage.

Following synaptic pairing of the zygotene stage, the threads become markedly shorter and thicker, and the nucleus enters the *pachytene* stage. In late pachytene, each of the two homologous chromosomes of each pair becomes double by a complete longitudinal split. Each pachytene thread is now quadruple, and composed of a *tetrad of chromatids.*

Homologous chromosomal threads at synapsis were very strongly attracted to each other. Following late pachytene, a strong repelling force is exerted, which causes the paired homologous chromosomes (each now composed of two daughter chromatids) to separate and pull apart sharply from each other. This separation is complete, except where the chromosomes have become joined together by bridges, or *chiasmata,* at points where they have "crossed over." Your instructor will explain the phenomenon of crossing over of chromosomes and its significance in inheritance. The nucleus is now in the *diplotene* stage (worksheet 5.2C).

The chromosomes have become progressively shorter and thicker as they have passed through the preceding stages. With further accentuated contraction, the chromosomes appear as compact and shortened tetrads lying well spaced in the nucleus, often near its periphery. This is the *diakinesis* stage. As diakinesis terminates, the nuclear membrane and nucleolus disappear, and the tetrads move to become arranged at the equator of the cell.

The tetrads of chromosomes become oriented along the equatorial plane of the cell, and *spindle fibers* (the achromatic figure) are then developed. This stage is *metaphase I* (worksheet 5.2D and E).

Homologous chromosomes, each composed of two daughter chromatids, now separate, and the resulting *dyads* (pairs of daughter chromatids) move apart toward opposite poles of the spindle. This constitutes *anaphase I* (worksheet 5.2F). Reduction of chromosome number from diploid to haploid is now apparent since each group of chromosomes at each pole of the spindle now contains the reduced (N) number of chromosomes. A wall develops between these two groups of chromosomes during *telophase I* to form two *secondary sporocytes* (worksheet 5.2G).

A brief *interphase* elapses, and each nucleus progresses through *metaphase II* (worksheet 5.2H), *anaphase II* (worksheet 5.2I), and *telophase II*. These divisions are equational (mitotic), and no change in chromosome number occurs. Following telophase II a quartet (tetrad) of microspores is formed, each of which rounds up as an isolated cell contained within the mother cell wall (worksheet 5.2J).

Study the selected phases of meiosis shown in worksheet 5.2 (diagrams A to J) and label the different structures identified.

D. Meiosis in Other Tissues

Meiosis is also studied in the formation of the megasporocyte, which gives rise to the female gametophyte, as is demonstrated in an examination of megasporogenesis and development of the female gametophyte in the flower (see exercise 19). Other places where the process may be observed is the sporophyte of *Anthoceros* or the formation of tetraspores of *Polysiphonia*.

Using colored modeling clay or colored pipe cleaners, make models of chromosomes as they would appear in each phase of mitosis and meiosis. Be able to demonstrate any phase to your lab instructor if asked.

Questions

1. What are chromosomes?
2. Why are they important?
3. Name the meristematic tissues of a plant.
4. Where are they located?
5. Does mitosis increase or decrease the number of chromosomes in a cell? Explain this answer.
6. What structures may be found in the cytoplasm?
7. What are the parts of the nucleus?
8. Name the phases of mitosis and briefly characterize each.
9. What is cytology? Cell biology?
10. What appearance of the nucleus indicates that division is being initiated?
11. Why is DNA so important to the study of molecular biology?
12. Why might a careful description of the shape and number of chromosomes in each plant species be essential to the study of plant evolution?
13. How does meiosis differ from mitosis? Compare and contrast the two processes. What is the importance of each to the plant?

Worksheet 5.1

Mitosis in Onion Root Tip (Courtesy of H. L. Dean)

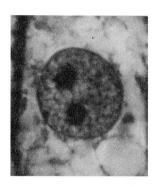

A Interphase

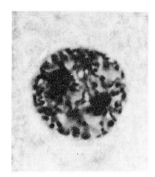

B Early prophase

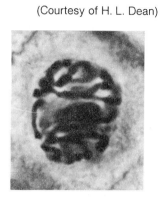

C Middle prophase

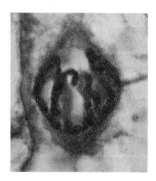

D Premetaphase

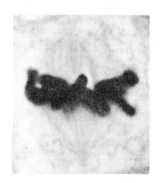

E Metaphase (side view)

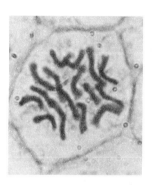

F Metaphase (polar view)

G Early anaphase

H Late anaphase

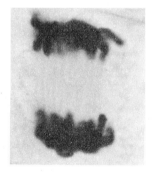

I Late anaphase—early telophase

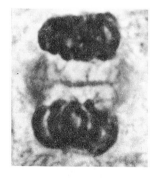

J Middle telophase

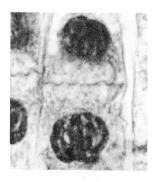

K Late telophase

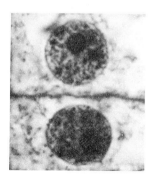

L Two daughter cells—
beginning of interphase

Meiosis, Microsporogenesis in Lilium *Anthers*

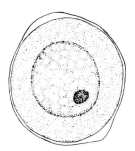

A Microsporocyte

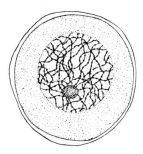

B Early prophase
leptotene stage

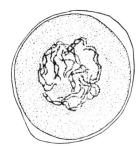

C Later prophase
diplotene stage

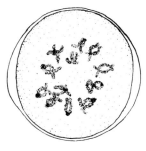

D Metaphase I, polar
view

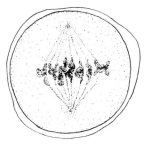

E Metaphase I, side
view

F Anaphase I

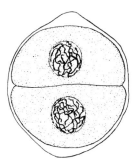

G Secondary sporocytes

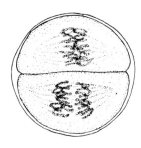

H Metaphase II, early
anaphase II

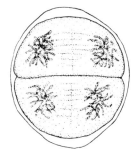

I Anaphase II completed

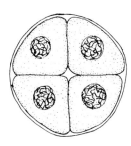

J Quartet of microspores;
meiosis completed

6

The Microscopic Structure of Leaves

Plant Materials

The materials needed are prepared slides with cross and paradermal sections of evergreen privet leaf or (less desirable) common privet or lilac leaf; complete leaf of lilac (fresh or pressed); living leaves of *Rumex, Fuchsia, Zebrina, Sedum, Tradescantia, Ficus,* elderberry pith, fresh carrot, prepared slides with cross and paradermal sections of a corn leaf and cross sections of oleander, Ficus, water lily, and pine leaves.

Equipment

The equipment requirements include a compound microscope; blank slides and cover glasses; dissecting needles; fine-pointed curved forceps; single-edged safety razor blades; scalpel; photomicrographs of cross and paradermal sections of evergreen privet leaf, corn leaf; Styrofoam and a metric ruler.

Introduction

In order to better understand the functions (physiology) of a living green leaf, it is necessary to know the fundamental details of its structure. Throughout this exercise an attempt should be made to correlate structural details with functions. Visualize how gases may enter and exit from the leaf, what pathways gases use in circulating within the leaf, what pathways water follows in the leaf, and what structures protect the leaf from injury and water loss. In a living green leaf the area of moist internally exposed cell wall surface is of great importance in photosynthesis and transpiration. From examination of material in this exercise, and from the textbook and lecture notes, attempt to explain how the internal atmosphere of a leaf is air-conditioned to maintain this moist situation.

In order to obtain a view of the interior of a leaf, it is necessary to cut it into very thin slices or sections that may be examined with a compound microscope. The simplest way to do this is to place a bit of leaf between the halves of a split piece of elder pith, Styrofoam, or fresh carrot, and cut thin slices of pith and leaf with a very sharp knife or razor blade (freehand sections). Excellent sections may be cut with a little practice. See section F and figures 6.3 and 6.4.

More uniformly thin sections of plant materials can be obtained by using a machine called a *microtome*. In this case, tissues are killed and embedded in paraffin for cutting. These thin sections are then fastened to glass slides, stained, and a cover glass is then sealed on with Balsam or similar medium. Prepared slides will be used for much of the work in this course. Most of the sections on these slides have been cut 5 to 15 micrometers (μm) in thickness. One millimeter = 1,000 micrometers. How many micrometers are in one inch? *Note:* Micrometer (μm) has replaced the now obsolete term, micron (μ).

A. Structure of a Typical Dicotyledon Foliage Leaf

Using l.p. and h.p., examine prepared slides of the cross section of a leaf from an evergreen species of privet, or similar leaf. Select a suitable section and identify the following parts: upper and lower epidermis, palisade and spongy mesophyll, veins (containing xylem and phloem), stomata, and cuticle. A *tissue* consists of a group of morphologically similar cells that have similar origins and general functions. An *organ* (such as a leaf) is composed of one or more tissues. Do the cells of each tissue have a characteristic size and shape? Note the chloroplasts in the cells. In what tissues do they occur most abundantly? In what tissues are they lacking? Look for the lightly stained, noncellular, waxy layer (the cuticle) on the outer surface of the epidermal cells. Suggest functions of the cuticle. How thick is it? How is the structure of a leaf adapted to photosynthesis?

Examine prepared slides and photomicrographs of the sections cut parallel to the epidermis (*paradermal*). Locate and identify the principal tissues of the leaf. Are there differences in the size and shape of the cells of the various tissues as compared with the same tissues seen in cross section? Enumerate. Where is the most cell wall surface exposed: the outer surfaces of the epidermal cells or the surfaces of the internal cells of the mesophyll? Can you estimate the ratio between the externally exposed surface and the internally exposed surface? What is the importance of this internally exposed surface to photosynthesis? to transpiration?

After careful study of the leaf sections and identification of all the parts, compare with figure 6.1. Label the diagram on worksheet 6.1.

Figure 6.1 Simplified stereodiagram of an evergreen privet leaf

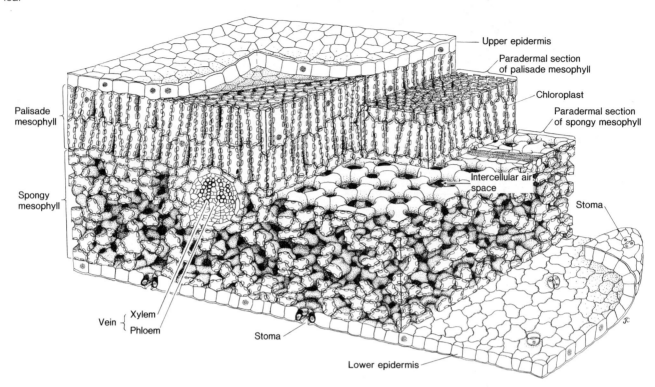

Study the stereodiagram of an evergreen privet leaf (fig. 6.1) and correlate its features with the named structures.

Optional Study

Measure a fresh or pressed lilac leaf and compute the total external surface. See Exercise 10 for a method of estimating the surface area of a leaf. It is known that the *internally* exposed cell wall surface of a lilac leaf is 13.2 times greater than the *externally* exposed cell wall surface. Take the figure derived and compute the area of internally exposed surface of the leaf. Express this area in mm², cm², or dm².

B. Cross Section of a Stoma

Examine the lower epidermis of a privet leaf carefully under l.p. and find a *stoma* (plural, *stomata*). Focus very carefully under h.p. Note relation of stoma to *guard cells* and to the *substomatal chamber*. Compare the guard cell with adjoining *epidermal* cells as to position, size, thickness, and uniformity of cell wall, cutinized surface, and chloroplasts.

C. Stomata in Surface (Face) View

Determination of stomatal numbers is optional.

Use a leaf of *Zebrina, Fuchsia, Rumex, Sedum, Tradescantia,* or some other plant from which the epidermis is easily separated. With a razor blade or sharp knife peel off a small piece of the lower epidermis and mount in a drop of water, outer side up. Add a cover glass and examine under l.p. Find a portion of the mount free from air bubbles and estimate the number of stomata visible in the field at one time. The diameter and area of the low-power and high-power fields of view were determined in Exercise 3. Using this information, estimate the number of stomata to the square millimeter (mm²) on this leaf. An ordinary square postage stamp has approximately 500 square millimeters of surface. With this data, estimate the number of stomata (on an area the size of a stamp) on a leaf of the species studied. Consult the accompanying table for stomatal numbers per square millimeter on leaves of other plants.

Locate a stoma and examine it under h.p. Note the relation of guard cells to surrounding subsidiary and other epidermal cells, also note their chloroplasts, nuclei, and thickened inner walls. Mount a portion of the upper epidermis of the same leaf. Are any stomata present on the upper surface of the leaves of this particular plant? How do these epidermal cells compare in size and shape with those of the lower epidermis?

After careful study of the material provided, complete worksheet 6.2.

Figure 6.2 Cross section of a monocotyledon leaf: corn

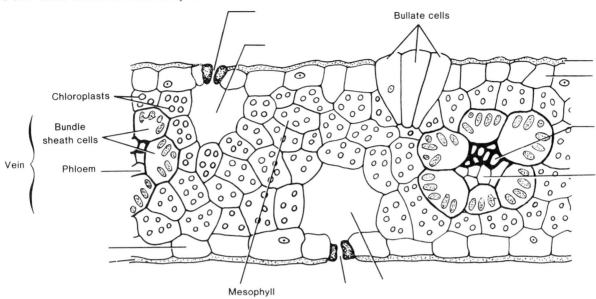

Bullate cells

Chloroplasts

Bundle sheath cells

Vein

Phloem

Mesophyll

D. Stomata Per Square Millimeter of Leaf Area

Species	Upper Surface	Lower Surface
Abies balsamea (balsam fir)	0	228
Lilium bulbifera (lily)	0	62
Morus alba (white mulberry)	0	480
Syringa vulgaris (lilac)	0	330
Nymphea alba (water lily)	460	0
Pinus strobus (white pine)	142	0
Helianthus annuus (sunflower)	175	325
Lycopersicon esculentum (tomato)	12	130
Phaseolus vulgaris (bean)	40	281
Triticum sativum (wheat)	33	14

In order to visualize the area size, carefully draw with a sharp pencil a square measuring exactly one millimeter on each side. With this square in mind, study again the preceding table of stomatal numbers for different species.

The actual size of a stoma (i.e., the opening between the guard cells) is very small. The area of an average pinhole is roughly equivalent to the area of 2,000 to 2,500 stomatal openings. A single stomatal opening may measure approximately 4 × 7 micrometers (μm) in size. Could the finest human hair be thrust through one such opening?

E. Structure of a Monocotyledon Leaf: Corn (*Zea*)

Using l.p. and h.p. examine prepared slides of a corn leaf. With the aid of figure 6.2 identify the following parts: upper and lower epidermis; cuticle; mesophyll, of angular and compact cells; stomata, in both upper and lower epidermis; bullate cells, in the upper surface; bundle sheath of large cells enclosing a vein; and chloroplasts.

Bullate cells are thin-walled, and lose much water on a hot day, which causes them to lose turgor and, more or less, collapse with a resulting curling or rolling inward of the leaf blade that extends on each side of the long midrib. Explain how rolling of the leaf could help reduce the water loss caused by transpiration.

In paradermal sections note that the veins are parallel to each other and not netted as in dicotyledons.

Corn is a C_4 plant. Its leaf has the recently discovered, and highly efficient, C_4 photosynthetic pathway (Hatch-Slack pathway) and Kranz anatomy (big bundle sheath cells with large chloroplasts). The evergreen privet is a C_3 plant and has the earlier known Calvin-Benson photosynthetic pathway and lacks the Kranz anatomy.

F. Cutting Freehand Sections

The following method of cutting freehand sections (or some variation of it) has long been used and may be considered a "standard" procedure:

1. Firmly grasp stem, root, or other object as illustrated (fig. 6.3). Brace both elbows solidly against ribs to steady hands. Use a new and SHARP single-edged, backed, razor blade (Gem or similar). Rest blade flat on left index finger as shown (fig. 6.3). By wrist and forearm action pull your right hand with the blade toward you across the stem or other object to cut the sections by a smooth, continuous slicing motion, using as much edge length as possible. PULL the blade to SLICE through tissues; don't push and don't chop. Keep right thumb and knuckle well below the cutting edge.

Figure 6.3 Method of cutting a freehand section

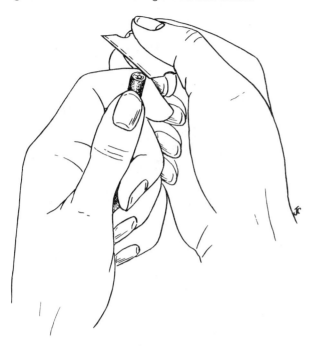

Figure 6.4 How to cut a leaf sample in elderberry pith

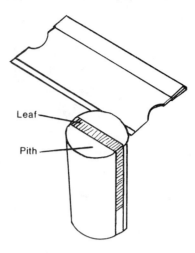

Leaf

Pith

2. Sometimes a combined, coordinated motion of both hands—the right pulling toward you and the left moving away at the same time—may produce good sections. Always SLICE, don't chop!

3. Don't try for a complete section (especially with harder materials). Attempt to cut a narrow, wedge-shaped section that tapers off to a very thin edge ("feather edge"). Cellular details are more easily seen under the microscope using the thinner edges.

4. Always cut many more sections than will be needed at one time. Float off sections into a watch glass of water or place directly on a microscope slide. Push off adhering sections with a dissecting needle or small brush. Pick out the best (thinnest) sections, place on a slide in a drop of water, and cover with a cover glass for observation under the microscope.

5. A piece of leaf can be placed and held firmly between the halves of a longitudinally split cylinder of elderberry pith, Styrofoam, or fresh carrot; and then both the leaf and its surrounding matrix can be cut at the same time, into sections (fig. 6.4). Similarly, small cylindrical or other shaped objects can be placed in suitably hollowed-out grooves of elder pith, Styrofoam, or fresh carrot split into cylinders and cut in the same way as leaves.

Note: Before cutting (ruining?) good tissues, practice on similar noncritical materials until a satisfactory proficiency is obtained. With reasonable practice, adequate (or better) freehand sections can be cut. REMEMBER:

Don't hurry.
Don't make jerky cuts.
Use a new SHARP blade.
Cut many sections; use the best ones.

G. Leaf Modifications

Examine various other leaves provided. Make cross sections of the living material and study the prepared slides. Label the diagrams provided in worksheet 6.3 or make drawings if directed.

In a cross section of the rubber plant *Ficus* find the large cells in the upper epidermis containing crystals. These crystals are called cystoliths. Explain what happens if a 1% solution of HC1 is added under the coverslip?

Compare the leaves studied as to presence of cuticle, number of upper and lower epidermal layers, location of the stomata, number of palisade layers, size of the air spaces in the spongy mesophyll and presence of epidermal hairs. What correlations can you find between the internal structure and the habitat in which the plant grows?

Consult recent textbooks of general botany and plant anatomy for further information.

Questions

1. What is chlorenchyma?
2. Name the functions of a vein.
3. How is a typical green leaf adapted for photosynthesis?
4. What is the importance of air spaces in a leaf?
5. Approximately how much more internally exposed cell wall surface is there in a leaf than externally exposed cell wall surface? What is the significance of this ratio?
6. Of what value is the cuticle of the leaf? the epidermis? List the main functions of the cuticle and epidermis.
7. Do epidermal cells usually have chloroplasts?
8. Of what value are chloroplasts in the guard cells of a stoma?
9. Why do leaves wilt?
10. What is a tissue? an organ?
11. Why must the internally exposed cell wall surface of a leaf be kept moist?
12. Name and locate the tissues of a typical green leaf.

Cross Section of a Dicotyledon Leaf: Evergreen Privet (Ligustrum).

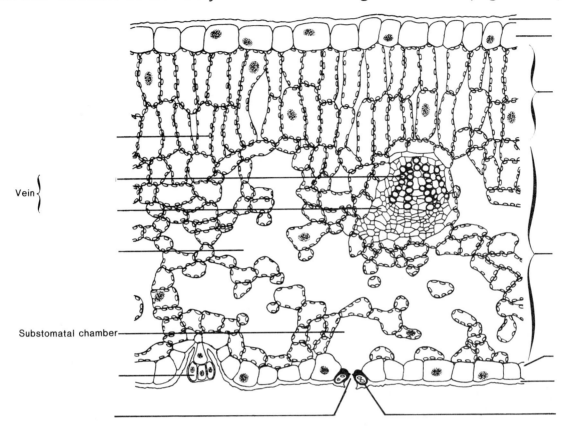

Vein {

Substomatal chamber ——————

Worksheet 6.2

Upper epidermis of *Tradescantia* leaf

Lower epidermis of *Tradescantia* leaf

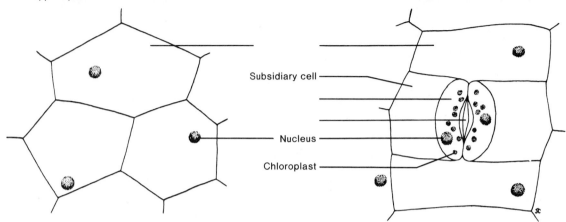

Subsidiary cell

Nucleus

Chloroplast

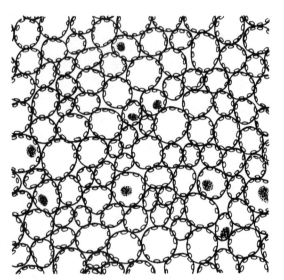

Palisade mesophyll paradermal section

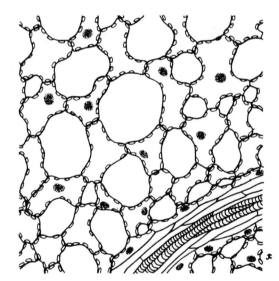

Spongy mesophyll paradermal section

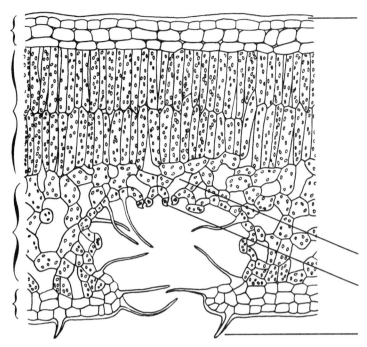

Cross section of oleander leaf

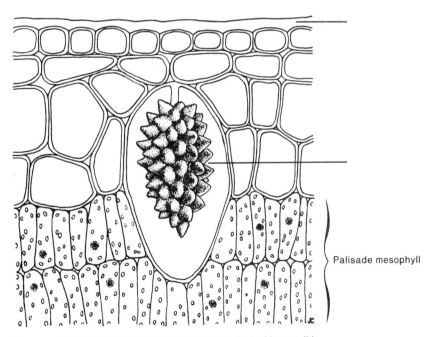

Palisade mesophyll

Cross section of the upper half of a rubber plant leaf with cystolith

The Formation of Food in Leaves: Starch

Plant and other Materials

Materials needed are fresh potato, any commercial dry starch, note paper, filter paper, cheesecloth, and muslin; geranium or *Coleus* leaves from plants kept in darkness (24–48 hours), and similar plants kept in full sunlight; *Coleus* or geranium with variegated leaves kept under similar conditions of light and darkness; fresh grass shoots, kale, garden beans, tobacco, spinach, or broccoli, *Elodea* shoot; dry starch of corn, wheat, potato, and others as desired; boiled 12-mm potato cubes, and diastase (amylase).

Equipment

You will need blank glass slides, several 1,500-ml glass beakers, several hot plates, heavy thread, petri dishes, light screens, India ink and fine pen, colored crayons, 2.5 × 15-cm test tubes; Whatman's No. 1 or No. 3 chromatography filter paper; glass rod or fine medicine dropper, assorted small beakers and Erlenmeyer flasks, spectroscope, scissors; thin glass rods, 15 cm long; flat, circular vials for use with spectroscope; bell jars, absorbent cotton; compound microscope, polarizing microscope (or polarizing discs); blank slides, cover glasses, millimeter ruler, glass plates (25 × 25 cm in size), Syracuse watch glasses, 1,000-ml beaker, hot plate, and 18 × 150-mm test tubes.

Reagents

Acquire an iodine potassium iodide solution, 95% ethanol, sugar (sucrose), 5% solution (glucose), Vaseline, petroleum ether, acetone; strong alcoholic solution of chlorophyll, and phenol red.

Introduction

Photosynthesis is the most important function of the green leaf. Carbon dioxide and water are essential raw materials; chlorophyll and sunlight are necessary for the reaction; sugar (glucose), oxygen, and water are the end products.

$$6CO_2 + 12H_2O \xrightarrow[\text{chlorophyll}]{\text{sunlight}} C_6H_{12}O_6 + 6O_2\uparrow + 6H_2O$$

carbon dioxide   water   glucose   oxygen   water

Radiant energy of sunlight is converted to available chemical energy of the glucose molecule. Photosynthesis is the most important chemical reaction to people worldwide because they are totally dependent upon photosynthesis for all their food and oxygen supply.

The entire photosynthetic process may be divided into two general parts:

1. The light reaction (photolysis) is a series of reactions for which light is necessary. This is an unbelievably fast (practically instantaneous) series of reactions during which water is broken down, oxygen released, and ATP and $NADPH_2$ are generated.
2. The dark reaction (carbon dioxide fixation) is a much slower (but still extremely fast) series of enzymatic reactions that do not require light but use the energy generated in the light to reduce CO_2.

An important end product here is phosphoglyceraldehyde (PGAL). Phosphoglyceraldehyde is an unstable and highly reactive compound that may be used immediately by the plant as food, for building and repair of cells, or converted into glucose.

Glucose is a comparatively inert compound and may be considered the first stable food product formed. When an abundance of glucose is formed in the plant, much of it is converted into starch (the first visible product of photosynthesis) and stored in this concentrated insoluble form.

This stored starch may later be changed back into sugar and translocated to other parts of the plant. The presence of starch in a leaf may thus be considered good indirect evidence of photosynthesis, even though it is not the first stable food product formed; therefore, the following simple tests outlined are for starch instead of sugar.

Directions for Writing Experiments

Experiments are to be recorded in worksheet 7.1. All lettered and numbered divisions of the directions for this exercise are similarly represented in worksheet 7.1. Carefully perform all experiments and make the suggested observations before filling in the blanks or making sketches. All sections of worksheet 7.1 are to be properly filled in before leaving the laboratory, except for certain parts necessarily carried over until the following period. Any additional material should be written on separate sheets of notepaper and handed in with worksheet 7.1.

A. Starch Test

Place a very small amount of starch in a drop of water on a glass slide, and add a drop of dilute iodine solution. What change occurs? Repeat the experiment, using sugar instead of starch. Apply this starch test to notepaper, filter paper, cheesecloth, muslin, or raw potato.

Storage of Starch in Leaves

As noted earlier, the presence of starch in a leaf may be considered good indirect evidence of photosynthesis. Starch may be detected in leaves by the following method:

1. Using a hot plate for heat, first remove any water soluble anthocyanin pigments from the leaves by immersing them in boiling water for a few minutes. Tie a long thread to the petiole of your leaf so that it can be handled with minimum risk of burns.
2. Then soak your leaf in ethyl alcohol that is heated by placing the alcohol beaker in a water bath. The hot alcohol will extract the chlorophyll and carotene pigments. Save the extract for use in part E.
3. When the chlorophyll has been removed, rinse the leaves in cool water to make them pliable. Test for starch by placing the leaves in petri dishes and adding enough iodine solution to cover them. What happens if starch is present? Apply this starch test to
   a. leaves picked from a plant at sunset, i.e., a plant that has been in full sunlight all day.
   b. leaves picked from a plant at sunrise, i.e., a plant that has been in darkness overnight.

B. Relation of Light to Photosynthesis

Place light screens on leaves of a plant that has been kept in total darkness for one to two days. Expose the plant with attached light screens to sunlight for several hours. Remove the leaves from the plant and test for starch as in A. Is starch present in any part of the leaf? What conclusion may be drawn from this experiment? Make colored sketches in the data sheet to show the results.

C. Relation of Chlorophyll to Starch Formation

Sketch a variegated leaf of a *Coleus* or geranium plant that has been kept in the sunlight (or use a leaf picked from such a plant). Outline the green portion of the leaf with India ink, then remove the chlorophyll, sketch the decolorized leaf, and test for starch. Record the results by means of a third sketch in the data sheet, then color the sketches properly.

D. Starch Synthesis without Photosynthesis

Photosynthesis does not occur in darkness, and plants kept in darkness do not manufacture sugars or store starch.

1. Use plants of *Coleus,* bean, or geranium that have been kept in darkness 48–72 hours or until starch free (test to make certain). Still keeping the plants in darkness, cut off several leaves and float the leaf blade(s) on a 5% solution of glucose in a petri dish. Now cover, and allow it to remain in complete darkness for another 48 hours.
2. After the 48-hour period in darkness on the glucose solution, bring the leaves into the light and test for starch as in previous parts of this exercise. Was starch present in any of the leaves? Explain what has happened.
3. Repeat the previous experiment using variegated leaves of *Coleus* or geranium. Did the colorless, nonphotosynthetic part of these leaves form starch? Explain your results.
4. Write a short paragraph on worksheet 7.1 concerning the previous experiments, explaining how starch may be formed in a leaf without photosynthesis occurring. Do you believe this could happen in nature?

E. Properties of Chlorophyll

1. Examine a filtered alcoholic solution of chlorophyll by holding it up to the light (viewed by transmitted light). Place the solution against a dark background (viewed by reflected light), and note the difference in appearance. What color is the chlorophyll with reflected light? This phenomenon is called *fluorescence.*
2. Place a few ml of a chlorophyll solution into a tightly corked vial, and place it in direct sunlight. Put a similar sample in a locker or some other dark place. Compare the vials' contents at the next laboratory period. Has any change occurred?
3. Use the chlorophyll extract obtained in part A or use several consecutive lots of chopped leaves of grass, kale, garden beans, tobacco, spinach (use frozen; thaw and blot dry before use), or broccoli shoots, and extract chlorophyll by gently boiling or simmering in 500 ml of 95% ethyl alcohol in a 1,500-ml glass beaker on a hot plate *(never use an open flame!)* until a dark green solution is obtained. Now cool, filter, and adjust (testing with a hydrometer) until the alcohol content of the solution is 80 to 85%. Filter again if necessary.
4. Place 10 ml of the chlorophyll solution into a test tube, and add up to 1 ml of distilled water. Then add 5 ml of petroleum ether, slowly and carefully. Note the color of each layer. Shake the tube vigorously and allow the mixture to stand

undisturbed for a few minutes. Describe the result. The yellow pigments that are separated from the chlorophyll are *xanthophyll* and *carotene*. Which rises to the upper half of the mixture, the alcohol or the petroleum ether?

Make colored sketches in the data sheet to record these results.

F. Paper Chromatography

Separation of the various pigments in a chlorophyll solution may be accomplished by simplified paper chromatography.

1. Use a strong, freshly prepared solution of chlorophyll, such as that extracted for part E3 of this exercise. Cut strips about 15 mm wide and 20–25 cm long from Whatman's No. 1 or No. 3 chromatography filter paper to fit inside (without touching) large diameter (2.5 cm) test tubes. Clip the corners off one end of the strip (minimize handling with the fingers to avoid getting oil on the paper).
2. Use a glass rod or pipette to place a drop of chlorophyll solution about 25 mm from the clipped end of a filter paper strip. Allow to air dry, then repeat the process until five to ten drops of chlorophyll have been added to the original spot. A very direct method of providing chlorophyll is to fold, twist, and tightly squeeze a fresh leaf of tobacco, bean, spinach, or similar leaf between the fingers to produce a green-colored fluid. Make a spot on the filter paper strip with four or five drops (drying after each) of this green fluid, or press the torn and wet leaf tissue directly on the paper several times to form a spot. Which of these methods of chlorophyll extraction gives the best results? Which one do you regard as the most scientific? Be prepared to explain your answer.
3. For the solvent, use five parts of petroleum ether mixed with one part of acetone.

   Warning! This mixture is extremely flammable. Keep away from open flames.

   Pour about 12 mm of this mixture into a vertically placed test tube and drop a paper strip into the solvent with the chlorophyll spot at the bottom of the tube but not immersed in the fluid. Allow it to remain undisturbed for 20 minutes or until a good separation of pigments occurs.
4. Observe the solvent as it ascends past the green chlorophyll spot, moving any soluble pigments upward with it. Each pigment migrates upward at its own rate, independently of any other pigment molecules present, resulting in a series of color bands or spots vertically spaced at different levels on the paper strip. The distance any pigment moves upward is specific for that pigment under a given set of conditions.
5. The approximate position on a paper strip occupied by a compound (in this case a pigment spot) is designated by a term called the R_f value. This is the ratio determined by dividing the distance traveled from the baseline by the solvent into the distance traveled from the same baseline by the solute (pigment spot). For example, assuming the solvent has moved upward 10 cm from the point where the pigment sample was applied, and the center of the chlorophyll A spot has moved 4 cm from the same location, then the R_f value of this pigment would be 4/10 or 0.40. In this manner, determine the R_f values for each of the pigment bands or spots formed on a chromatogram. Note that the yellow-green chlorophyll B is most strongly adsorbed and forms the first color band or spot nearest the bottom of the strip. The blue-green chlorophyll A appears next above chlorophyll B. Xanthophylls are yellow and occur above the chlorophyll A, while the orange, red, or deep yellow carotenes appear as a band some distance above the xanthophylls.
6. Make a natural-sized diagram of the paper strip, showing the exact dimensions and location of the original color spot, and the bands or spots of chlorophyll A, chlorophyll B, xanthophylls, and carotenes. Indicate the R_f values for each.

   Other types of chromatography are thin layer (TLC), column, and gas.

   Consult the catalogs of supply houses for ready-to-use chromatography kits.

G. The Spectrum of Chlorophyll

White light may be split into its component colors by means of a spectroscope, diffraction grating, or prism. The colors appear as a band, called the *spectrum,* ranging from red to violet as indicated by the diagram in worksheet 7.1.

1. Observe the normal spectrum, then insert a vial of an alcoholic chlorophyll solution into the spectroscope, or place it between the light source and the grating or prism, and note any changes from the normal spectrum. Are these changes due to the chlorophyll or the alcohol in which it is dissolved? What effect would the glass of the vial have on the spectrum? How would you determine whether the alcohol or the glass affected the normal spectrum?

   Indicate the *absorption bands* of chlorophyll by shading the diagram of the spectrum in the proper regions. Explain the significance of the absorption of the color bands by the chlorophyll solution.

2. A more precise measure of the absorption spectrum may be obtained by using a spectronic 20 or similar spectrometer and recording the extinction over a range of wavelengths. On a graph, plot the percent of light absorbed against the wavelength and compare with similar graphs in your textbook. Is there any difference? Explain why.

Consult the text for further details.

H. Gas Utilized by Photosynthesis

1. Use two *Coleus,* bean, or geranium plants that have been kept in darkness 48–72 hours, or until starch free (test to make certain).
2. Control plant: Place one plant along with a 125-ml beaker of water under a large, open-topped bell jar (sealed to a glass plate with Vaseline). Loosely plug the open top with absorbent cotton. Note that air with a normal concentration of CO_2 may enter this jar freely.
3. Experimental plant: Place another plant under a similar bell jar along with a 125-ml beaker two-thirds filled with a 30% solution of potassium hydroxide (absorbs CO_2). Plug the open top with a rubber stopper. Note that this plant will be living in a CO_2 free atmosphere.
4. Expose both plants 4–6 hours in bright sunlight, then remove a leaf from each plant and test it for starch. Was starch present in the leaves from both plants, or in the leaves of one plant only? Describe your results.

Does this experiment indicate that carbon dioxide is or is not necessary for photosynthesis? Give reasons for your answer, and include them in a short paragraph on worksheet 7.1, explaining the results of this experiment.

I. Starch

More starch is stored in plants than any other food material. Other foods commonly stored in plants are proteins, sugars, fats, and oils. Various other substances are found within plant cells or encrusting the walls, but these will not be considered at this time because of the greater economic importance of starches as human food; for example, cornstarch is used to make corn syrup and glucose. Starch is also of great importance industrially, as it is used for sizing paper and textiles, for stiffening, and in making dextrin (an adhesive and sizing agent).

Chemically, starch is a polysaccharide and yields glucose on complete hydrolysis, or following phosphorolysis. Each plant forms a starch granule of characteristic structure and shape that is usually different from the starch granules of other plants. Because of this fact, it is usually possible to identify the various starches by means of direct microscopic examination. See figures 7.1, 7.2, and 7.3.

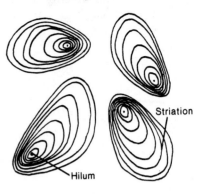

Figure 7.1 Potato starch granules

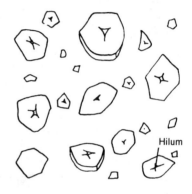

Figure 7.2 Corn starch granules

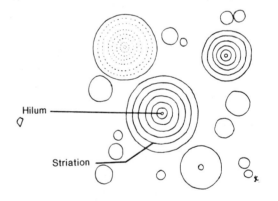

Figure 7.3 Wheat starch granules

J. Preparation of Starch Samples

Because small quantities of starch are difficult to obtain commercially, a simple procedure will be outlined for its extraction from plant parts.

Soak dry seeds or fruits (achene, caryopsis) in water overnight, or until the pericarp or seed coats are completely loosened. Remove and discard the seed coats or pericarp, embryos, or other nonstarchy materials, then pound and grind cotyledons or endosperm in a mortar, using a small amount of water to make a smooth paste.

Spread the paste on a clean glass plate to air dry. When dry, remove from glass, crumble into small pieces, and grind into a fine powder.

Peel or debark tubers, rhizomes, roots, or similar fleshy structures and chop them into small pieces. Pound and grind in a mortar to make a smooth paste, dry on a glass plate, then regrind into a fine powder.

Bits of broken vascular tissues and cell walls will appear in the powder but are easily distinguished from starch granules. With the starch samples provided, use the key on page 55 to identify and name each unknown starch.

K. Potato Starch

Cut a thin section of raw potato tuber and mount it in water. Look for starch granules within the cells. About how many granules are there in a single cell? Do the granules vary much in size? If the section has been cut from near the cork layers (peel) of the tuber, one may find small cubical crystals of protein in the cells with the starch.

Draw (to proper scale) several starch granules. Add the title and labels.

Carefully lift the cover glass and remove the section of potato tuber. Replace the cover and examine the starch granules that have remained in the water. If the section is to be kept for later examination, make a fresh slide by lightly scraping the cut surface of a potato tuber, then mount a small portion of the scraping in water. Avoid too much material; the water of the mount should be only faintly milky. Carefully study the starch granules. What is their size? Measure a large one by comparison with the diameter of the field (h.p.), and note the range of variation in size. What is their shape? Tap the coverslip gently or tilt the microscope while observing them. Do the grains slide or roll? What does this indicate regarding their shape? Note the faint concentrically arranged markings or *striations* (striae). These represent successive layers of starch deposited about the growth center, the *hilum* (plural, *hila*). Is the starch deposited equally on all sides of the hilum?

Add a little dilute iodine solution to one side of the cover glass and draw through with filter paper. Examine the starch grains after treatment with this reagent. What has happened? The blue color disappears on heating, reappears after cooling.

L. Cooked Starch

Boil several 12-mm cubes of potato tuber until soft. Study a water mount of cooked starch granules, l.p. and h.p., and compare with the uncooked starch. Are the cooked granules different in appearance? What is the reaction of cooked starch to iodine solution? to polarized light? How is a simple starch paste prepared?

Draw several granules of cooked starch.

M. Enzymatic Digestion of Starch

Make a thin aqueous suspension of starch in a Syracuse watch glass. Stir in a small quantity of *diastase* (amylase), cover, and allow to remain several hours in a warm place or in an oven at 37°C. The starch granules will be variously digested or degraded, depending on the length of treatment by the enzyme. Study a water mount of digested starch granules under the microscope and compare with the untreated starch, noting differences in appearance of the two samples.

Draw several granules of digested starch. Make a thin (0.5%) aqueous suspension of starch. Pour about 20–25 mm (4–5 ml) of this into a test tube and test for sugar by adding an equal amount of Benedict's solution and heating five minutes in a water bath or very carefully to boiling over a flame. A copper red precipitate indicates that sugar is present. One presumes the test should be negative. Why?

To another test tube add 20–25 mm (4–5 ml) of the starch suspension, then stir in a small amount of diastase. Allow to stand in a warm place (37°C) for 1–1½ hours. Test this starch suspension with iodine solution every 15 minutes or until a blue color no longer appears. Then test for sugar with Benedict's solution as directed above. Is sugar now present in the suspension? If so, explain how it was formed.

N. Demonstration

Examine various starches under a polarizing microscope or a compound microscope fitted with polaroid discs. What is the appearance of a starch grain under polarized light? Why are starch grains said to be doubly refractive (anisotropic) under polarized light? Where do the dark bands cross in a starch grain under this light? What is polarized light? What are crossed Nicols?

O. Optional

Draw starch grains from several species of plants as they appear under polarized light. Make the largest grain about 6 cm in length, with the others in direct proportion.

The Plant's Uses of Its Photosynthetic Sugar

The photosynthate, a mixture of glucose and fructose ($C_6H_{12}O_6$), is used by the plant directly or may be employed in the construction of various substances in different parts of the plant, many of them not only useful to the plant but to man as well.

A. Cell Walls (Cellulose)

Cell walls constitute the mechanical framework. Cellulose ($C_6H_{10}O_5$)n, variously modified in the plant by cutin, suberin, or lignin, is of great economic importance (wood, lumber, fuel, coal, lignite, peat, cork, paperpulp, fibers of flax, hemp). Cellulose is vitally important in certain chemical industries.

B. Reserve Foods

1. *Carbohydrates*
    a. *Sugars:* glucose, fructose ($C_6H_{12}O_6$), and sucrose (cane sugar, $C_{12}H_{22}O_{11}$). Sugars are important foods. They are not usually stored in great amounts in many plants, but some like sugar cane or sugar beet may contain a high percentage of sugar.
    b. *Starches* ($C_6H_{10}O_5$)n are formed in plastids from sugar. This is the form in which plant food is most commonly stored, and is the most important source of food for man.
    c. *Hemicelluloses* are formed as extra layers on walls and are modified forms of cellulose. Examples are date seeds or certain other palm seeds (vegetable ivory).
    d. *Pectins* or fruit jellies.
    e. *Gums:* examples are gum arabic and cherry gum.
2. *Lipids:* (fats, oils, waxes, fatty acids). Proportion of O is small compared with C and H. Common fats in plants are olein ($C_{57}H_{104}O_6$), palmitin ($C_{51}H_{98}O_6$), and stearin ($C_{57}H_{110}O_6$).
3. *Proteins* are highly complex compounds forming the most important, even if not the most abundant, of the reserve foods. Proteins contain C, H, O, N, S, and sometimes phosphorus. Examples are aleurone, globulins, nucleoproteins, gliadin of wheat, and zein of corn. Protein molecules are large and complex; for example, zein of corn ($C_{736}H_{1161}N_{184}O_{208}S_3$).

C. Secretions

The following are some diverse substances formed by the living cells:

1. *Essential oils* (volatile): examples are clove oil, cedar oil, peppermint oil.
2. *Resins, pitch, spruce gum, Canada balsam.*
3. *Camphor:* a gum of unknown use to the plant.
4. *Caoutchouc:* basic of natural rubber.
5. *Pigments:* chlorophyll, xanthophyll, carotin, anthocyanin, flavones.
6. *Alkaloids:*
    a. Morphine from *Papaver*
    b. Nicotine from *Nicotina*
    c. Aconitine from *Aconitum napellus*
    d. Strychnine from *Nux vomica*
    e. Cocaine from *Erythroxylon*
    f. Codeine from *Papaver*
    g. Berberine from *Berberis*
    h. Atropine from *Atropa*

7. *Enzymes* cause chemical changes without themselves entering permanently into the reactions as follows:
    a. Diastase converts starch into sugar.
    b. Zymase converts sugar into alcohol and CO_2.
    c. Lipase converts fats to soluble fatty acids.
    d. Pepsin converts proteins into peptones.
    e. Invertase (sucrase) converts sucrose into glucose and fructose.

D. Protoplasm

Some of the plant's food is used to build up the living protoplasm.

E. Energy

Much of the plant's food is used in the plant's respiration and is broken down to release energy.

Questions

1. In this experiment, why are the tests made for starch instead of glucose?
2. During the night what happens to starch stored in the leaf?
3. Why is there so much starch in leaves at the end of the day?
4. What four pigments may be found in a chlorophyll solution?
5. Why is carotene important in the diet of animals?
6. What may cause the yellow and brown colors of autumn leaves?
7. What gases diffuse into and out of a leaf?
8. Can one gas diffuse into a leaf at the same time that another diffuses out? Can a poisonous gas diffuse into a leaf? Explain.
9. What happens to the energy derived from sunlight during photosynthesis?
10. Name the gases present in the atmosphere and state the proportions (percentages) in which they occur.
11. What is the spectrum?
12. What does the term *control* mean as applied to an experiment?
13. Name and describe pigments in a chlorophyll solution in the order of their appearance (bottom to top) on a paper chromatogram.
14. What is the value of starch to the plant?
15. In what parts of the plant is starch most commonly stored?
16. Why is starch an ideal storage product for plants?
17. Why is sugar a poor storage product for plants?
18. What is a simple test for starch?
19. Why is starch a polysaccharide?
20. What is hydrolysis? phosphorolysis?
21. What happens to starch granules when cooked?

Key to the Identification of Starch Grains

1a. Hila Centric, or apparently lacking
  2a. Individual granules largely polygonal in outline
    3a. Aggregates present
      4a. Aggregates elliptical or rounded
        5a. Granules larger (commonly 5 to 10 μm) **Oat**
        5b. Granules smaller (commonly 3 to 7 μm) **Rice**
      4b. Aggregates not rounded, linear or small groups **Buckwheat**
    3b. Aggregates wanting, hila very distinct (granules 15 to 35 μm) **Corn**
  2b. Granules not polygonal, rounded or more or less irregular
    3c. Granules kidney shaped, large fissured hila
      4c. Outline quite regular **Bean**
      4d. Outline quite irregular
        Few or no aggregates or compound granules **Pea**
    3d. Not kidney shaped, rounded with facets *Cassava* **(tapioca)**
      4e. Some compound granules, very irregular **Acorn**
  2c. Granules distinctly round, quite variable in size
    3e. Larger granules showing occasional fissured hila **Rye**
    3f. Hila indistinct, barely perceptible
      4f. Granules smaller (18 to 30 μm) **Barley**
      4g. Granules larger (28 to 50 μm) **Wheat**
1b. Hila Excentric
  2d. Granules ovoid, pear shaped to elongated
    3g. One end truncately cut
      4h. Truncate end abruptly tapering, hila indistinct **Ginger**
      4i. Truncate end not tapering, large v-shaped hila **Orris root**
    3h. Not truncate
      4j. Hila usually at larger end, fissures *Maranta* **(arrowroot)**
      4k. Hila usually at smaller end, pinpoint
        5c. Distinctly pear-shaped, lamellations very distinct
          6a. One end with distinct projection **Canna**
          6b. End projection usually wanting **Potato**
        5d. Granules elongated and more or less curved
          6c. Broad end more or less truncate **Yam**
          6d. Broad end not truncate, irregular **Banana**
          6e. Truncate end narrower with blunt tip **Curcuma**
        5e. Bell-shaped granules, some compound granules **Sweet Potato**
  2e. Granules quite irregular as to shape and outline
    3i. Hila usually at broader end, many small granules **Horse Chestnut**
    3j. Large fissured hila **Chestnut**
  2f. Granules showing facets
    3k. Hila transversely fissured **Sago**
    3l. Hila radiately fissured **Sweet Potato**

Worksheet 7.1

Test for Starch

A. The Iodine Test for Starch

1.

Substance tested	Original color	Color after addition of iodine solution
Starch solution		
Sugar solution		
Potato		

2. Storage of starch in leaves
   a. Results of the application of iodine test for starch:
      1. Leaves picked from plant at sunset

      2. Leaves picked from plant at sunrise

   b. Conclusions

B. Relation of Light to Photosynthesis

Sketch leaves below

1. Results of iodine test.
   a. Color of portion of leaf exposed to light

   b. Color of portion of leaf kept from light

   c. Conclusions

C. Relation of Chlorophyll to Starch Formation

Sketch leaf below

1. Results of iodine test.
   a. Color of portion of leaf containing chlorophyll

   b. Color of portion of leaf lacking chlorophyll

   c. Conclusions

D. Starch Synthesis without Photosynthesis

Write your paragraph here. Use a separate sheet of paper if necessary.

E. Properties of Chlorophyll

1. Fluorescence of chlorophyll
   a. Color by reflected light

   b. Color by transmitted light

2. Action of light on chlorophyll
   a. Describe appearance of chlorophyll solution left in light

   b. Describe appearance of chlorophyll solution left in dark

   c. Conclusions

3. Pigment Separation
   a. Pigment(s) found in alcohol layer

   b. Pigment(s) found in petroleum ether layer

F. Chromatography

1. Make a drawing of a chromatogram on a separate sheet.

G. The Spectrum of Chlorophylls

1. Fill in the absorption bands of a chlorophyll solution:

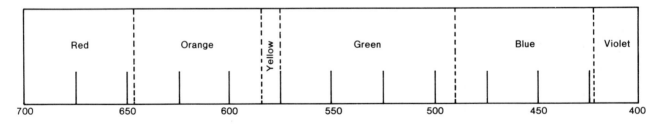

Wavelengths indicated are in nanometres (nm).

H. Gas Utilized by Photosynthesis

Write your paragraph here. Use a separate sheet of paper if necessary.

8 Respiration

Plant and Fungus Materials

You will need eight or more 500-ml lots of germinating wheat seeds, two or more 500-ml lots of wheat seeds killed by boiling in water; root, stems, leaves, and flowers of geranium, tobacco, petunia, or similar plants, and a moist yeast cake.

Equipment

Obtain absorbent cotton, window screening, assorted-sized beakers (some 2,000 ml), two bell jars, dark colored paper, two widemouthed bottles with stoppers, one similar stopper fitted with thistle tube and bent glass delivery tube; six test tubes (25 mm × 15 cm), shell vials (8 dram); four 500-ml-size thermos bottles, three laboratory thermometers (marked in both C and F scales); five plain glass cylinders 25 × 4.5 cm in size, each containing a strip (20 × 4 cm in size) of 7-mm mesh hardware cloth (wire screen) and fitted with stoppers; several pieces of 7-mm glass tubing 20 cm long; incubator; fermentation tubes, test tubes (15 mm × 15 cm); Erlenmeyer flasks (50 ml, 250 ml, and 500 ml), Erlenmeyer flask (500 ml) with side arm, several 150-ml widemouthed bottles with rubber stoppers and fitted with bent glass delivery tubes, short section (6 cm) of 3-mm glass tubing, 7-mm glass tubing 90 cm long to make simple still, No. 7 rubber stopper (with one hole) to fit simple still, No. 7 solid rubber stopper for 500-ml side arm flask; hot plate, ring stands and clamps, Drink-O-Meter alcohol testing tubes, 7-mm bore rubber tubing, beakers (30 ml, 100 ml, and 250 ml), glass rods for mixing, and a 10-ml graduated cylinder.

Reagents

Required reagents are baryta water, phenol red, 5% sodium hydroxide solution, sodium hydroxide pellets, pyrogallic acid (to make sodium pyrogallate), iodine potassium iodide solution, white Karo syrup; 10% solutions of sucrose, glucose, fructose, lactose, galactose, maltose, dextrin, and starch.

Introduction

Living cells of all plants need energy to maintain life, and this energy is obtained from food by the process of respiration.

Respiration is the oxidation of complex foods within all living cells of an organism to form simpler compounds (eventually carbon dioxide and water) with an accompanying release of energy. It occurs continuously, day and night, in all living cells and if it stops, the cell dies. Respiration is not a single quick reaction, but involves a gradual series of intermediate steps (perhaps 50) and compounds before carbon dioxide and water are finally produced; a specific enzyme catalyzes each step, and the food being oxidized is the substrate. The energy released by respiration is of vital importance to a plant, although much of it is lost as heat. But not all energy escapes as measurable heat; some of it is retained and utilized within the cells to support metabolism. The retained energy is used to synthesize fatty acids, amino acids, and glycerol, and for growth and repair of cell contents. Respiration is a complex and extremely important process, and a fundamental knowledge of its characteristics is absolutely essential to the understanding of any living organism.

Aerobic Respiration

Aerobic respiration occurs mostly in higher plants, and is characterized by the oxidation of organic substances (i.e., foods, sugars commonly) in living cells by free atmospheric (molecular) oxygen (O_2) to produce, eventually, carbon dioxide and water plus the release of energy. Aerobic respiration proceeds gradually, step by step, with a small amount of energy released at each step. The overall reaction is shown as follows:

$$\underset{\text{glucose}}{C_6H_{12}O_6} + \underset{\text{oxygen}}{6O_2} \xrightarrow{\text{enzyme}} \underset{\substack{\text{carbon}\\\text{dioxide}}}{6CO_2\uparrow} + \underset{\text{water}}{6H_2O} + \underset{\text{energy (heat)}}{673 \text{ kcal*}}$$

Early stages of aerobic respiration occur in the cytoplasm and the final stages in the mitochondria.

Anaerobic Respiration

Anaerobic respiration occurs in the absence of free oxygen (O^2) and results in the incomplete oxidation of food to yield

---

*kcal = kilocalorie. The amount of heat required to raise the temperature of 1,000 ml (1 liter) of water 1°C.

intermediate compounds, each capable of still further oxidation, plus the release of energy. It occurs commonly in fungi and bacteria. When the anaerobic breakdown of food is accompanied by evolution of gas, the process is called fermentation. Alcoholic fermentation by yeast is such an anaerobic process and is called the anaerobic respiration of yeast. This, however, is not exactly the same as that characteristic of certain strictly anaerobic bacteria.

The disaccharide sucrose (cane sugar) is not fermentable by yeast and must first be split outside the yeast cells by the enzyme sucrase (invertase) of yeast into its component monosaccharides, glucose, and fructose, each of which is fermentable.

$$C_{12}H_{22}O_{11} \xrightleftharpoons{\text{sucrase}} C_6H_{12}O_6 + C_6H_{12}O_6$$

sucrose (left), glucose (right), fructose (right)

Glucose or fructose diffuses into yeast cells where it is acted upon by the enzyme zymase of yeast to produce ethyl alcohol (ethanol) as an intermediate product plus carbon dioxide and energy.

$$C_6H_{12}O_6 \xrightarrow{\text{zymase}} 2C_2H_5OH + 2CO_2\uparrow + 28 \text{ kcal}$$

glucose; ethanol; carbon dioxide; energy (heat)

Alcoholic fermentation by yeast is important in baking where the carbon dioxide bubbles produced by it in rising bread dough cause bread to become light and porous when baked.

Such fermentation is necessary for brewing alcoholic beverages (beer, wine), the production of distilled beverages (whiskey, gin, vodka), and the production of ethyl alcohol for industry, gasohol, and medicinal uses.

Aerobic Respiration

A. Relation of Oxygen to Respiration

Place a few germinating wheat seeds on a disc of moist cotton laid on top of a small platform made of wire screening. Put this setup in a glass dish, tumbler, or beaker, and invert a smaller beaker over it. Pour in enough sodium pyrogallate to cover the lip of the small beaker, then cover with a bell jar. Sodium pyrogallate absorbs all oxygen from the air. What happens to the solution inside the smaller beaker? How much oxygen is in the atmosphere? Does the solution rise an equivalent volume in the smaller beaker? Set up a similar apparatus as a control, using water instead of the sodium pyrogallate. Cover both bell jars with paper. Why? Examine after three to four days. What has happened? How may these results be explained? Enter the results in worksheet 8.1.

To make sodium pyrogallate, add 20 ml of 30% NaOH to 80 ml of 10% pyrogallic acid. Use immediately after mixing.

B. Relation of Carbon Dioxide to Respiration

1. Fill a widemouthed bottle one-third full of germinating wheat seeds and put a tight stopper on the bottle. Use a control bottle containing similar seeds that have been killed by boiling. After an hour and one-half, replace the stopper with one equipped with a thistle tube and bent glass delivery tube so that air in the bottle may be bubbled through *baryta water*. Place the end of the delivery tube in a test tube containing baryta water and note any changes that occur as the air bubbles pass through it. Repeat the experiment with the control bottle.

    Barium hydroxide (in baryta water) and carbon dioxide unite to form a white, water-insoluble precipitate of *barium carbonate*.

$$Ba(OH)_2 + CO_2 \longrightarrow BaCO_3\downarrow + H_2O$$

    Blow gently through a glass tube into some baryta water. Compare the results with those obtained from the two bottles of seeds. What do these tests indicate?

2. Use three vials or test tubes, each two-thirds filled with a dilute solution of phenol red (delicate pink in color). Place several living germinating wheat seeds in one tube, several killed germinated wheat seeds in another, and, as a control, leave one tube empty. If the color of the phenol red (pH range 6.8–8.4) changes immediately on placing the germinating wheat in the solution, it will be necessary to add a drop or two of 0.1% sodium bicarbonate or lithium carbonate to restore the original pink color. When the color has been adjusted properly in all tubes, proceed with the following directions. Keep all tubes in subdued light and examine at intervals of 5 minutes, 15 minutes, and 30 minutes. Has the color of the phenol red changed in any tube? In which tube? To what may this change be attributed? What is the source of the carbon dioxide causing this color change?

C. Respiration and Temperature in Germinating Seeds

Disinfect and germinate a quantity of wheat seeds under sterile conditions for 18 to 24 hours. Fill a sterile thermos bottle two-thirds full of the germinating seeds and plug with cotton carrying a thermometer. The bulb of the thermometer should be placed deep in the middle of the seed mass. Prepare a second thermos bottle, using similar seeds that have been killed in boiling water and then cooled to room temperature. Add a small amount of 4% formalin to the dead seeds in order to check the growth of microorganisms. Why must bacteria and other microorganisms be prevented from growing in the dead seeds? Equip a third thermos bottle with a cotton plug and thermometer, but omit the seeds. Why is it desirable to include this empty bottle (control) in the experiment? Record the temperature of the seeds in each bottle and of the room every 2 hours for a period of 18 to 24 hours. Make a record of these readings on worksheet 8.1.

D. Respiration in Plant Parts

Partition each of five plain glass cylinders (about 25 × 4.5 cm in size) into two sections by a strip of coarse (7-mm mesh) wire screen. In one side of each cylinder loosely pack leaves, stems, roots, and flowers, respectively, leaving one cylinder empty for a control. Stopper each cylinder. After about 2 hours, pour a little baryta water down the side of each cylinder, or force out the contained air through baryta water by means of a delivery tube as in part B 1 of this exercise. Do all living plant parts respire? Do all parts respire at the same rate? Describe and explain the results of this experiment.

Anaerobic Respiration

A. Evidence of Yeast Fermentation

Fermentation within a two-hour laboratory period may be demonstrated as follows:

1. Use a 50% solution of white Karo syrup or molasses or a 10% solution of glucose (dextrose). Place 10 ml of this solution in a fermentation tube.
2. Thoroughly mix one cake of moist yeast or a packet of dry yeast in 100 ml of distilled water.
3. Add 5 ml of this yeast suspension to the fermentation tube, invert several times and manipulate to disperse the yeast and to fill the upright (closed) arm of the tube. At room temperature, gas (carbon dioxide) will collect in the closed arm of the tube. Measure in millimeters the amount of gas collected. Much quicker results will be obtained by using warm solutions of syrup or sugar or by incubating the tube at 50°C (about 122°F). Observe the tube at intervals shown on worksheet 8.2.

B. Fermentation of Different Carbohydrates

Your instructor will add 5 ml of the yeast suspension previously described to fermentation tubes, each containing 10 ml of a 10% solution of a different carbohydrate: glucose, sucrose, lactose, fructose, galactose, maltose, dextrin, and starch. The yeast should be thoroughly dispersed within the tubes. The tubes may be kept at room temperature, but quicker results will be obtained if they are incubated at 50°C or placed close to a warm radiator.

Figure 8.1 Testing for carbon dioxide

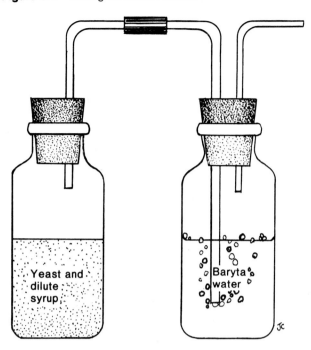

Measure in millimeters the amount of gas collected in each tube. Note which carbohydrate ferments first and which one eventually forms the most gas.

Fill in the chart (worksheet 8.2) to show the amount of gas produced by each carbohydrate at the times indicated. Are all carbohydrates fermentable? Define fermentation.

C. Testing for Carbon Dioxide

Use two 125-ml or 150-ml widemouthed bottles. In one bottle place 100 ml of 50% white Karo syrup or 10% glucose solution to which has been added one cake of moist yeast. Mix well to disperse the yeast. In the second bottle place 100 ml of baryta water. Fit a bent glass delivery tube through the rubber stoppers so that any gas formed in the yeast culture will be bubbled through the baryta water (fig. 8.1). Add a 3-mm glass tube to the stopper in the bottle of baryta water to permit escape of air; allow to stand at room temperature or incubate at 50°C. If the gas slowly bubbling through the baryta water contains an appreciable amount of carbon dioxide, a white precipitate will be formed.

D. A Chemical Test for Ethyl Alcohol (Ethanol)

For rapid fermentation, add 50 ml of white Karo syrup to 100 ml of water in a 500-ml side arm distilling flask, then crumble and thoroughly mix it in with one cake of moist yeast (Fleischmann's). Allow it to ferment 1 to 1 1/2 hours in a warm place, shaking gently at intervals.

Respiration   57

Figure 8.2 Reflux air-cooled distilling aparatus. Note: the vertical glass tube measures 30 cm from the rubber stopper to the curve at top. See text

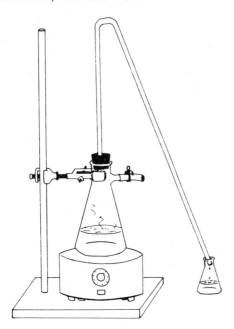

Figure 8.3 Testing for ethyl alcohol vapor with Drink-O-Meter tube

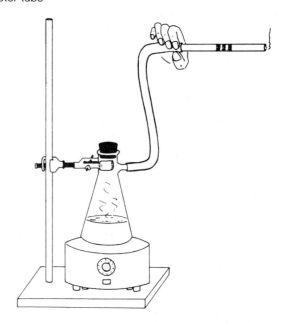

Use the simple air-cooled reflux distilling apparatus (fig. 8.2) to distill gently and slowly 20–25 ml of the above mixture into a 50-ml flask. Note the odor of ethanol near the apparatus and in the distillate itself.

WARNING! Simmer the flask on a hot plate **very slowly** and carefully to avoid boiling over of mixture. Remember alcohol boils at 78°C, so don't overheat.

Pour 5 ml of the distillate into a test tube, then add 2 ml of strong iodine potassium iodide solution followed (with gentle shaking) by 2–3 ml (or enough to just decolorize the iodine) of 5% NaOH. Allow it to stand two to three minutes. Ethanol in the presence of NaOH reacts with iodine to form iodoform, which first appears as a pale turbidity, soon settling out as a yellow precipitate. Note the characteristic odor of iodoform at the mouth of the test tube.

E. Testing for Alcohol Fumes with Drink-O-Meter Tubes

Remove the distilling apparatus from the side arm flask, plug it with a rubber stopper and continue to gently heat until the contents bubble again, and vapor is seen coming from the side arm. Take a 30 to 35 cm length of 7-mm rubber tubing, insert a freshly opened Drink-O-Meter tube in one end, then attach the other end to the side arm of the distilling flask (fig. 8.3). Hold the Drink-O-Meter tube horizontally about 25 cm above the flask, thus allowing the rising vapors to pass through it (do not allow the crystals to become wet). If the yellow crystals in the tube change to green, this indicates that ethyl alcohol is present.

The green color appears gradually and spreads slowly with very dilute concentrations of alcohol. With higher concentrations the color appears quickly and spreads rapidly throughout the crystals. How many seconds did it take for this color change to occur in each of the three color bands in your tube?

Special Note: One should be aware that many law enforcement officers, especially those of the Highway Patrol, may use a breath-testing tube of this type to help screen out drunken drivers.

Write for Drink-O-Meter tubes to

Luckey Laboratories, Inc.
7252 Osbun Road
San Bernardino, California 92404

Questions

1. What is respiration?
2. Does respiration occur in living green cells? in living colorless cells? in dead cells?
3. What is the importance of respiration to plants?
4. Why do germinating seeds release so much heat?
5. What problems do the respiration of stored grains, fruits, and vegetables present?
6. Contrast aerobic and anaerobic respiration.
7. What are the differences between respiration and breathing?
8. Contrast photosynthesis and respiration.
9. What is metabolism? catabolism? anabolism? Which of these apply directly to respiration?
10. What is the role of enzymes in respiration?
11. What is the economic importance of yeast?

Aerobic Respiration

A. Relation of Oxygen to Respiration

Sketch of apparatus

1. What has happened to the seeds over the sodium pyrogallate?

   What is the condition of the seeds over the water (i.e., the control)?

   How do you account for these changes?

   Conclusions:

B. Relation of Carbon Dioxide to Respiration

1. Results with live seeds:

   Results with dead seeds:

2. Record the color changes of the phenol-red solution in the following chart:

Experimental Material	Color of Phenol Red after		
	5 Minutes	**15 Minutes**	**30 Minutes**
Vial containing living germinating wheat			
Vial containing killed wheat			
Control (no seeds)			

To what do you attribute the color change?

Conclusions:

C. Respiration and Temperature in Germinating Seeds

1. On the following chart indicate the temperature of the room by means of a dotted line (. . . . . . .), the temperature of the dead seeds by a broken line (- - -), the temperature of the living, germinating seeds by a continuous line (—), and the temperature of the air within the empty bottle by (oooo).

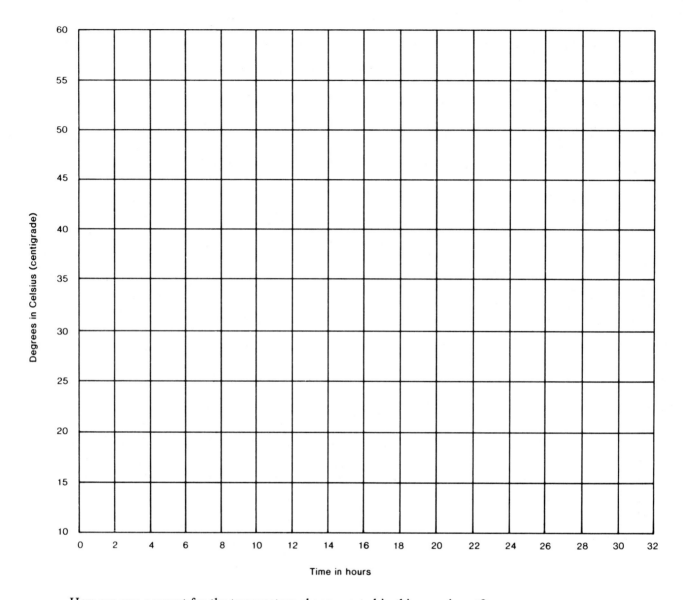

How can you account for the temperature changes noted in this experiment?

D. Respiration in Plant Parts

1. In the following chart record the amount of precipitate as large, medium, small, or none.

	Roots	Stems	Leaves	Flowers	Control
Amount of precipitate					

Worksheet 8.2

Anaerobic Respiration

A. Evidence of Yeast Fermentation

Millimeters of Gas in Fermentation Tube after				
15 Minutes	30 Minutes	45 Minutes	1 Hour	2 Hours

Temperature in degrees Celsius _____

B. Fermentation of Different Carbohydrates

	Millimeters of Gas in Fermentation Tube after				
Carbohydrate	15 Minutes	30 Minutes	45 Minutes	1 Hour	2 Hours
Sucrose					
Glucose					
Fructose (Levulose)					
Lactose					
Galactose					
Maltose					
Dextrin					
Starch					

Temperature in degrees Celsius _____

C. Testing for Carbon Dioxide

How long did it take for a precipitate to appear? Was it light, medium, or heavy in amount?

D. A Chemical Test for Ethyl Alcohol (Ethanol)

What is the reason for not testing a portion of the fermenting mass of yeast and sugar without first distilling it?

What are the medical uses of iodoform?

E. Testing for Alcohol Fumes with Drink-O-Meter Tubes

How long did it take for the first yellow band in the Drink-O-Meter tube to turn green? the second band? the third band?

Comment on the importance of commercially produced ethyl alcohol (ethanol) for gasohol and industrial, scientific, and medical uses.

Write here the usual chemical equations for:

Photosynthesis:

Aerobic respiration:

What is the essential difference in energy relationship between photosynthesis and aerobic respiration?

Comment critically on the importance of each in the life of a plant.

Contrast photosynthesis and respiration according to the following:

	Photosynthesis	Respiration
a. Energy relationships (stored or released)		
b. Raw materials		
c. Function		
d. Period of greatest activity		
e. End products		

9 Transpiration

Plant Materials

You will need shoots of geranium, *Coleus, Zebrina, Tradescantia, Sedum, Impatiens;* wheat or oat seedlings 3.8 cm tall grown in 50-mm pots; two potatoes, two apples, each pair matched for size; and celery stalks.

Equipment

Obtain widemouthed 250-ml Erlenmeyer flasks, tumblers, 10 × 10-cm cardboard squares (paraffined), potometers, atmometer bulb, large bell jar, and heavy glass plate; laboratory scales, absorbent cotton, a paring knife, and a small electric fan.

Reagents

Eosin solution, 1%, and Vaseline are needed.

Introduction

Transpiration is the loss of water vapor from the aerial parts (especially leaves) of the living plant. Because transpiration is essentially the evaporation of water from the wet surfaces of the internally exposed cell walls of a leaf, it is thus subject to the same physical laws that govern evaporation and diffusion. Excessive transpiration is an ever-present danger to a plant and is probably the greatest single factor in the death of plants during drought. It prevents mesophytic plants from thriving in arid regions and causes loss of seedlings and cuttings, and wilting of garden, crop, and ornamental plants. About 90% of the water lost by transpiration escapes through the stomata (stomatal transpiration); the remaining 10% is lost through the cuticle (cuticular transpiration).

Transpiration is probably the principal force concerned with the ascent of sap in plants, and also functions in cooling the plants as liquid water is converted to water vapor.

Guttation is the loss of liquid water from the aerial parts of the living plant and occurs through continuously open pores, the *hydathodes.*

A. Evidence of Transpiration

1. Insert a vigorous geranium leaf or shoot of *Zebrina* or *Tradescantia* without removing it from the plant into a widemouthed Erlenmeyer flask and plug with cotton carefully fitted around the petiole. Place it in such a way that the leaf will assume its natural position. Take care not to injure the leaf. Similarly, plug an empty flask and set it up for a control. Observe at the end of one hour, two hours. Explain your results.

2. Fill a tumbler nearly full of water, put Vaseline on the edges, and cover with a 10 × 10-cm square of paraffined cardboard with a hole punched through the center. Insert the stem of a geranium (a single leaf of geranium may also be used), *Coleus, Zebrina,* or *Tradescantia* shoot through this hole until it is immersed in the water. Remove the lower leaves of the shoot if necessary. Seal the hole around the plant with Vaseline and cover with a second tumbler (make certain it is dry) sealed to the cardboard with Vaseline. For a control set up a similar apparatus without a plant. Place both sets of tumblers in direct sunlight or in a warm place and observe at the end of one hour, two hours. Has water condensed on the inside of any of the tumblers? If so, how did it get there?

    Which experiment appears most convincing? Give reasons for your belief, and enumerate the advantages of the experiment selected.

B. Rate of Transpiration (Demonstration)

1. Examine *potometers* set up by the instructor (figure 9.1). Each of the smallest divisions on the graduated tube represents 0.01 ml. After the plant has established a uniform rate of transpiration, measure the rate by timing the movement of the air bubble along the tube. Measure rates of transpiration in sunlight, in shade, and in a gentle breeze. Tabulate in worksheet 9.1 and explain any variation in the results. Make a sketch of the apparatus, indicating how it operates.

2. Examine a potometer fitted with an atmometer bulb instead of a plant. Do not touch this bulb with your fingers, for the oil from them will slow down the rate of evaporation from its porous surface. Is more water lost from a living plant shoot or from the atmometer bulb? Compare the rates of water loss from the plant and from the atmometer bulb and explain why one is so much greater than the other.

Figure 9.1 Potometer

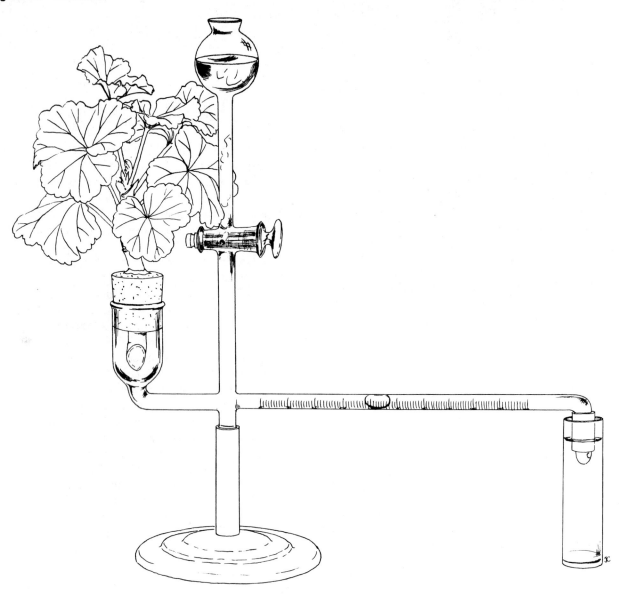

C. Guttation

1. Place a bell jar over a pot of young wheat or oat seedlings (about 3.8 cm tall) that have just been watered. Droplets that subsequently appear on the leaves are water of guttation. This same phenomenon may often be observed on lawns early in the morning, especially during spring. What term is then applied to these drops of water? Is water of guttation real dew? How does real dew differ from water of guttation? Is there any water condensed inside the bell jar? If so, explain its presence.

D. Protective Coverings and Loss of Water

1. Select two potatoes and two apples of uniform size and shape. Peel one potato and one apple, keeping the other (unpeeled) as a check, and weigh each one separately. Weigh each potato and each apple at 2-hour intervals for 24 hours and make a record of the results in worksheet 9.1.

2. Peel off the epidermis from three leaves of *Sedum*, or from leaves of a similar plant, keeping three unpeeled leaves as controls. On a sheet of paper expose all the leaves to the air of the laboratory. Observe at the end of one hour, two hours, the next laboratory period. Explain the results.

E. Rise of the Transpiration Stream

1. Use the stems of *Coleus, Impatiens,* sunflower, or the stalks of celery. Cut off the stems under water and quickly immerse them in a solution of eosin or fast green. Make two or three setups for each plant. Carefully split the stem at intervals to determine the rise of water as shown by the dye in the vessels. Experiment by placing one plant in the sunlight, another in the shade, and one in the breeze of an electric fan or hand held hair dryer. Explain any variation in results. Calculate the rate of water rise per minute for one plant used.

2. Cut off several leafy woody stems under water and quickly place in the dye solutions. Observe at regular intervals by splitting a stem. Determine the rate of water rise per minute in one woody stem such as *Eucalyptus.*

   At this rate how long would it take the water column to reach the top of a tree 25 meters tall?

F. Optional

Observe other experiments which may be set up by your instructor, or you may devise one of your own.

Note: Suitable laboratory transpiration kits are available from the various biological supply houses.

Questions

1. Contrast transpiration and guttation.
2. How is a leaf adapted for the function of transpiration?
3. Does transpiration serve any useful purpose to the plant?
4. May the plant be harmed by excessive transpiration?
5. What are the pores called through which water escapes from the leaf by transpiration? by guttation?
6. Correlate transpiration with the ascent of sap in plants.
7. How strong is the lifting power of transpiration?
8. Comment briefly on the rate of transpiration.
9. How do protective coverings check loss of water from plants or plant parts?
10. What are the protective coverings of a plant?
11. What is cuticular transpiration?
12. What is a xerophyte? a hydrophyte? a mesophyte?

Worksheet **9.1**

Name _____

Transpiration and Guttation

A. Evidence of Transpiration

1. Results No. 1.

2. No. 2.

    Experiment No.   is most convincing to me because

B. Rates of Transpiration; Use of the Potometer

1. In the following chart represent the transpiration rates (in the form of a block graph) of plants under the conditions stipulated. Fill in the entire column for the condition under which most transpiration occurs, with the other columns in direct proportion. Use the following markings:

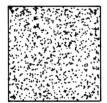  

Sunlight	Shade	Breeze	

2. Results of experiment with atmometer bulb

C. Guttation

Sketch of plants below

1. The conditions necessary for guttation are:
   a.

   b.

   A hydathode is

   Guttation differs from transpiration in that

D. Protective Coverings and Loss of Water

Experimental Material	Original Weight	Weight in Grams at Two-Hour Intervals											
		2	4	6	8	10	12	14	16	18	20	22	24
Peeled apple													
Control (unpeeled apple)													
Peeled potato													
Control (unpeeled potato)													

1. Conclusions

On the following graph plot the figures given on page 68 in terms of actual weight. Indicate the peeled apple by a solid line (—), the control (unpeeled apple) by a broken line (- - -), the peeled potato by a line of dots (. . . .) and the control (unpeeled potato) by a line of small circles (oooo).

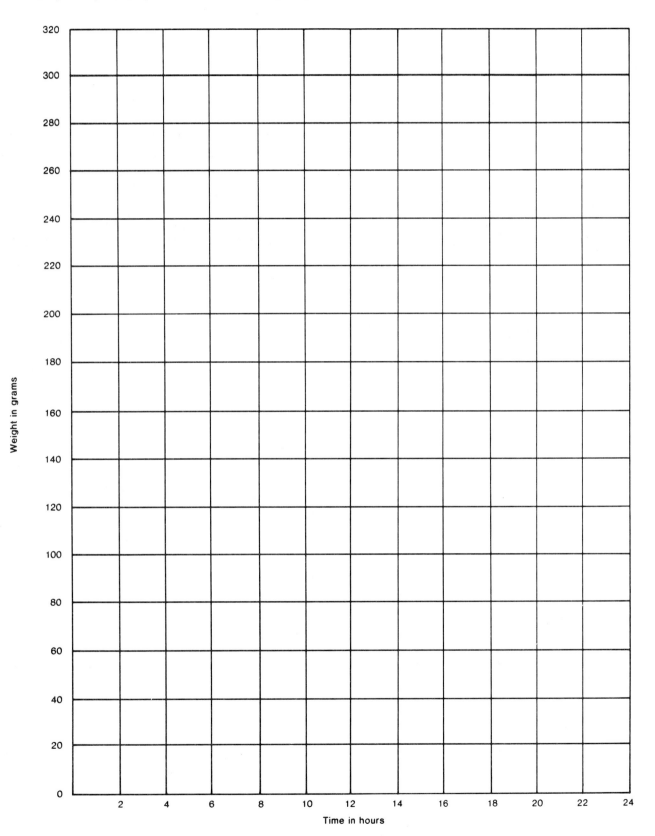

2. Note any changes in the leaves at the end of the laboratory period.

What changes did you note the next period?

What conclusions may you draw as to the efficiency of the epidermis (and its cuticle) in preventing water loss?

E. Rise of the Transpiration Stream

1. Chart the rate of rise in millimeters or centimeters per minute for the plants and conditions as indicated below.

Experimental Conditions	Rise Per Minute in Millimeters or Centimeters			
	Celery	Coleus	Sunflower	
In shade				
In sunlight				
In breeze (fan)				

2. Follow directions of your instructor in setting up these experiments.
What is the calculated rate of rise per minute in the woody stem used?

Time required to reach the top of tree 25 meters tall?

10 Features of Herbaceous Stems

Plant Materials

You will need *Helianthus* plants 15–20 cm tall, each in a 7.6-cm pot.

Equipment

Obtain blank slides and cover glasses, single-edged safety razor blades, 100-ml beakers, tumblers; prepared slides of young *Helianthus* stem (cross section), median longitudinal sections of *Coleus* stem tip, cross sections of *Coleus* stem tip, longitudinal sections of *Elodea* stem tip.

Reagents

A 1% eosin solution will be needed.

Introduction

The stem of a typical plant functions primarily to support the leaves so that they are always exposed to sunlight. Flowers and fruits are also borne on the stem and its branches. The stem serves to conduct water and dissolved mineral salts upward and to transport elaborated food materials downward. Many stems are greatly modified for food storage; others are the main photosynthetic organ of the plant; some are important in the vegetative propagation of the plant (reproduction). The stems studied in this exercise are herbaceous; they are not woody or treelike, and usually die each year. Other types of stems will be studied in later exercises. A fundamental knowledge of structure is essential in order to understand the functions and mechanical features of stems.

A. Comparison of Stem and Leaf Area

Examine a young *Helianthus* (sunflower) plant 15–20 cm tall, or a similar herbaceous plant (a weed?). What is the color of the stem? Is it photosynthetic? Measure it for length and diameter, then compute its surface as if it were a true cylinder. Determine the area of a leaf in the following manner. Trace the outline of the leaf lightly and accurately with a sharp pencil on the millimeter cross-section paper reproduced on worksheet 10.1. By counting the number of complete squares, the approximate area of the leaf may be quite accurately estimated. The area of any flat, irregularly shaped object may be estimated in a similar manner.

Note: Each of the larger squares formed by the boldly inked lines is one square centimeter; the smaller, lighter ruled squares are each four square millimeters in area.

Cut the stem near the base under water, and after a few seconds place the cut end in a solution of eosin. Remove the stem after 10 minutes and split it a distance of about 4 cm from the cut end and note any localization of the dye. Does it rise through definite passageways, or is it diffused throughout the stem? Cut cross sections of the stem above the split part, and locate the same conducting tissues in this plane. What may be deduced from this experiment? In a latter part of this exercise, these channels of conduction will be more clearly defined under the microscope.

B. Cross Sections of an Herbaceous Stem

Make a freehand cross (transverse) section through an internode near the tip of a young sunflower stem, mount in water, and examine with the hand lens and under l.p. of the microscope. Then study the labeled diagram of a young sunflower stem in cross section (fig. 10.1) to help locate the various parts and tissues. Compare this section from the living stem with a similar, stained section on a prepared slide. Enumerate the advantages and disadvantages of each kind of section for this type of study.

The outermost layer of cells is the *epidermis*. Is it as clearly defined as in the leaf? Does it have similar functions? Are there stomata in this tissue? Note the band of firmer tissues about midway between the epidermis and

Figure 10.1 Diagram of young sunflower stem cross section showing location of parts and tissues

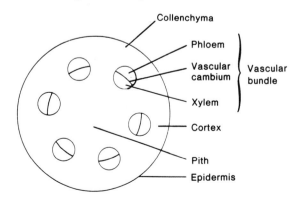

the center of the stem. This is the *vascular ring*, and it is divided into a number of separate *vascular bundles*. The tissue inside the vascular ring is the *pith* (parenchyma); the tissue outside is the *cortex*. The layers of cortical cells with thickened corners just inside the epidermis are *collenchyma cells*. The remainder of the cortex is filled with *parenchyma* cells.

C. The Vascular Bundle

Using prepared slides, again locate the epidermis, collenchyma, cortex, vascular ring, and the pith. Focus on a single vascular bundle. The tissues are stained with two dyes. One stains woody (lignified) walls red; the other stains cellulose walls green. Note the red-stained, thick-walled cells of large diameter. These are the *vessels*, or *tracheae* (singular, *trachea*), of the vascular bundle. Are they nearer the cortex or the pith? If the section is from an older stem there may be other red-stained, thick-walled cells in this section. Where are they located? Is their function the same as that of the vessels?

The red-stained vessels of the bundle are part of the *xylem*, or wood, which is responsible for the upward movement of water and dissolved substances. The vessels also provide some measure of mechanical support to the stem. The *fibers* (sclerenchyma) function entirely for the mechanical support of the stem. Note that the large vessels toward the outside of the xylem are still in the process of differentiation and have not yet become lignified.

Locate the *phloem*, mainly concerned with the downward movement of elaborated food materials. The phloem is composed of sieve elements (*sieve tubes*) and *companion cells*. An occasional *sieve plate* (end walls of cells pierced with holes) may be found in the phloem, but these structures will be seen more clearly in another stem to be studied later.

The red-stained, thick-walled cells in patches on the outer side of the bundles, forming layers outside the conducting phloem, are mechanical tissues, fibers or *sclerenchyma* called the bundle cap. Separating the xylem and phloem is the *vascular cambium*, which contributes to the formation of new cells. This *meristematic layer* cuts off cells that develop into xylem on one side, and cells that develop into phloem on the other side. Is there any evidence that this cambium extends laterally (*interfascicular cambium*) beyond the limits of the vascular bundle? Suggest a reason or advantage for this extension.

Label all parts of the detailed drawing (worksheet 10.2) of a single bundle of a sunflower stem and the accompanying outer tissues as shown.

D. The Stem Tip

The aboveground parts of the plant arise from a mound of continuously dividing cells, the *apical meristem,* found in the tip of every stem and branch. The *primary tissues* of leaves, young stems and branches, vascular bundles, and cortex all differentiate directly from cells derived from the stem tip. Is the epidermis a primary tissue? *Secondary tissues* usually originate from cells derived from the vascular or cork cambium. The instructor will explain these points in detail. The particular study that deals with the development and differentiation of organs and tissues is called *developmental anatomy*. The perennial habit of woody stems is possible because of the meristematic nature of the cells in the stem apex.

Examine on l.p. and h.p., median longitudinal sections cut from stem tips of *Coleus* or a similar herbaceous plant (fig. 10.2). Note the low, concave mound of meristematic cells of the stem tip itself; the young leaves in various stages of development; the *primordia* of buds in the leaf axils; provascular (procambium) strands; and the development of the epidermis, pith, and cortex. An apical meristem is covered by one or more layers of cells called the *tunica*, which encloses a central mass of cells called the *corpus*.

Similarly, study a cross section of a *Coleus* stem tip (fig. 10.3), noting the distinct opposite arrangement of the developing leaf pairs and the circular mass of cells (stem tip cross section) in the center between the youngest (smallest) pair of leaves.

Find the following structures on the median longitudinal section of *Coleus* and label these on figure 10.2: epidermis, cortex, provascular strand of stem, the leaf gap area above the point in the stem where the provascular strand enters the leaf.

Examine a longitudinal section of the stem tip of *Elodea* and compare with the *Coleus* stem. List the differences found. What structural adaptations does the *Elodea* show to its underwater habitat?

No detailed study will be made of the stem tip in this course, but every botany student should know the working fundamentals of this important plant part, and have some appreciation of the universal role it plays in plant development.

Figure 10.2 Longitudinal section of *Coleus* stem tip

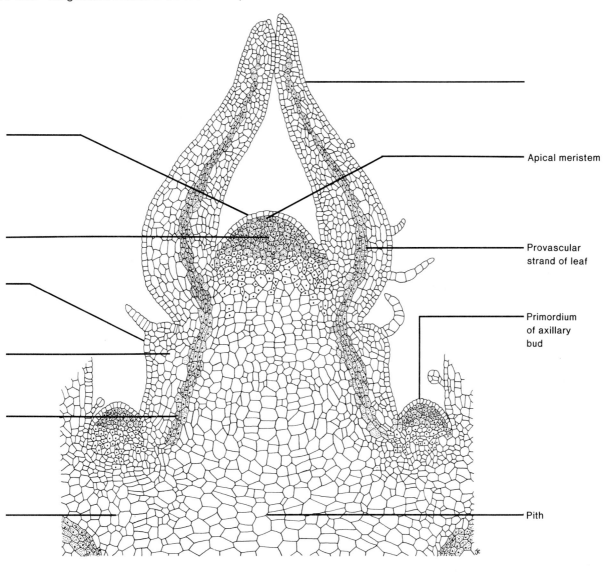

Apical meristem

Provascular
strand of leaf

Primordium
of axillary
bud

Pith

Figure 10.3 Cross section of *Coleus* stem tip

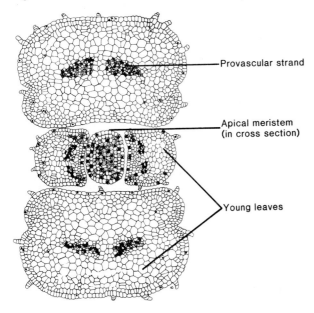

Provascular strand

Apical meristem
(in cross section)

Young leaves

Questions

1. How is an herbaceous stem structurally adapted to serve its functions?
2. What tissues give it mechanical support?
3. What happens when an herbaceous stem loses its turgor?
4. Define *herbaceous stem*.
5. What tissue conducts water upward and elaborated foods downward in a stem?
6. Does the stem of an herbaceous plant ever carry on photosynthesis?
7. What are the parts of a vascular bundle?
8. What is collenchyma?
9. What is the vascular cambium? the interfascicular cambium?
10. Is the herbaceous type of stem characteristic of annuals, biennials, or perennials?
11. Give the functions and characteristics of each stem tissue.
12. Explain the importance of the stem tip in the development of the plant.
13. Briefly discuss the tunica-corpus concept of an apical meristem.

Worksheet 10.1

Name _____

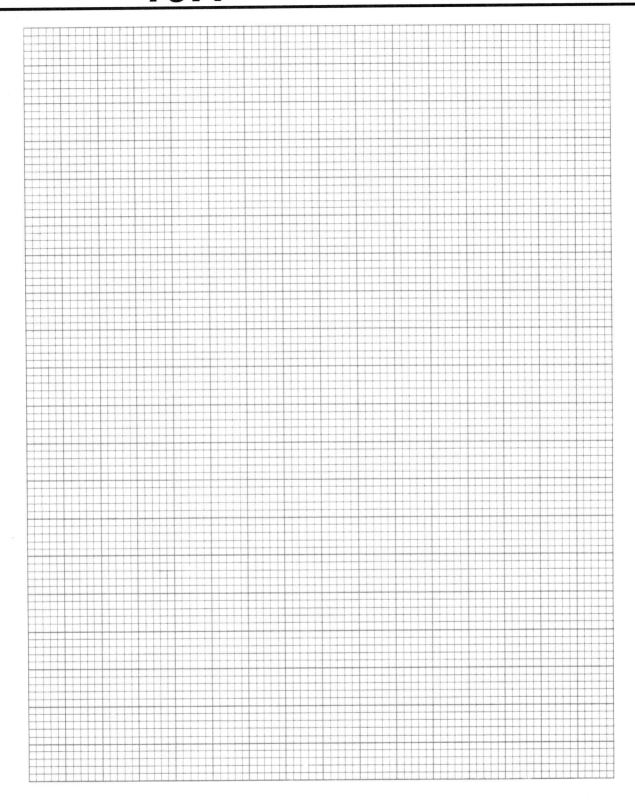

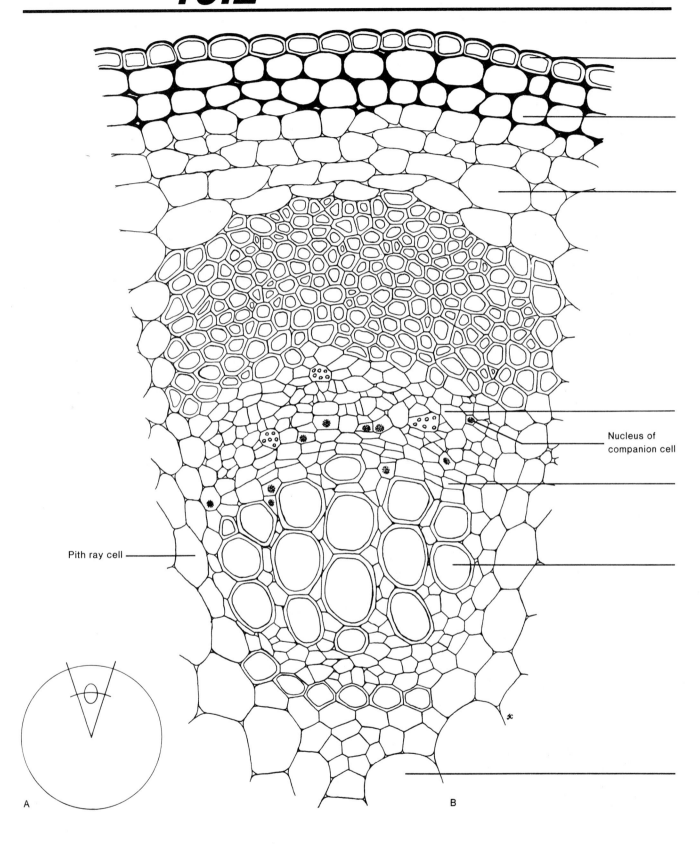

Nucleus of
companion cell

Pith ray cell

A

B

11 Features of Woody Dicotyledonous Stems

Plant Materials

Needed are twigs of hickory, buckeye, lilac (flower and leaf buds); substitutes—*Forsythia*, elm, soft maple, sweetgum, or cottonwood; cross sections (4 cm thick) of 10–20-year-old mulberry, or similar woody stem sanded and polished on one side; a variety of locally occurring leafy twigs (10–15 genera) for parts D and E; basswood twigs, elderberry stems, geranium (*Pelargonium*) shoots, bottle corks, bark of cork oak, sheet cork, and a cork strip showing the stages in cutting bottle corks. *Liriodendron* twigs may be substituted for basswood.

Equipment

Obtain single-edged safety razor blades, a hand lens, 10×; compound microscope, prepared slides of three-year-old basswood stem, (or *Liriodendron* stem), elderberry lenticels; elderberry pith, Styrofoam or fresh carrot.

Reagents

You will need 70% ethanol.

Introduction

Woody stems are permanent structures and, as such, possess certain features not well developed in herbaceous plants. The formation of a strong, woody, central axis is characteristic of them. Other structures, buds and bark, protect the stem during the winter season, in periods of drought, and from injuries due to fungi, bacteria, or mechanical agents. An important function of woody stems is the production of new leaves each spring.

Buds are characteristic structures of woody stems. When they produce only leaves, they are called leaf buds; flowers only, flower buds; both leaves and flowers, mixed buds. The following exercises are designed to present a brief survey of important structures, functions, and taxonomic features of woody stems.

External Features of Woody Stems

A. Twig of Hickory or Buckeye

Note bark, lenticels, buds, leaf scars, bundle scars, and terminal-bud scale scars. Where do you find the largest bud? Are the remaining buds all the same size? What is the length, in millimeters, of the largest bud? of the smallest? Where are the nodes? the internodes? On the cut end, note bark, wood, cambium region, and pith.

When the previously mentioned structures have been identified, add proper labels to worksheet 11.1A. Draw in bundle scars, and label the larger drawing of a leaf scar (worksheet 11.1B).

B. Cross Section of Tree Stems

Examine the polished surface of a cross-section cut from a young mulberry or similar tree. Identify the bark, cambium region, growth rings, early and late wood, sapwood, heartwood, wood rays, and pith. Each growth ring usually represents one year's growth. How old is this block? Could the age of a large tree be estimated by counting the annual rings? What modern uses have been made of tree rings in dating ancient ruins, or the study of climatic conditions of the past?

Diagrammatically draw a triangular segment of the mulberry stem, and label all parts.

C. Buds of Lilac. (*Forsythia*, sweetgum, elm, soft maple, and cottonwood are good substitutes.)

On a lilac twig note features corresponding to those indicated on the hickory stem. How does the lilac twig differ as to position of lateral buds? Is a terminal bud present? Are there any other differences? Select a large bud, and with a sharp knife or razor blade cut it longitudinally in two, being careful to cut exactly in the center. Using a hand lens, carefully examine the inside. Is it a leaf bud or a flower bud? How can you tell?

Continue cutting buds until one is found to be distinctly different inside from the one previously examined. State very carefully, but briefly, the way in which it is different.

Properly identify and label worksheet 11.1C and D.

D. Twigs in Winter Condition

Study a number of twigs from shrubs and trees in winter condition, learn their names, and make a record of their taxonomic characteristics in the accompanying chart (worksheet 11.2). What is winter botany?

E. Optional

Make a simple key for trees in winter condition (use a form similar to that for leaves in exercise 2).

Structure of Woody Stems

F. Basswood Twig in Third Year of Growth

Study prepared slides of a basswood twig, first using l.p. and later h.p. Identify the epidermis, if still present, cork, collenchyma, cortical parenchyma, phloem fibers ("bast"), phloem, phloem rays, cambium, xylem, growth rings, late wood, early wood, wood fibers, vessels, wood rays, and pith. An endodermis-like layer is present in most sections. Note the crystals of *calcium oxalate* in the parenchyma cells of the cortex, and in the dilated *phloem rays*.

Note the circle of alternating triangular- or wedge-shaped areas just inside the cortex. The triangles, with their blunt apices pointing *outward toward the cortex*, have a banded appearance (see worksheet 11.3) due to layers of thick-walled phloem fibers, or "bast" (stained red), interspersed with layers of sieve tubes and companion cells (stained green or blue). A number of phloem rays extend radially through this area, where short rows or small groups of phloem parenchyma cells are present. Carefully note the size, shape, and arrangement of the sieve tubes, companion cells, phloem fibers, phloem rays, and phloem parenchyma cells.

The alternating triangles with their apices pointing *toward the center of the stem* (see worksheet 11.3) are composed of rectangular appearing parenchyma cells. Each of these sectors results from the extreme fan-shaped dilation of a phloem ray. The apex of each connects directly with a primary wood ray extending from the cambium to the pith.

Find the vascular cambium. In what part of the stem is it located? How many cells thick does it seem to be? Describe the shape, size, and arrangement of the cells as they appear in cross section.

When the structures outlined previously have been identified and located, add labels to worksheet 11.3. Examine the cross sections of other woody plants provided. Record your observations as directed by your laboratory instructor.

The xylem should be stained red, although it should not be so bright a red as that of the phloem fibers. Identify the vessels and wood fibers; also describe the cell walls, and the size of the cell cavities. Describe the size, form, and arrangement of the parenchyma cells in the wood rays. What causes the annual growth rings? Where are the largest cells found? Were these formed early or late? How many layers of cells are formed during one growing season?

G. Lenticels

Note the large, corky lenticels of an elderberry twig. With a sharp knife or razor blade, cut off a thin longitudinal portion of the bark, including a lenticel, place it between pieces of elder pith, and cut a transverse section through the bark and lenticel. Place it on a slide, quickly wet it with alcohol, then with water, cover, and examine.

Prepared slides may be used instead to study lenticel structure, but they won't show the chlorophyll-bearing tissue (chlorenchyma) in its living green condition.

Which is the more efficient structure for the interchange of gases, a lenticel or a stoma? Explain.

Make a neat diagram of a section of elderberry bark showing cork, cork cambium, lenticel, and immediate underlying tissues. Indicate by neat green shading any chlorophyll-bearing tissue (chlorenchyma).

H. Cork

Examine cross sections of the stem of *Pelargonium* (house geranium). The outermost layers of this stem are made up of *cork cells*. Examine, using l.p. and h.p., and note the cell's shape and the character of the walls. Are cork cells living? Do they have any contents? What is the *phellogen*?

Compare the cork layers of basswood and elderberry with those of the house geranium.

Study thin sections of bottle corks and compare with the cork cells previously examined. The walls contain *suberin*, which gives cork its characteristic properties.

Examine the demonstration of cork. Note the bark of the cork oak, sheet cork, and stages in cutting bottle corks. List commercial uses of cork. In what region does the cork oak grow? Is there a satisfactory substitute for cork?

Questions

1. Contrast woody and herbaceous stems.
2. What structural features are characteristic of a perennial plant?
3. What is the economic importance of woody stems?
4. List commercial uses of woody stems.
5. How may tree rings (annual rings) be used to determine the date ancient ruins were built? to study climates of the past?
6. What is a bud?
7. Name three kinds of tree buds according to their contents.
8. During what time of the year are buds formed?
9. What prevents buds from freezing in winter?
10. Name taxonomic features of woody stems that are useful in identifying them in winter condition.
11. What mechanical problems arise when a tree has a tall, heavy trunk?
12. How tall may trees grow? Name several very tall trees and give the regions in which they grow.
13. List differences in structural details of woody and herbaceous stems.
14. What is the main structural element in woody stems?
15. What parts of a woody stem are dead? what parts are living?
16. How did the basswood tree get its name?
17. What use has been made of the ''bast'' fibers of basswood in Europe?
18. What is the function of a lenticel?
19. What are the properties of cork? to what are these properties due?
20. Of what value is cork in the plant?
21. List commercial uses of cork.
22. What is an ''annual'' ring?
23. Explain how cork originates and develops in a stem.

Name _____

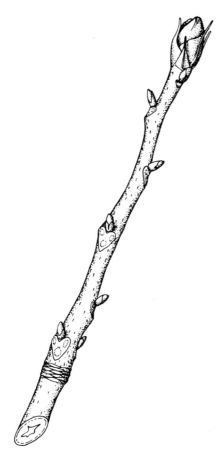

A   Hickory twig

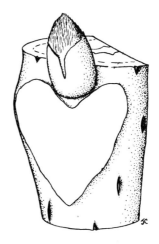

B   Hickory leaf scar (enlarged)

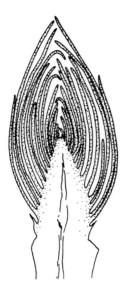

C   Lilac leaf bud

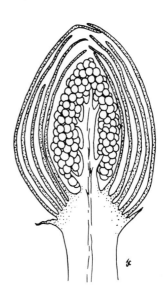

D   Lilac flower bud

Twigs in Winter Condition

Name of Tree	Leaf Arrangement	Twig Color	Leaf Scar (sketch)	Other Conspicuous Characters (thorns, bud-scales, etc.)	Distinguishing Characters (list three)

Cross Section of a Three-Year-Old Basswood Stem (Tilia Americana). *A, Entire Stem Cross Section; and B, Enlarged Stem Segment.*

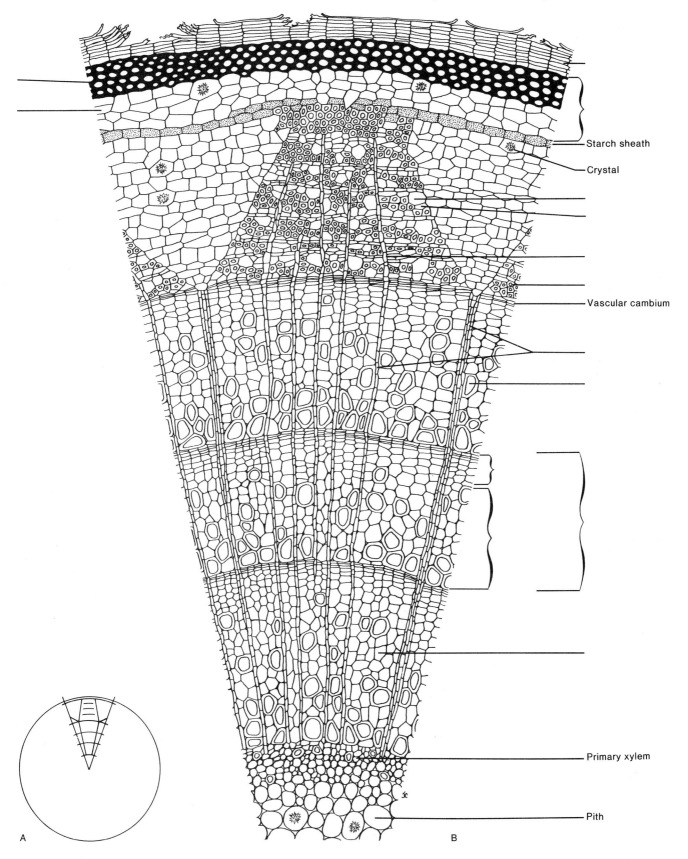

Starch sheath

Crystal

Vascular cambium

Primary xylem

Pith

A

B

12 Structure of Coniferous Wood: Pine

Plant Materials

You will need prepared slides (cross sections) of white pine twigs 3–5 years old; prepared slides of cross, radial, and tangential sections of white pine wood; large (5 × 5 cm) cross, radial, and tangential sections of white pine wood bound between two glass plates; smoothly sanded 5-cm cubes of white pine wood clearly showing cross, radial, and tangential surfaces; similar cubes or blocks of other coniferous woods for identification (see the key on page 99 for examples). Number each block to correspond to the similarly numbered name of each wood type as listed in the instructor's identification sheet.

Equipment

Use a compound microscope, blank slides and cover glasses, single-edged safety razor blades, screw topped widemouth jar, 400 ml capacity; rectangular hot plate, fine pointed curved forceps, and a hand lens, 10×.

Reagents

Cupric acetate, 10% solution; 10% glycerine, glycerine jelly, and nail polish will be required.

Introduction

Coniferous woods (soft woods) have *tracheids* as the main structural element in their composition; wood fibers and vessels characteristic of angiosperm woods (hard woods) are entirely lacking. Coniferous wood, having no vessels (pores), is often termed *nonporous* wood (fig. 13.2A). Resin ducts are found in coniferous woods. Pine tar, resins, and turpentine are obtained from coniferous woods, and much of the paper pulp is made from spruce. Much of the lumber supply of the world comes from coniferous woods. In this exercise, there will be an opportunity to study in detail the three standard cuts of a coniferous wood, namely, *transverse* (cross), *radial,* and *tangential.*

A. Pine Stem

Examine prepared slides of transverse sections of a young pine stem. Note and describe the relative size of areas occupied by pith, vascular elements, and cortex. Note the

resin ducts. What is their size and shape? In what tissues do they occur? Are the cell walls lignified, or of cellulose? How may this be inferred? Do the ducts as they appear in the section contain resin? Explain why it may be lacking. Note the demonstration of pine tar, commercial resins, and turpentine in the display cabinet.

B. Transverse Section of Pine Wood

Study prepared slides of pine wood cross sections, first under l.p., then in detail using h.p. Instead of vessels and wood fibers, the xylem here is composed entirely of tracheids. Are the cell walls of uniform thickness throughout? Are there indications of openings from one cell to another? Study and describe the size and modifications of the tracheids at the line of junction between two growth rings. How do the cells of the wood rays differ from the tracheids?

Check worksheet 12.1A representing a group of tracheids, two wood rays, and a resin duct at the junction between two "annual" growth rings. Label all structures.

C. Radial Section of Pine Wood

Examine prepared slides of pine wood cut in a radial longitudinal plane, first under l.p., later in detail using h.p. Note the elongated tracheids with bordered pits (seen in worksheet 12.1B in face view), and the wood rays crossing the tracheids at right angles. Why is a tracheid considered to be a single cell? Identify the bars of Sanio. What is the shape of an entire tracheid as seen in this section? Can the yearly growth rings be identified in this section? If so, by what means? Is it possible to determine which part of the section was nearest the center of the tree? Explain. Describe the resin ducts as they appear in this section.

Check the diagrammatic drawing of a radial section of pine wood (worksheet 12.1B). Label all parts.

D. Tangential Section of Pine Wood

Examine prepared slides of pine wood cut in a tangential longitudinal plane, first under l.p., then in detail using h.p. Describe the shape of the wood rays (seen in worksheet 12.1C in cross section), their arrangement, and the average number of cells in each. How many cells wide are the rays? How does the width of the tracheids as seen in this view compare with their radial dimension? What is the shape of an entire tracheid as seen in this section? Locate the bordered pits. How do they differ from those found in the radial section? Describe the resin ducts as they appear in the tangential section.

Check the diagrammatic drawing of a tangential section of pine wood (worksheet 12.1C). Label all parts.

E. Three Standard Sections

Study the simplified stereodiagram (fig. 12.1) of a pine wood cube showing enlarged features of the cross, radial, and tangential sections as seen in their three-dimensional relationship to each other and compare with the microscopic slides of these sections.

F. Demonstrations

Large (5 × 5 cm) sections of pine wood cut in three planes as previously described have been mounted between glass plates. Examine them closely with a hand lens, and l.p. of the microscope. Using a hand lens and the unaided eye, identify the diagnostic features of each section, and learn to recognize each of the three standard sections at sight. Examine the blocks of coniferous wood placed on display. Identify the structural details of this material, and learn to recognize a number of these woods at sight.

Sketch three 5-cm squares, each representing one of the three standard cuts of a coniferous wood. Indicate in these squares the characteristic features (grain) of each cut, as determined by the unaided eye or the hand lens.

Properly identify and label each square. Make similar sketches for each additional kind of coniferous wood as indicated by the instructor.

Note: If 5 × 5-cm thin sections are unavailable, use smoothly sanded 5-cm cubes of pine wood clearly showing representative cross, radial, and tangential surfaces.

G. Demonstrating Resin in Resin Ducts

Use fresh 5–10-year-old twigs of white pine, spruce, or other conifer known to contain resin ducts. Cut and quickly immerse a number of 3–4 cm long pieces in a 10% aqueous solution of cupric acetate, and allow to remain 2–3 weeks or until the resin in the ducts has turned green. Then cut cross sections 60–100 micrometers (μm) thick with a razor blade (sliding microtome is better), and mount temporarily in 10% glycerine. Any resin in the resin ducts or other tissues will be stained a beautiful emerald green color. Sections may be stored in 10% glycerine, or permanently mounted in glycerine jelly.

Blank slides, cover glasses, and all instruments used should be placed on a warming plate kept at 55–60°C. Place a portion of glycerine jelly about the size of a match head in the center of a slide, and wait until it melts. Blot away excess glycerine from the section, and slide it into the melted glycerine jelly. Allow to penetrate a few minutes, then add a warm cover glass. Keep on the warming plate until the glycerine jelly fills the cover glass, then remove and cool on a flat surface. Clean away excess glycerine jelly, and seal the cover glass edges with nail polish.

Questions are at the end of exercise 13.

Figure 12.1 Pine wood cube

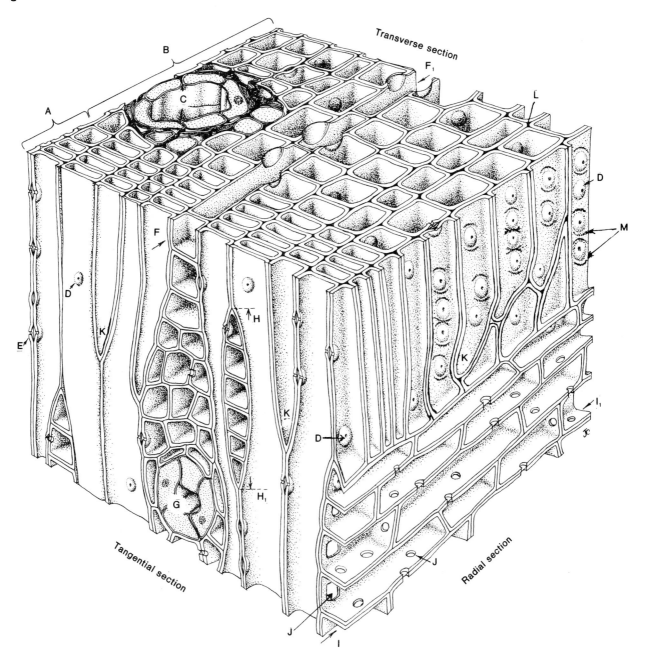

Key to Pine Wood Cube Labels

A. Summer wood
B. Spring wood
C. Vertical resin duct, cross section
D. Bordered pit, face view
E. Bordered pit, in section
F. F and F_1—wood ray, longitudinal section
G. Transverse view of horizontal resin duct in large wood ray
H. H and H_1—wood ray, cross section
I. I and I_1—longitudinal section of wood ray
J. Simple pit in wood ray cell
K. Tracheid ending
L. Intercellular space
M. Bars of Sanio (crassulae)

Name _____

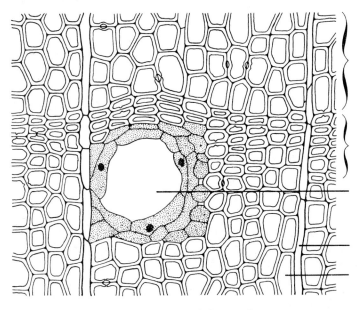

A Cross section of pine wood

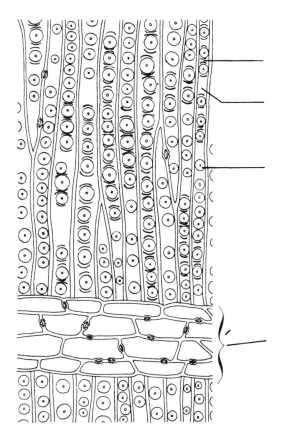

B Radial section of pine wood

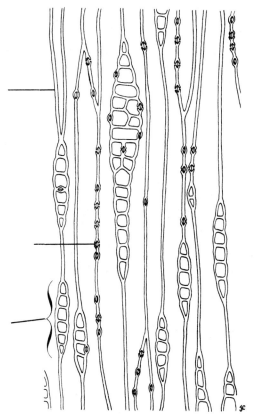

C Tangential section of pine wood

Exercise 13

Structure of Angiosperm (Dicot) Wood

Plant Materials

Materials required are oak and maple twigs 3–5 years old; prepared slides (cross sections) of oak and maple stems 3–5 years old; prepared slides of cross, radial, and tangential sections of oak and maple wood; large 5 cm (square) cross, radial, and tangential sections of oak and maple wood, each set of sections bound between two glass plates; smoothly sanded 5-cm cubes of oak and maple wood clearly showing cross, radial, and tangential surfaces; and similar cubes or blocks of other angiosperm wood for identification. (See key on page 99 for example.) Each cube or block will be numbered to correspond to its similarly numbered name as listed on the instructor's identification sheet.

Equipment

You will need a compound microscope, hand lens (10×), and single-edged razor blades.

Introduction

Angiosperm (dicotyledonous) woods have wood fibers and vessels (tracheae) as the main structural elements in their composition. Tracheids may be present, but they never constitute the bulk of the xylem as they do in coniferous woods. The vessels of some dicotyledonous woods are visible to the naked eye and are often called pores. Dicotyledonous wood, as lumber, is important in many kinds of building operations, trimming and finishing, furniture manufacture, and making certain grades of paper pulp. Each kind of wood has definite physical and structural characteristics that make it suitable for certain specific uses.

In this exercise there will be an opportunity to study in detail the three standard cuts of dicotyledonous wood; namely, transverse (cross), radial, and tangential. Facts learned about coniferous and dicotyledonous woods in this and the preceding exercise will be used immediately in the very practical task of identifying common woods by means of a simple key.

A. Oak Stem

Examine prepared slides of the cross section of a young (3 to 5 years old) oak stem. Note and describe the relative areas occupied by pith, vascular elements, cortex, fibers, and cork. What shape is the pith in this section? Compare this stem with the section of a young pine stem previously studied. Enumerate the differences between these stems.

B. Transverse (Cross) Section of Oak Wood

Study prepared slides of oak wood cross sections, first under l.p., then in detail using h.p. The xylem is composed essentially of tracheae (vessels) and wood fibers; however, tracheids and wood parenchyma are also present. Are the larger vessels (pores) arranged in any definite pattern? Why is oak called a ring-porous wood? Identify early wood, late wood, and the annual growth rings. Are the wood rays all the same size? Describe the simple (uniseriate) rays, and the compound (multiseriate) rays. Tyloses may be found (especially in white oak) in the larger vessels, frequently filling the lumen of the vessel.

Identify and label the previously named parts and check the diagrammatic drawing (worksheet 13.1A) representing a transverse section of red oak wood at the junction between two annual growth rings.

C. Radial Section of Oak Wood

Examine radial longitudinal sections of oak wood, first under l.p., then in detail using h.p. Note the wood fibers and vessels as they appear in this longitudinal section. How long are the wood fibers in proportion to their thickness? How thick are the walls? What elements seen in this section contain pits? Are the pits simple or bordered? How does the (trachea) vessel of oak differ from the tracheid of pine? What is the distribution of tyloses (if present) in the longitudinal cut of a vessel? Note the wood rays crossing at right angles to the wood fibers and vessels. Identify narrow (simple) and broad (compound) rays. The sections of the larger rays (flatsided view) exposed in the radial sections of oak wood help give quarter-sawed oak its characteristic grain.

Identify and label the parts, and check the diagrammatic representation (worksheet 13.1B) of a radial section of red oak wood.

D. Tangential Section of Oak Wood

Examine prepared slides of oak wood cut in a tangential longitudinal plane, first under l.p., then in detail using h.p.

List the essential differences between the wood fibers and vessels as seen in this view as compared with their appearance in the radial section. The wood rays are seen in cross section (end-on view) in this cut of oak wood. How many cells wide is a simple ray? a compound ray?

Identify and label the parts, and check the diagrammatic representation (worksheet 13.1C) of a tangential section of red oak wood.

E. Three Standard Sections

Study the simplified stereodiagram (fig. 13.1) of an oak wood cube showing the enlarged features of the cross, radial and tangential sections as seen in their three-dimensional relationship to each other and then compare with the microscopic slides of these sections.

F. Maple Stem

Examine prepared slides of a young (3 to 5 years old) maple stem. Identify and describe the pith, vascular elements, cortex, wood fibers, and cork, comparing these with similar features of the oak stem. Compare this stem with the sections of pine and oak previously studied. Enumerate the similarities and differences between these stems.

G. Maple Wood

Using l.p. and then h.p. of the microscope, study cross, radial, and tangential sections of maple wood. In contrast to oak wood, which is ring porous (fig. 13.2B), maple wood is diffuse porous (fig. 13.2C), with its vessels (seen in cross section) scattered uniformly throughout the width of an annual ring. Can this difference be seen with the unaided eye? Compare maple wood with oak, noting similarities and differences between the vessels, wood fibers, wood rays, early wood, late wood, and annual growth rings.

Draw representative selected areas from cross, radial, and tangential sections of maple wood, illustrating structural details comparable to those found in oak wood.

H. Demonstrations

Large (5 cm square) sections of white oak and sugar maple, cut in the three planes previously named, have been mounted between glass plates. Using both the unaided eye and the hand lens, locate and identify the diagnostic features of each section. Inspect the blocks of various kinds of angiosperm wood and the sections of angiosperm wood on display. Learn to identify a number of these woods at sight.

Draw three 5-cm squares, each representing one of the three standard sections of oak wood, and similarly, three squares representing similar sections of maple wood. Sketch within these squares the characteristic grain pattern for each section as determined by the unaided eye and the hand lens. Make similar sketches for each additional kind of angiosperm wood as indicated by the instructor.

Note: If 5 × 5-cm-thin sections are unavailable, use smoothly-sanded 5-cm cubes of oak, maple, or other angiosperm woods clearly showing representative cross, radial, and tangential surfaces.

I. Identification of Common Woods

Using the accompanying key, identify each of the various kinds of wood represented by the numbered blocks or cubes on the supply table. Upon completion of this work, a student should be able to identify immediately on sight, any of the woods studied. Before leaving the laboratory, practice with a partner until proficient in this identification.

Note: In order to see maximum detail with a hand lens of pores, vessels, tracheids, wood rays, etc., you may have to slice cleanly (don't chop) a thin 2 to 3-mm² portion from the corner of a wood block to remove saw marks and other confusing details. Moisten the freshly cut portion with water, let dry briefly, and observe. Moisten again if necessary. Check with your lab instructor before cutting any wood samples.

Questions

1. What is the characteristic structural element of coniferous woods?
2. Contrast coniferous wood with that of an angiosperm, such as oak or maple.
3. What are the commercial uses of coniferous (soft) woods? dicotyledonous (hard) woods?
4. What are resin ducts?
5. What are naval stores?
6. In what sections of the United States and Canada do coniferous forests grow? forests of dicotyledonous trees?
7. What does the term *coniferous* mean?
8. Do bordered pits weaken the tracheid walls? Why or why not?
9. Why is coniferous wood said to be without pores?
10. Enumerate the identifying characteristics of the transverse, radial, and tangential cuts of pine wood, and also a dicotyledonous wood.
11. Based on the arrangement of pores, how may woods be classified?
12. Be able to name several very hard woods, hardwoods, softwoods, and extremely light and soft woods.

Figure 13.1 Oak wood cube

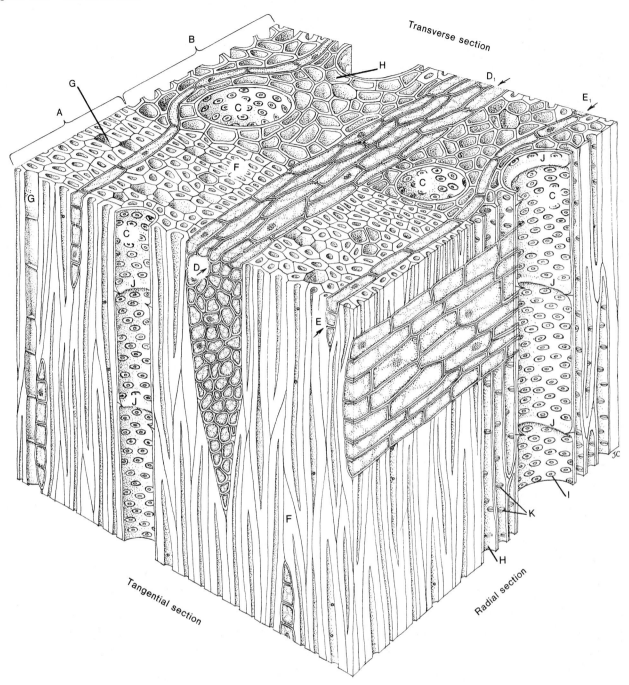

Key to Oak Wood Cube Labels

A. Summer wood
B. Spring wood
C. Vessels (tracheae)
D. D and D_1—multiseriate wood ray
E. E and E_1—uniseriate wood ray
F. Wood fibers
G. Wood parenchyma
H. Tracheids
I. Pits in vessel (trachea) walls
J. Junction of vessel elements
K. Pits in tracheid walls

Figure 13.2 Appearance of wood in cross sections

A Coniferous nonporous (pine)

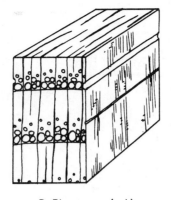
B Ring-porous (oak)

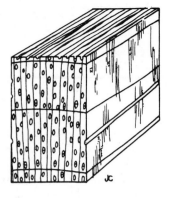
C Diffuse-porous (maple)

Key to Common Woods

1. Wood without pores **Coniferous nonporous woods 3**
1. Pores present **2**
2. Pores numerous, usually large, massed in early wood **Ring-porous woods 12**
2. Pores numerous, usually small, evenly distributed **Diffuse-porous woods 18**

Coniferous Woods (Nonporous)

3. Resin ducts absent **4**
3. Resin ducts present **9**
4. Heartwood not distinct, hence, light colored **5**
4. Heartwood distinct from sapwood, hence, light brown or darker **6**
5. Color yellowish white in transverse section **Fir**
5. Color pinkish in transverse section **Hemlock**
6. Heartwood differing slightly in color from sapwood, hence, light brown **7**
6. Heartwood differing decidedly in color from sapwood, dark brown or brownish red **8**
7. Odorless **Cypress**
7. With mild aromatic odor **White Cedar**
8. Heartwood purplish to brownish red, odor aromatic **Red Cedar**
8. Heartwood maroon or terra cotta to deep brownish red, no odor **Redwood**
9. No distinct heartwood, color white, resin ducts very small but numerous **Spruce**
9. Distinct heartwood present, resin ducts larger, color white to orange or reddish brown **10**
10. Resin ducts unevenly distributed, usually in groups of 8 to 30, forming lines in cross section **Douglas Fir**
10. Resin duct groups numerous, evenly distributed **11**
11. Transition from early to late wood gradual, color white to yellowish red, wood soft and light **Soft Pines**
11. Transition from early to late wood abrupt, color light to deep orange, wood medium hard and heavy **Hard Pines**

Ring-porous Woods

12. Pores of late wood in radial branching lines **13**
12. Pores of late wood either not in lines or these not radial **14**
13. Rays very minute, barely visible **Chestnut**
13. Rays very broad and conspicuous **Oak**
14. Pores of late wood only slightly smaller than those of early wood, very heavy and hard, color tinged with red **Hickory**
14. Pores of late wood minute **15**
15. Pores single or in groups or in short broken lines which are never radially oriented **16**
15. Pores of late wood in concentric, wavy, sometimes branching lines **17**
16. Rays minute, not yellowish **Ash**
16. Rays fine, but distinct, color yellowish brown **Black Locust**
17. Rays fine, but distinct, color greenish white **Hackberry**
17. Rays indistinct, heartwood reddish brown **Elm**

Diffuse-porous Woods

18. Pores varying in size from large to minute, approaching ring-porous **19**
18. Pores nearly uniform in size **20**
19. Wood heavy and hard, color chocolate brown **Black Walnut**
19. Wood light and soft, color light reddish brown **Butternut**
20. Rays indistinct, even with hand lens **Cottonwood**
20. Rays large or small but always distinct **21**
21. Pores large, plainly visible, filled with gum **Mahogany**
21. Pores minute, most numerous in early wood, hence, approaching ring-porous appearance, color vinous reddish **Cherry**
21. Pores minute, but evenly distributed **22**
22. Rays of two thicknesses **23**
22. Rays all nearly the same thickness **24**
23. Broad rays predominant **Sycamore**
23. Narrow rays predominant **Beech**
24. Rays very small, pores visible only as grayish specks on cross section **Birch**
24. Rays somewhat larger, pores distinct **25**
25. Wood hard, color pinkish white, rays appearing as orange-brown flakes in radial section **Maple**
25. Wood soft **26**
26. Pores not crowded, occupying not over one-third of space between rays, wood soft **Basswood**
26. Pores crowded, occupying nearly all of space between rays **27**
27. Color yellowish white, often with a greenish tinge **Tulip-Poplar**
27. Color light to dark reddish brown **Sweet Gum**

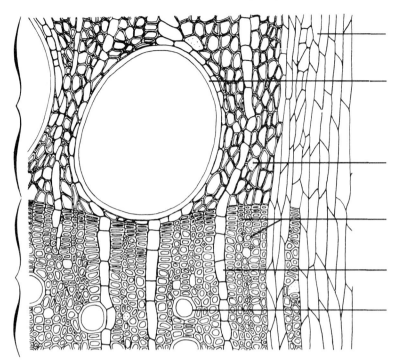

A Cross section of oak wood

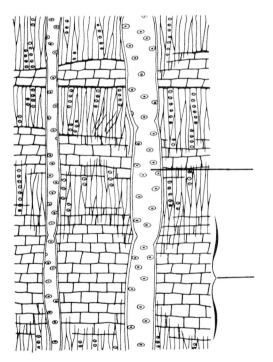

B Radial section of oak wood

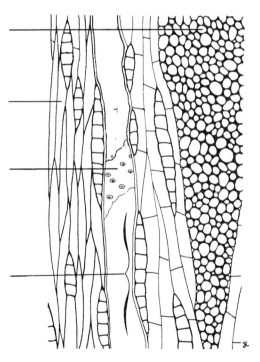

C Tangential section of oak wood

Exercise 14

Monocotyledonous Stems

Plant Materials

Materials required are lengths of older maize stems 30–35 cm long, with each including at least one node; prepared slides of cross and longitudinal sections of maize stem; sections of a large palm stem, rattan stem (usually coiled), stems of bamboo, and *Smilax*.

Equipment

Obtain a meter stick and a hand lens (10×).

Introduction

Monocotyledonous stems differ from those of dicotyledons in that the vascular bundles typically are scattered throughout the stem (seen in cross section), and a cambium is usually lacking. The secondary thickening characteristic of certain dicot stems usually does not occur in monocot stems, and never in any case results in the large woody cylinder so typical of certain dicots. Most monocot stems in our climate are not woody or perennial. *Smilax* is a notable exception, since it is both woody, and perennial.

A. Stem of Maize (Indian Corn)

Examine a piece of maize stem, including a node and an internode. Cut a transverse section from near the end of the internode, and note the hard outer rind enclosing the central pith that contains numerous independent and scattered vascular bundles. Cut the stem longitudinally through the node and internode; note the appearance of the several parts and also the relations of the leaf base to the node. What happens to the vascular bundles at the node?

Make and label a neat diagram of the maize stem as seen in transverse and longitudinal sections.

B. Prepared Section of Corn Stem

Examine under l.p., a cross section of corn stem. Note the epidermis, and immediately beneath it, the few rows of small thick-walled sclerenchyma cells, the hypodermis. The epidermis and hypodermis together form the *rind*. The inside of the stem is composed of pith or ground tissue (parenchyma) in which the vascular bundles are embedded. Are parenchyma cells in the center exactly like those near the rind?

Using h.p., study the epidermis and underlying cells. Is a cuticle present? What mechanical advantages or engineering principles are exemplified by the arrangement of the rind, cortex, and bundles in this stem?

Examine a single bundle under h.p. Note the xylem, consisting typically of several conspicuous vessels, connected by smaller vessels and tracheids. The two largest vessels (which look like eyes) are metaxylem vessels, which are among the last to differentiate as the bundle matures. The large central vessel is the last of the protoxylem. Earlier protoxylem vessels disintegrate as the bundle matures leaving a large air space (at the "mouth" location). Often parts of these vessels can be seen in the air space. The protophloem, quite evident in a young bundle, is crushed by the development of the metaphloem and may be hard to find in a mature bundle. The metaphloem, composed of sieve tubes and companion cells, is partly between the two larger vessels of the xylem and lies toward the outside of the bundle (at the "forehead" location). Sieve plates may be seen clearly in some of the sieve tubes. Xylem and phloem parenchyma may be present. The whole bundle is surrounded by a sheath (bundle sheath) of thick-walled cells (fibers), which are more conspicuous toward the outside and the inside of the bundle than towards the sides.

After the parts of the vascular bundle have been located and studied, label worksheet 14.1.

C. Longitudinal Section of Corn Stem

Examine under l.p., and note the vascular bundles running longitudinally through the pith. How does the length of the pith cells compare with their width? Identify and describe the appearance in this section of as many as possible of the vascular elements noted in the transverse section.

D. Perennial Monocotyledon Stems

Examine sections of a palm stem. Could satisfactory boards be made from this type of stem? Study the coiled stem of the liana, rattan. This plant does not stand erect, but grows up through and over other jungle plants. Compute the length of this stem and measure its diameter. Examine the stems of *Smilax* and bamboo, comparing them with palm and rattan.

Questions

1. Contrast the stem of maize with those of sunflower and basswood.
2. To what great family of plants does corn belong?
3. What is the economic importance of this plant family?
4. What products are made from corn stalks?
5. How are corn stalks structurally adapted for this use?
6. What monocotyledon is woody?
7. How does rattan keep its leaves exposed to sunlight since it does not have a rigid vertical stem?
8. What are the structural (mechanical) advantages of the monocot type of stem?

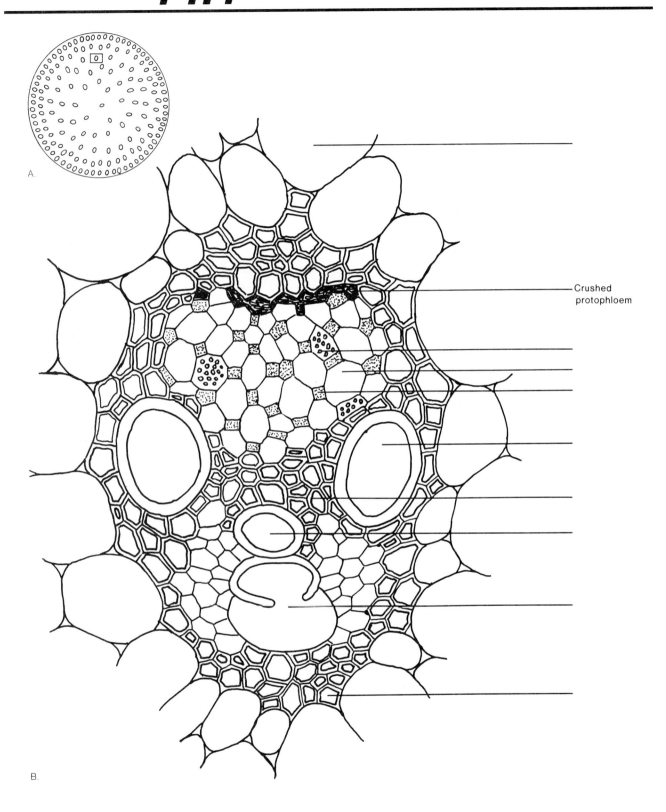

A.

Crushed
protophloem

B.

Exercise 15 — Modified Stems

Plant Materials

Obtain runners of strawberry or cinquefoil; rhizomes of *Iris,* May apple, Solomon's seal, quack grass or a fern; tubers of white potato. Corms of *Gladiolus* or *Crocus;* bulbs of tulip, hyacinth, or onion.

Note: Almost any good example of runner, rhizome, tuber, corm, or bulb may be substituted for the above.

Equipment

A sharp knife will be needed.

Introduction

All stems do not grow vertically above ground. Various stems are modified to function primarily for storage and reproductive purposes. Some of these grow prostrate on the soil surface, while others remain completely underground. Leaves and shoots sprout upward into the air from these stems, and roots grow downward into the soil; underground stems furnish much of the starchy foods of the world. Many ornamental flowers are grown from bulbs and corms.

A. Runners

Study runners (slender stolons) of strawberry or cinquefoil. Do these horizontal stems grow above ground or beneath the soil? Note the young plants attached to the parent plant by means of the runners. Do these young plants develop at every node or at every other node? How may one determine this? Are the internodes of a runner long or short in length? Contrast the runner with the rhizome described in section B.

Sketch the parent plant, runners, and attached young plants. Label all parts and indicate the ground line.

B. Rhizome (Worksheet 15.1A *Iris* Rhizome)

Examine rhizomes of May apple, Solomon's seal, *Iris,* quack grass, or other plants provided. Note leaf scars, nodes, internodes, and scale leaves. What are the advantages or disadvantages of this type of underground structure compared to the runner, bulb, corm, or tuber as a reproductive organ? as a storage organ?

C. Tuber (Worksheet 15.1B Potato Tuber)

Examine tubers of the white (Irish) potato. Determine which end was attached to plant (stem end). How does it differ from the other end? What is the arrangement of the eyes? Exactly, what is an eye? What is the "eyebrow"? Why is it desirable to include several eyes in each seed piece cut from a potato tuber?

Cut a longitudinal section of a tuber, being careful to cut through both stem scar and terminal eye. Where is the vascular system? What is the relation between the vascular system and the eyes? In a stem enlarged as this one, would the epidermis persist? What is the outer protective covering of an old potato tuber? How does this tissue develop? Give reasons for considering the potato tuber a modified stem. Which is the better storage organ, a rhizome or a tuber? Compare the structural features of a runner, rhizome, and tuber.

D. Corm (Worksheet 15.1C and D *Gladiolus* Corm)

Study corms of *Crocus* or of *Gladiolus* in external aspects, and as they appear in longitudinal sections. Note that a corm is a solid structure invested with dry scale leaves. Identify the parts of this structure corresponding to a leaf, stem, or root.

E. Bulb (Worksheet 15.1E and F Hyacinth Bulb)

Examine bulbs of tulip, onion, or hyacinth in external aspects and as they appear in longitudinal sections. How much of this structure is leaf, stem, or root? Are there any other parts present? Note the greatly reduced stem, and the thick, fleshy scale leaves. Compare the structural features of a corm and bulb.

After study and comparison of the modified stems outlined, add proper labels to worksheet 15.1A–F.

Questions

1. What are some advantages and disadvantages of underground stems?
2. List economic uses of these stems.
3. How does a bulb differ from a bud?
4. What laws govern the importation of bulbs and corms into the United States from abroad?
5. Why are these laws necessary?
6. How do the runner and rhizome types of stem aid in the rapid spread of a plant?
7. Are rhizomes injured by ordinary prairie fires?
8. Define runner, rhizome, tuber, corm, and bulb.
9. Explain why the popular use of the term *bulb* is often incorrect.

Name _____

A *Iris* rhizome

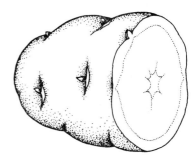

B Potato tuber

C *Gladiolus* corm, external

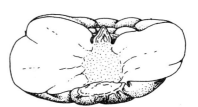

D *Gladiolus* corm, longitudinal

E Hyacinth bulb, external

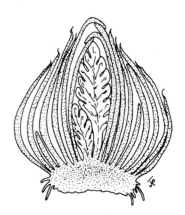

F Hyacinth bulb, longitudinal

Exercise 16   Roots of Plants

Plant Materials

You will need sunflower plants 20–25 cm tall removed from the soil to show their roots; similar root systems of ragweed, alfalfa, English plantain, and dandelion; corn plants 15–20 cm tall removed from the soil to show their roots; similar root systems of blue grass, rye, and wheat; mature roots of carrot (10–20 cm long), sugar or common beet, and turnip; *Dahlia* root system, sweet potato; sprouting sweet potato grown in a liter jar of water; cuttings of *Coleus,* geranium, willow, or *Tradescantia* grown in sand; Virginia creeper, English ivy, poison ivy, and older corn stem with adventitious roots; redtop seedlings 4–7 days old grown on the surface of water in a glass bowl; and seedlings of radish, mustard, or cucumber grown on wet filter paper in petri dishes.

Also needed are prepared slides with longitudinal sections of onion, hyacinth, spiderwort, or corn roots; prepared slides with cross sections of buttercup root, corn root, and of lupine, buttercup, or willow with lateral roots; and sawed sections of any woody (tree, usually) root.

Equipment

Obtain perlite flats, flowerpots, glass dishes 10–12 cm in diameter, petri dishes; a quart mason jar or similar container; and a compound microscope.

Reagents

Prepare an iodine potassium iodide solution diluted until light amber in color and a 0.1% solution of neutral red.

Introduction

Roots are typically underground structures, and function mainly for anchorage and absorption. The problem of anchorage becomes acute in large trees and other tall plants. Tremendous stresses and strains are imposed on the roots when large trees are subjected to strong winds. Typical roots have hairlike extensions of the epidermal cells: the root hairs that absorb water from the soil. All of the water lost by a plant during transpiration must enter through the root hairs. Roots differ further from stems since they do not have nodes, never produce leaves, and have a special covering (the root cap) that protects the delicate growing point from injury as it pushes through the soil.

Some roots, like stems, are used for food, and others are sources of important drugs. Because of the great abundance of cell divisions occurring in the meristem of the root tip, it is used almost universally for the study of mitosis in elementary classes. All the primary tissues of a root originate from cells derived from the apical meristem of the root tip in much the same fashion that stem tissues arise from similar cells of the stem tip. Consult the text for root types and modifications not described in these exercises.

General Directions

The seedlings called for have been grown in perlite and are easily removed without injury to the roots. Other roots must be taken from the soil as carefully as possible to avoid breakage and loss of the smaller members of the root system. Wash them carefully in water to remove any attached particles. Float the roots in a shallow dish of water placed against a black background and allow them to remain undisturbed for observation. Gently tease out the roots to show favorably the extent of the root system and to make evident details of the smaller roots.

External Features of Roots

A. Taproots

Examine the taproot system of a young sunflower plant. The central tap (primary) root appears to be an underground extension of the stem shaft. Observe the method of branching and the characteristic tapering of primary and secondary roots. Close examination of suitable material may reveal tertiary and quaternary roots. Review figure 1.1, exercise 1, showing primary, secondary, and tertiary roots on a plant. Ragweed, English plantain, alfalfa, and dandelion furnish other good examples of taproot systems.

Add labels to the drawing of a sunflower root system (fig. 16.1A).

B. Fibrous Roots

Examine the root system of a young corn plant. These roots are characteristically long, cylindrical, and fiberlike in appearance. This is a fibrous root system, sometimes termed

Figure 16.1 *A,* taproot system: sunflower; *B,* fibrous root system: corn

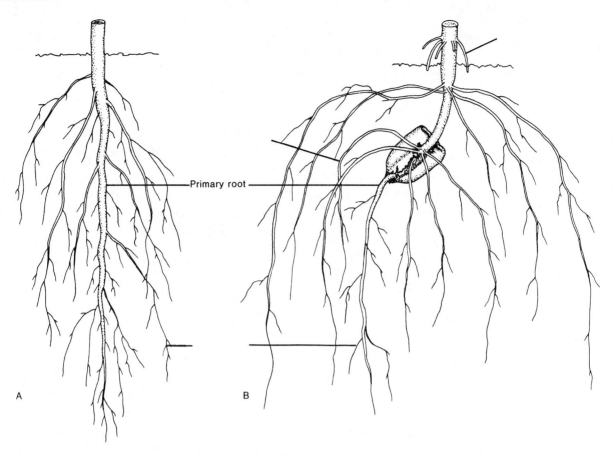

Primary root

A   B

a diffuse root system because of the manner in which the roots ramify throughout the soil. Fibrous roots are characteristic of the grasses, and are the chief reason why these plants are such efficient soil binders. Note how the root system of corn differs from that of the sunflower and carrot. What happens to the primary root of corn as the plant develops? Where do the permanent roots originate? Examine the root systems of blue grass, rye, and wheat on display.

Add labels to the drawing of the root system of a corn seedling (fig. 16.1B).

C. Storage Roots

Some taproots become fleshy and much enlarged for the storage of food. Plants with this type of root are often biennials. Can the biennial habit of plants be correlated with the presence of a storage root? The sugar beet is an example of a commercially important storage root and is unusual because it stores considerable amounts of sugar (sucrose). Examine the mature roots of a turnip or carrot, also roots of *Dahlia* (fascicled roots), and of the cultivated sweet potato (a tuberous root). Note the characteristic form and habit of each of these roots. Where do the secondary roots arise? Examine a sprouting sweet potato

growing in a container of water. What functions other than food storage does this root perform? What is an adventitious bud?

D. Adventitious Roots

Examine cuttings of *Tradescantia, Coleus,* willow, or geranium that have been naturally rooted in perlite. The roots arising from the stems of such cuttings are termed *adventitious.* What does this term mean? Compare with the adventitious roots of Virginia creeper, English ivy, poison ivy, and the prop roots of an older corn plant. Adventitious roots may also arise from leaves.

Add labels to the drawing of adventitious roots (fig. 16.2).

E. The Root Tip

Make a water mount of a young seedling root of redtop (or other grass), radish, mustard, or cucumber. Examine the entire length of the root. Note the region of absorption, the region of elongation, the region of maturation, the apical meristem (region of cell division), and the root cap. At what part of the region of absorption are the root hairs longest? Where are they shortest? Is there a sharp

Figure 16.2 Adventitious roots: geranium

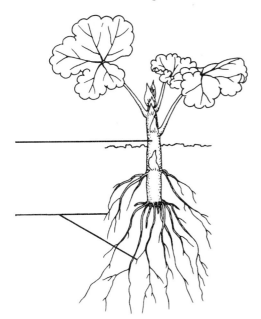

Figure 16.3 Development of root hairs

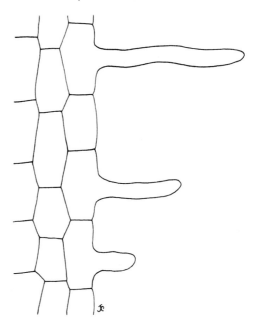

gradation in their size? How long may root hairs become? Where are the new root hairs formed? Compare the diameter of the root above and below the region of root hairs.

Note: To grow redtop seedlings, scatter seeds on the surface of water in a small dish 4–6 days before they are needed.

Diagrammatically sketch the seedling root showing the root hairs and root cap.

F. Root Hairs

Mount a young redtop seedling root with root hairs and study it under the microscope. What cells give rise to root hairs? What is the diameter of a root hair? Do they have cross walls? How many cells are in a single root hair? Identify the nucleus and cytoplasm. Draw a weak iodine solution under the cover glass or mount in 0.1% neutral red. Are any of the features more evident?

Carefully fill in (stipple) the contents of the root hairs represented by the outline drawing (fig. 16.3).

G. Total Length and Surface of Roots and Root Hairs of a Single Plant

The root system of a single plant of winter rye was measured, and roots of all categories (primary, secondary, tertiary, and quaternary) were carefully counted. A total of 13,815,672 roots was obtained. The combined length of all roots was 387 miles. The total surface of these roots was 2,554 square feet. Root hairs numbered over 14 billion and had a total length of 6,603 miles. The total area of root hair surface was 4,321 square feet. All of these roots grew in slightly less than 2 cubic feet of soil.

The significance of these figures is apparent when one stops to consider the value of such roots for absorption, as soil binders in checking erosion, and when such roots die and decay, their help in aerating the soil by leaving myriads of small tunnels to form a network in the soil.

The tremendous root-hair surface is of vital importance because practically all the water supply taken in by the plant must pass through this surface.

Internal Structure of Roots

H. Longitudinal Section of a Young Root

Examine prepared slides bearing longitudinal sections of onion, spiderwort, hyacinth, or corn root tips. Under l.p., identify the root cap extending beyond the tip and back along the sides of the section; the region of cell division (apical meristem) composed of cubical cells with dense cytoplasm and relatively large nuclei, some of which are in the process of division (mitosis); the region of cell elongation; and the region of maturation.

Is there a definite boundary between the root cap and the rest of the root? between the region of cell division and that of cell elongation? As the cells elongate, what position does the nucleus assume? What is the appearance of the cytoplasm? Note the differentiation of tissues into epidermis, cortex, endodermis, and stele.

Make a neat diagram of a median longitudinal section of a root tip, showing the root cap and division into the tissues named.

I. Transverse Sections of a Dicotyledon Root: Buttercup (*Ranunculus*)

Examine prepared slides bearing sections of young and older buttercup roots. Identify the epidermis, cortex, endodermis, pericycle, stele, xylem, and phloem. Which section was cut from a young root? The xylem and phloem have a definite pattern in the stele. Why is this called a radial arrangement? Where does the vascular cambium form in a dicotyledon root? Is there any evidence of it in the older root? What is the light blue, stained material stored in the cortical parenchyma cells? Suggest how roots differ in structure from stems.

Study and identify the parts of the young and older roots of buttercup, then add proper labels to the drawing (worksheet 16.1) representing a segment of the older root.

Inspect the sections of a woody root on display. How do these differ in structure from similar sections of woody stems?

J. Transverse Section of a Monocotyledon Root: Corn (Maize)

Examine the transverse sections of a corn root, and identify the main tissue groups. Note that the radial arrangement of the xylem and phloem includes more groups of these tissues than are found in a dicot root. Is there any evidence of a pith? No cambium is developed in this root, and secondary thickening does not occur. Is it logical to associate this lack of cambium with the fibrous root system of corn?

Study and identify the parts of the corn root and compare with similar tissues of the buttercup root; then add proper labels to the drawing of a segment of a corn root (worksheet 16.2).

K. Origin of Lateral (Branch) Roots

Examine prepared slides bearing cross sections of lupine, buttercup, willow, or other roots showing the origin of lateral roots. From what root tissue do lateral roots usually originate? Do they arise from superficial layers or from cells deeper within the root? In what respect does the origin of lateral roots differ from that of stem branches?

Make neat diagrams to illustrate the origin of lateral roots and to show their emergence from the parent root.

L. Development of a Dicotyledon (*Ranunculus*) Root Tip

Study the simplified stereodiagram (fig. 16.4) of a buttercup (*Ranunculus*) root tip showing three-dimensional aspects of a dicot root structure at progressive levels of development drawn from serial sections of the entire root tip. Compare it with worksheet 16.1.

Questions

1. How are roots structurally adapted to perform their functions?
2. How much of a large plant is underground?
3. Name the important regions of a root tip.
4. How long do root hairs live?
5. What is a root hair?
6. What are the functions of root hairs?
7. Why is the absorbing surface of root hairs important in the life of a plant?
8. Be prepared to comment on the interdependence of plant organs; in this case, specifically, roots, stems, and leaves.
9. What plants have root systems that make them ideal soil binders? Comment on their practical application from the standpoint of soil conservation.
10. In what external respects do roots differ from stems?

Figure 16.4 Development of a dicotyledon (*Ranunculus*)

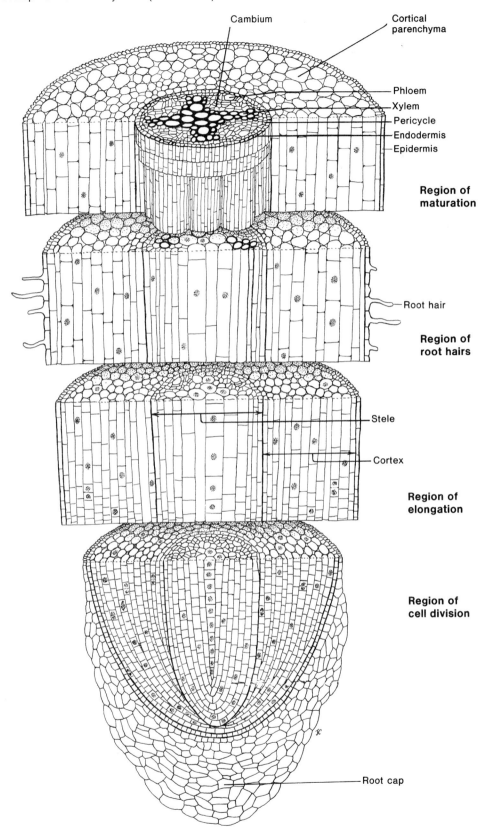

Cambium

Cortical parenchyma

Phloem
Xylem
Pericycle
Endodermis
Epidermis

Region of maturation

Root hair

Region of root hairs

Stele

Cortex

Region of elongation

Region of cell division

Root cap

Name _____

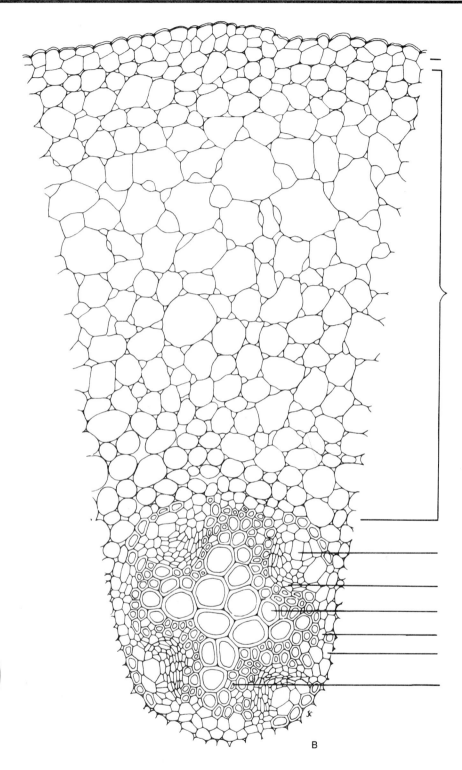

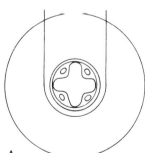

A

B

Name _____

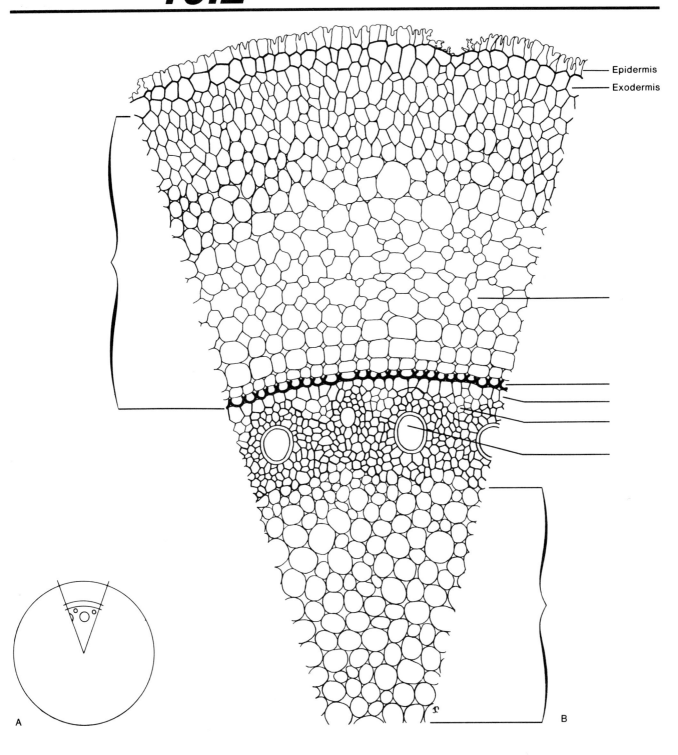

Epidermis

Exodermis

A

B

Exercise 17
Diffusion and Osmosis

Plant Materials

You will need *Elodea* shoots, potato tuber, carrots, dry peas, and cornstarch; Bacto-agar.

Equipment

Obtain a small moist chamber, glass tubing 40 × 3.8 cm in size, ring stand and clamps; test tubes 2.5 × 15 cm, medicine droppers; dialysis tubing 44 mm (1¾ inch) flat diameter, animal membrane 75 mm (3 inches) in diameter, 1-mm bore glass tubing 60 cm long, 6-mm bore glass tubing; 1,000-ml beakers; auger and 12-mm bit, #2 split one-hole rubber stopper, #4 rubber stopper; compound microscope, blank slides and cover glasses; single-edged razor blades, 12-mm cork borer, cheesecloth, absorbent cotton; two-ounce, screw-capped, widemouthed glass bottles, fine sand; plastic thistle tube bulb with removable 6-mm plastic tube; strong twine; scales for weighing; petri dishes; watch glasses; and cork borer.

Reagents

Reagents needed are chloroform, peppermint oil, citronella, clove oil, concentrated ammonium hydroxide, concentrated hydrochloric acid, potassium permanganate, phenolphthalein, white Karo syrup, sodium chloride, potassium hydroxide pellets, 90% ethanol; F.A.A.; potassium ferricyanide, ferrous sulfate, silver nitrate, iodine-potassium iodide (IKI) solution; bacto agar, red food coloring, sucrose, neutral red, and India ink.

Introduction

The movement of water and dissolved substances into, out of, and through plants, cells, or plant parts involves various physical processes. The necessary energy is derived from molecular motion; the turgidity of plants (and cells) is dependent upon these forces. If a plant loses its turgor it will wilt and possibly die shortly thereafter. All gases pass into and out of a leaf by *diffusion*. Also, water may enter plant roots, and move from cell to cell by *osmosis*. When much water moves out of a cell, the cell membrane shrinks away from the enclosing walls, and the cell is said to be *plasmolyzed*. A detailed account of these processes and their significance will not be given in these brief directions.

A. Brownian Movement

Brownian movement is the irregular, nondirectional movement of very minute solid particles or microscopic organisms suspended in water and is caused by the random motion of water molecules as they repeatedly bump into them.

Add a cover glass to a drop of dilute India ink, and observe under h.p. of the microscope. Note the constant irregular jiggling movements of the ink particles. They are not alive, and their movement is due to the constant jostling by the surrounding water molecules. This movement is slower when cooled, and faster when warmed.

Similar molecular motion enters directly into the processes described in this exercise.

B. Imbibition

Imbibition is the uptake of water accompanied by swelling and the release of heat by colloids such as cellulose, starch, and proteins. It is important in the germination of seeds and the uptake of water by hydrophilic colloids in root hairs and in certain cacti.

1. Select two lots, each of 20 dry pea seeds, and weigh each lot. Put one lot of seeds in a small beaker, cover with water, and allow to soak overnight. After soaking, weigh again, and record the difference in weight from their original dry condition. Compare the two lots of seeds as to weight, size, and smoothness of surface.
2. Tightly pack a two-ounce, screw-capped, widemouth glass jar with dry pea seeds, and then sift in fine sand to completely fill all remaining spaces. Tap it on a desk top to be sure it is well packed, then slowly fill the bottle to the top with water, making sure that everything inside is completely wet. Screw the top on tightly and place in a large beaker where it can remain undisturbed. Note the time this was started. How long did it take for the bottle to break? Explain why this happened.

C. Diffusion

Diffusion is the movement of molecules from an area where they are most concentrated to a region where they have less, or zero, concentration. This movement will continue until the entire space concerned is filled with the same concentration of molecules. The molecules have then reached a state of equilibrium.

Diffusion is based upon the fundamental principle that all molecules are in constant motion.

Gases into Gases

Highly volatile materials having marked characteristic odors will be used. A moist chamber containing cheese-cloth saturated with ammonium hydroxide, chloroform, oil of peppermint, cloves, citronella, or another suitable substance will be opened in a remote corner of the laboratory. Note the time in minutes until the odor can be detected. Is diffusion of gases rapid or slow? What is the significance of this experiment? Apply principles of diffusion to the problem of gaseous exchange in a leaf.

Relative Rates of Gas Diffusion

Firmly attach a piece of glass tubing (40 × 3.8 cm in size) in a horizontal position to a ring stand or other support. Saturate a cotton plug with concentrated NH_4OH (ammonia) and a similar plug with concentrated HCl (hydrochloric acid). Insert these plugs simultaneously into opposite ends of the glass tube. Do not disturb the apparatus after the plugs have been inserted. Why? HCl gas diffuses from one end of the tube to meet NH_3 gas diffusing from the opposite end. When these gases meet and combine they form the compound ammonium chloride (NH_4Cl), a white crystalline salt. Inspect the tube at two-minute intervals and note the white frosty ring deposited at the point where the gases meet. Is it exactly in the center? Which gas has diffused more rapidly? How can one tell? Suggest reasons why one gas should diffuse more rapidly than another. Record your observations and sketches on a separate sheet. Use plastic gloves or a large forceps when handling the cotton plugs. Wash your hands *immediately* in cold water if any solution is spilled on them.

Liquid into a Liquid

Fill a test tube one-third full of distilled water containing a small quantity of phenolphthalein. Phenolphthalein is colorless when in a neutral or acid medium but becomes red in an alkaline solution. Carefully pipette an equal volume of 80 to 90% alcohol, made alkaline by the addition of a few drops of sodium hydroxide solution, into the test tube. Note the red color at the junction of the two liquids. Place the tube (against a white background) where it will be undisturbed, and observe at intervals. Which way does the color spread? What is happening? Shake a similar tube to thoroughly mix the fluids, and note the color. Would the same thing occur if the first tube was left undisturbed for a long period of time?

Figure 17.1 J tube. Diffusion of a solid into a liquid

Solid into a Liquid

Hold a 6 mm, 20 cm long, glass J tube flat underwater, and fit a small cork into the long arm of the tube while it is still underwater, making sure there are no air bubbles (see fig. 17.1).

Stand the tube in a vertical position, drop a crystal of potassium permanganate into the short arm of the tube, and place the tube where it can remain undisturbed. Record the time it takes for the color to diffuse to the top of the long arm. Where is the color most concentrated? Can you note a diffusion gradient?

Optional Experiments

1. Place a single crystal of potassium permanganate in the center of a petri dish partly filled with water. Diffusion will begin immediately. Note how long it takes for the color to form a disc 1 cm in diameter and 4–5 cm in diameter. Compare this rate with the speed of a solid (silver nitrate) diffusing into a colloid.

2. Drop a single crystal of potassium permanganate into the short arm of a fermentation tube filled with water, and observe at intervals of 20 to 30 minutes. Where is the color most intense? Can you explain why? Allow it to remain overnight and record any further changes.

Figure 17.2 Agar wells in Petri dish

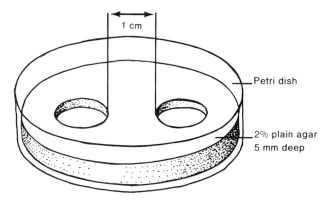

In the previous experiments, explain how the color can rise against gravity in the long vertical arms of the tubes.

Liquids through a Colloid

Use a petri dish containing 2% plain agar 5 mm deep. Push the open end of an 8 dram shell vial straight down through the agar to the bottom of the petri dish, and gently flip out the disc of agar formed, leaving a clean-edged well in the agar. Remove a similar disc of agar so that the edges of the two wells are 1 cm apart (see fig. 17.2). Place the petri dish on a level surface where it can remain undisturbed.

Using a dropping pipette, fill one agar well with a dilute aqueous solution (a pale orange color) of potassium ferricyanide taking care not to overfill. Similarly fill the other agar well with a dilute aqueous solution of ferrous (not ferric) sulfate, again taking care not to overfill.

Note: When solutions of potassium ferricyanide and ferrous sulfate meet, they form an intense blue precipitate of Prussian blue. Mix drops of each solution together on a spot plate and note the immediate formation of Prussian blue.

Look for a thin blue stripe midway between the agar wells indicating the formation of Prussian blue as the solutions diffuse to meet each other. How long did it take? Observe at 30-minute intervals thereafter, until the close of the laboratory period. Allow it to remain overnight, or until the next laboratory period, and record any further changes. Explain what has happened.

Use a petri dish containing 2% plain agar 5 mm deep. With a sharp-pointed, curved forceps, place a single crystal of silver nitrate in the center of the agar. Observe after 5 minutes, and at 20-minute intervals thereafter until the close of the laboratory period. Make notes concerning the outward (radial) spread of color and any other changes that may occur. Allow it to remain until the next laboratory period, and make note of any further changes. Keep it covered.

D. Osmosis

Osmosis may be defined as the movement (diffusion) of water through a differentially permeable membrane (i.e., a membrane that permits one substance to pass through it more readily than another).

During osmosis smaller water molecules pass freely through such a membrane in any direction while larger molecules of sugar pass through the same membrane very slowly, and still others do not pass through it at all (starch for example).

It is helpful to think of osmosis in terms of concentration of water molecules. In other words, the water moves from a place where it is most concentrated to a place where it is less concentrated. Where are the most water molecules, in a 50% sugar solution, or in pure water alone?

Devices used to demonstrate osmosis are called osmometers.

Thistle Tube Osmometer

Assemble an osmometer by attaching a soaked 75-mm (3-inch) diameter piece of animal membrane to a plastic thistle tube bulb as shown in figure 17.3. Fill the bulb with 50% Karo syrup or a 25% sucrose or glucose solution (colored red with food coloring), and attach to a 6-mm bore plastic or glass tube. Clamp it to a support stand, and place it so that the rim of the bulb is well underwater (see fig. 17.3). Mark the level of the colored solution at the beginning of the experiment and at regular intervals thereafter.

Note: In osmosis experiments, work in groups of two or four.

Osmosis experiments should be started early (even before the laboratory period begins) because they are sometimes slow to start.

Use a 1-mm bore glass tubing to show a faster rise in the solution than the 6-mm bore tubing.

Dialysis Tubing Osmometer

Use a 15 cm length of 44-mm flat diameter dialysis tubing. Soak it in water for 60 seconds, then roll one end briskly between your fingers and thumb to separate the two layers. Run water through, or blow through, to open the tube full length. Close one end by twisting tightly for about 2.5 cm, and tying strong twine tightly over the twist. Add enough 50% Karo syrup or 25% sucrose or glucose solution (colored red) to almost fill the tubing. Insert a #4 one-hole rubber stopper containing a length of 6-mm bore plastic tubing into the open end of the dialysis tubing, and tie it tightly with strong twine. A 1-mm bore glass tubing will show faster results than the 6-mm tubing. Rinse off any syrup or sugar spilled on the tube. Clamp it to a support stand and immerse the entire length of dialysis tubing in water (fig. 17.4). Mark the location of the syrup or sugar solution level at the beginning of the experiment and at regular intervals thereafter. How fast does the colored solution rise in the tube? Explain what is happening.

Figure 17.3   Thistle tube osmometer

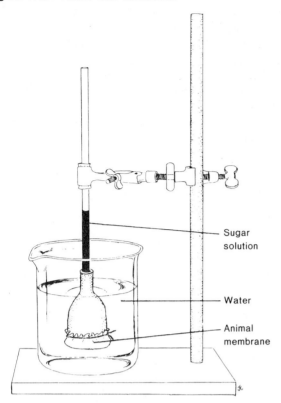

Sugar
solution

Water

Animal
membrane

Figure 17.4   Dialysis tubing osmometer

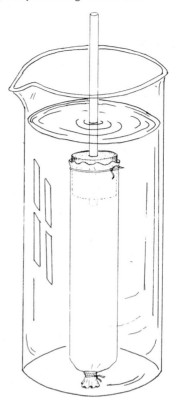

Osmosis in a Nonliving System

The dialysis tubing of the following artificial "cells" sim-
ulates the plasma membrane of living cells, the contents
of a sausage represent the cell contents (protoplast), and
the surrounding medium represents the prevailing environmental conditions.

Dialysis tubing sausages. Use 15-cm lengths of 44-
mm flat diameter dialysis tubing. Soak them 60 seconds
in water, then roll briskly between your fingers and thumb
to separate the two layers. Run water through, or blow
through, to open the tube full length. Twist one end tightly
for about 2.5 cm and tie strong twine tightly over the twist.

Add enough of the experimental solution to fill a dialysis tube two-thirds full, and then close the free end of
the tube as directed. Do not fill the sausage completely
with solution, and remove as many air bubbles as possible
before the final tying. Rinse it in cold water to wash away
any spilled solution. The completed sausage should now
be limp.

Prepare five dialysis bags, or sausages, to contain the
following solutions: (1) 1% starch suspension; (2) Iodine
(I2KI); (3) 25% sucrose (colored red); (4) pure water; and
(5) pure water (colored red). The numbers correspond to
those in worksheet 17.1.

Weigh and record the weight of each sausage in worksheet 17.1, then immerse each of them in the solution indicated by its matching number in worksheet 17.1. After
2 hours or more, examine and weigh all sausages, and then
supply any information called for in the remaining blank
spaces in worksheet 17.1.

Write a short paragraph commenting upon the osmotic behavior of the artificial "cells" (sausages) named
in worksheet 17.1. List ways in which they are like and
unlike living cells.

Osmosis in Living Systems

Plasmolysis. Mount a leaf of *Elodea* in fresh water, examine, and note the normal condition of cells. Place a drop
of 10% salt solution under the cover glass by dropping it
at the edge of the cover glass and drawing it under by
absorbing water on the opposite side with a piece of filter
paper. Quickly examine the cells under the microscope
again, watching for any change in the cell contents. Those
near the margin of the leaf should react first. What has
taken place in the cell to account for this change? How
does a salt solution bring this about? Would a weaker solution accomplish the same result? What practical application has been made of plasmolysis in some types of weed
eradication?

Kill an *Elodea* leaf by immersing it in F.A.A. for 10
minutes. Rinse it in water, mount it in salt solution, and
observe it under the microscope as directed earlier. Does
plasmolysis occur in these dead cells? Explain what has
happened to the plasma membrane of these cells.

No. 1. Make drawings showing several stages in the plasmolysis of an *Elodea* cell. Wash all salt water from the slides, and dry them before leaving the laboratory. Be certain to remove any salt solution spilled on the microscope.

A living osmometer. Lightly scrape off the outer tissues of a carrot, or peel a potato, and carefully hollow out with an auger bit a deep cylindrical cavity in the upper portion. Completely fill the cavity with 50% Karo or other syrup, and seal with a rubber stopper or cork carrying a capillary glass tube. Immerse the carrot or potato in water colored with 0.5% neutral red (does not harm living cells) to within 1/2 inch of the top and observe at regular intervals to note any rise of the liquid within the tube. Explain why the liquid in the tube is colored. What acts as the differentially permeable membrane in this case?

Turgidity. With a razor blade or cork borer, cut two pieces of potato tuber exactly the same size. They should measure about $30 \times 5 \times 5$ mm. Place one piece in a watch glass containing 10% salt solution, and the other in a watch glass of distilled water. After three minutes, and every few minutes thereafter, compare the flexibility of the two pieces. In the light of the observations being made, what is happening in the cells of the potato that may account for the change in flexibility? When a marked difference in the flexibility of the two pieces is apparent, rinse in tap water the piece that has been in salt water, and place it in distilled water. Continue comparing the two pieces and account for any change. Will living plant tissues recover from severe or prolonged plasmolysis?

For plastic thistle tube bulbs, plastic tubing, animal membranes, and other osmosis and diffusion equipment, consult the catalog of the

Carolina Biological Supply Company
Burlington, North Carolina 27215
or
Gladstone, Oregon 97027

Questions

1. What is Brownian movement? diffusion? imbibition?
2. What is osmosis? osmotic pressure?
3. How is each process important in the life of the plant?
4. How does water accumulate in vacuoles?
5. Salt in the soil will kill plants; explain why this is true.
6. How may weeds be eradicated?
7. What is turgor?
8. What happens when a plant loses its turgor?
9. Explain what is meant by physiological drought.
10. What is a differentially permeable membrane?
11. Does a similar membrane exist in plant cells?
12. Differentiate between diffusion and convection currents.
13. Why is starch a good storage product for plant cells?
14. Why is sugar a poor storage product for plant cells?

Osmotic Behavior

Bag Number	Contents of Sausage (bag)	Original Weight at Start (in grams)	To Be Immersed in	Weight after Two Hours	Appearance after Two Hours (add sketch)
1.	1% starch suspension		Iodine (I2KI)	1.	
2.	Iodine (I2KI)		1% starch suspension	2.	
3.	25% sucrose (colored red)		Pure water	3.	
4.	Pure water		25% sucrose	4.	
5.	Pure water (colored red)		Pure water	5.	

18 Growth Movements

Plant Materials

Materials needed are potted single sunflower plants 15–20 cm tall; germinated seeds of radish, mustard, or cress; kidney bean, lima bean, or oat; radish or wheat seedlings 3.8–5 cm tall growing in 5-cm pots; redtop seedlings 1.3–2 cm tall grown on surface of water in a 10.3-cm glass bowl; pressed cork, a block of soft wood, or a large cork.

Equipment

Obtain a needle and thread, straight pins, Scotch tape; petri dishes with filter paper discs to fit, bell jar with heavy glass plate; light-tight cardboard box with 7-mm square hole cut in the center of one side, and a similar box without a hole cut in the side; India ink and fine pen, wax pencil; ring stand and clamp.

Introduction

Plants and their organs exhibit characteristic growth responses to external, unilateral stimuli such as light, gravity, chemicals, contact, and water.

Responses of this kind are termed *tropisms* and are the most common and most important plant movements. They are usually named by adding the word *tropism* to a term designating the kind of stimulus involved: for example, photo + tropism = phototropism, or the bending response of a plant to the stimulus of light. When the plant or organ moves toward the source of a stimulus, the response is said to be positive. When the organ moves away from the stimulus, the response is said to be negative. Because these are growth movements, they are rather slow in occurring and require time before they become evident. These movements appear greatly accelerated by time-lapse photography. Several such motion pictures may be shown in the course of this work. In growth movements an organ (such as a stem) elongates more rapidly on one side than on the other, causing the characteristic bending associated with a tropism. This unequal growth rate is caused by the action of growth substances (auxins).

Auxins may stimulate or retard cell elongation, depending on the concentration of the growth substance and the kind of organ affected. When a stem is placed in a horizontal position, auxins accumulate in the lower part of this organ, stimulating cell elongation on that side, and causing the stem to bend and grow upright. A root in a similar horizontal position will turn and grow downward; in this case, the accumulation of auxins retards cell elongation in the lower side of the organ.

There are plant movements other than tropisms, but they will not be considered in this exercise. Consult the text, lecture notes, or library references if additional information is desired.

A. Negative Geotropism of Stems

Place a potted sunflower plant 15 to 20 cm tall in a horizontal position on the laboratory table. Carefully measure the shortest distance from the tip of the stem to the surface of the table. Repeat this measurement at 15 minute intervals. Also note any bending of the stem, and the location of the region of curvature. Compare this with the location of the region of curvature in a plant that has been lying in a horizontal position for 24 hours. What differences are there between the two plants? Suggest a possible explanation for these differences.

Before the close of the period, sketch the plant, showing the curvature as it then is. Indicate by dotted lines the original position of the stem.

B. Geotropism of Roots and Stems

Seeds of mustard, radish, or cress have been germinated in the dark on moist filter paper in petri dishes with the covers sealed in place with gummed paper or Scotch tape. Each dish has been kept on its edge by use of a clamp or other means. Note that the seedlings have developed definite roots and stems, and that they are growing in a vertical position. Mark on the glass with wax crayon the position of the seedlings, then rotate the petri dish through 90 degrees so that the seedlings are now horizontal. Clamp it in place, observe at the end of the laboratory period, and at the beginning of the next laboratory period. What changes in the position of the seedlings are evident? What typical responses to gravity are exhibited by the roots? by the stems? Make a sketch of the seedlings, indicating the position before (by dotted lines) and after (by solid lines) their position was shifted.

A variation of this experiment is to take a straight, uninjured seedling, carefully fasten it to a disc of filter paper (several sheets) with a needle and thread, and place the assembly in a petri dish. Wet the paper (not dripping), seal the dish, and proceed as directed in the previous paragraph.

Use germinating lima bean seeds on which the roots are about 1–2 cm long. Pin them firmly to a large cork, soft board, or block of wood so that the uninjured roots are pointing in various directions. Mark the position of the roots with India ink, wax crayon, or else make exact sketches. Allow them to stand in a moist atmosphere under a bell jar for two to three days. In what direction do the roots now point? What has happened?

Sketch the seeds showing the roots as they were originally and as they appear after two to three days.

C. Phototropism

Pots of oat, radish, or wheat seedlings will be grown until they are 4–5 cm tall. Keep them overnight in darkness before beginning the experiment. Still keeping the seedlings in darkness, place one of the pots in a light-tight box that has a 7-mm opening on one side. Expose it to daylight so that light is admitted only through the opening. Prepare a similar setup as a control, but without the opening in the light-tight box. At the end of two hours remove the boxes and observe the results. Allow another set of seedlings to remain undisturbed until the next laboratory period. What has happened? Sketch to show the position of seedlings before and after exposure to one-sided illumination.

Seedlings of redtop will be grown 1.2–2 cm tall on the surface of tap water almost filling a glass bowl. Expose one bowl of seedlings to strong one-sided illumination by placing it on a windowsill. Place another bowl of seedlings 8–10 meters away from the window in subdued light. What happens after two hours? half a day? Sketch a bowl of seedlings as they were before exposure to light and as they appear after a period of exposure to one-sided illumination. Comment briefly on the tropistic movements of plants and their parts as they occur in nature. What advantage are these movements to the plant?

Record the results as indicated in the above directions.

Questions

1. What causes a stem to bend following a stimulus such as light or gravity?
2. How does the characteristic response of roots and stems to hormones apparently determine the vertical growth habit of a typical plant?
3. What is a tropism?
4. What is meant by positive and negative responses?
5. List a number of forces or stimuli that cause tropisms, and give the characteristic response of the plant to each.
6. What part do growth substances play in causing tropisms?
7. Describe a number of tropistic responses of plants as they are found in nature, and list the possible advantages of each to the plant.

Exercise 19 The Flower

Plant Materials

Materials needed are flowers of tobacco, petunia, lily, snapdragon, sweet pea, or others of similar structure; prepared slides of lily stamen and pistil cross sections; prepared slides of lily ovary showing development of the embryo sac and double fertilization; whole mounts of *Polygonum,* tobacco, or other pollen tubes, flattened stigma and style of *Datura,* lily or other plant with contained pollen tubes; germinated pollen in 95% ethanol of elderberry, lily, lemon, tobacco, or similar plant; hay fever and other pollens in 10% glycerine, including ragweed, sunflower, corn, plantain, rose, goldenrod, pine, timothy, and others; preparations of lily (or similar plant) microsporocytes showing meiosis; and prepared slides of *Capsella* embryos.

Equipment

Obtain a compound microscope, hand lens (10x), dissecting needles, single-edged safety razor blades, dissecting microscope, blank slides, and cover glasses.

Reagents

You will need 10% glycerine, and 95% ethanol.

Introduction

The flower of an angiosperm functions primarily in the reproduction of the plant and is the precursor of fruits and seeds. Flowers vary greatly in size, shape, number of parts, and colors, but most of these variations cannot be studied in this exercise. These and other characteristics of flowers (especially of pistils and stamens) are of great importance in the identification and classification of plants. One of the smallest flowers (duckweed) is almost microscopic in size, while one of the largest (*Rafflesia*) may measure more than one meter across a single blossom.

The most popular use of flowers is for decorative purposes, and nearly all persons derive pleasure from seeing flowers, either cut or naturally growing in gardens. Millions of dollars are spent annually on flowers for decorative purposes. Flowers are the traditional source of perfumes, and some have been recommended for medicinal use. The use of flowers for the aforementioned purposes, however, is insignificant when compared to the enormous value of the fruits and seeds derived from them.

Much popular and scientific interest has been shown in the study of the pollination of flowers by wind, insects, and other means. A more personal interest in pollens may be found in the fact that many persons are sensitive to them, causing the decidedly uncomfortable allergy known as hay fever. The instructor will discuss some of the hay-fever pollens, pointing out their characteristics, distribution, time of shedding, and toxicity.

All hay-fever pollens provided for study are suspended in a glycerine solution and consequently cannot escape into the air or cause discomfort to hay-fever sufferers.

A. The Flower as a Whole

A complete flower has four sets of floral organs: (1) the *calyx,* of which the individual parts are called *sepals;* (2) the *corolla* made up of a group of *petals* (the calyx and corolla together constitute the *perianth*); (3) the *stamens;* and (4) one or more *pistils.* These parts may vary in number from only a few to several and may be separate or united, either to members of the same set or to the other floral organs. All are produced from the *receptacle,* which is the slightly expanded tip of the *peduncle,* or flower stalk. Nectaries may be present.

Flowers having perianth parts alike in size and shape and arranged to resemble a wheel or star when viewed from above, are called *regular* flowers; they may also be *radially symmetrical* or actinomorphic. Examples are tulip, lily, poppy, petunia, and primrose. When one and more perianth parts are of a different size or shape than the others, the flower is not radially symmetrical and is then called an *irregular* flower. If the right and left sides of an irregular flower are alike in size and shape when viewed from the front, the flower is then said to be *bilaterally symmetrical* or zygomorphic. Examples are sweet pea, redbud, orchid, violet, and snapdragon.

Flowers are *hypogynous* (having a superior ovary) when sepals, petals, and stamens arise below the ovary (figs. 19.1 and 19.2). Flowers are *epigynous* (having an inferior ovary) when sepals, petals, and stamens arise from the upper part (top) of an ovary (fig. 19.2).

Carefully study the longitudinal vertical section of a hypogynous, radially symmetrical flower represented in

Figure 19.1 Longitudinal section of a hypogynous radially symmetric dicotyledonous flower with a superior ovary (*Geranium maculatum*, a native wild flower often called cranesbill)

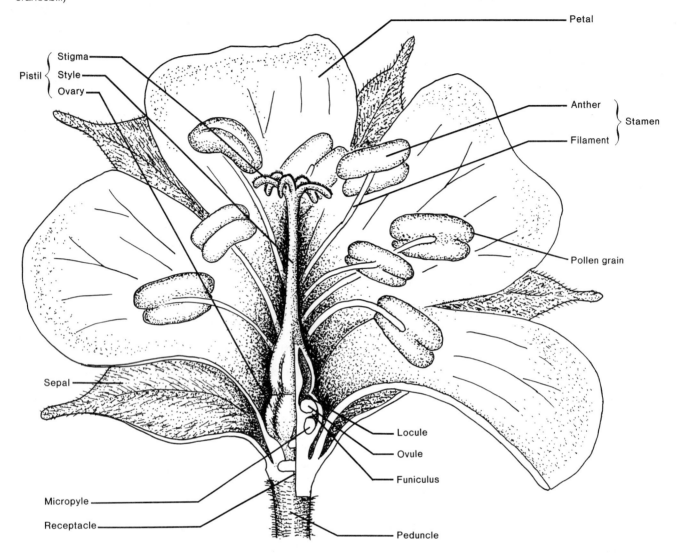

Petal

Pistil { Stigma — Style — Ovary —

Anther } Stamen
Filament }

Pollen grain

Sepal

Locule
Ovule
Funiculus

Micropyle
Receptacle

Peduncle

figure 19.1. It shows the described parts, plus details of ovary contents. Use this figure as a guide in the following studies:

1. Examine the flower provided. Is it *radially* or *bilaterally* symmetrical? How many of the floral organs can be seen without disturbing any of them? Carefully remove each set of floral organs, beginning with the outermost ones. Note the position of each part in relation to others near it. Arrange the parts on a sheet of paper in the relative position in which they occurred in the flower.
2. Examine a *stamen* with the dissecting microscope. It is composed of a *stalk,* or *filament,* and *anthers,* or *pollen sacs.*
3. The *pistil* is made up of an enlarged part called the *ovary* and a sticky receptive spot, the *stigma,* which is usually found at the tip of a slender *style.* Are there any pollen grains adhering to the stigma?

4. Split the pistil lengthwise with a razor blade and note the internal cavity or cavities (cells or locules) of the ovary, in which a number of ovules are produced. If there is more than one locule, cut a transverse section also. Subsequent to fertilization, the ovules may develop into seeds.
5. Examine a water mount of the pollen grains under the compound microscope. Before fertilization can take place, pollen must be transferred from the anthers to the stigma (pollination). In some plants this may take place within the flower (closed pollination); in others, the parts are modified to ensure cross pollination—the transfer of pollen from another plant.

Draw, on a fairly large scale, a diagrammatic vertical section of the flower, including all structures and labeling all parts.

Figure 19.2

Flower Inflorescences

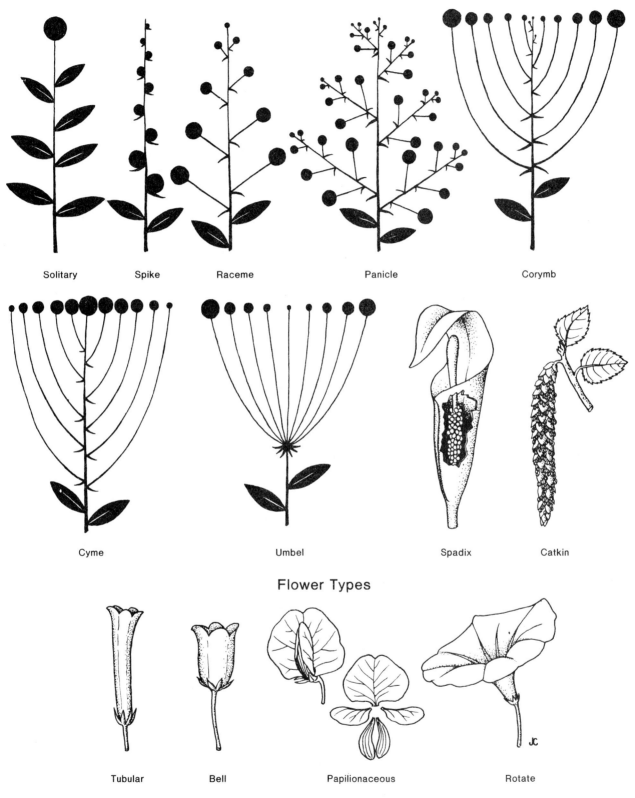

Solitary   Spike   Raceme   Panicle   Corymb

Cyme   Umbel   Spadix   Catkin

Flower Types

Tubular   Bell   Papilionaceous   Rotate

Figure 19.2 continued

Flower Types

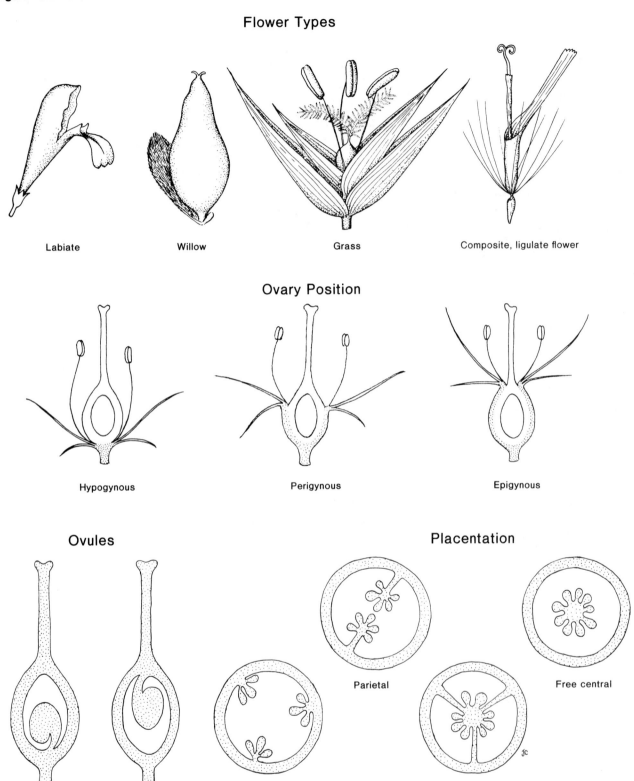

Labiate   Willow   Grass   Composite, ligulate flower

Ovary Position

Hypogynous   Perigynous   Epigynous

Ovules

Basal   Pendulous

Placentation

Parietal

Free central

Parietal

Central (axile)

Examine cross sections of a young lily flower bud. Identify the principal parts of the flower.

Check with the diagram (worksheet 19.1A) of the cross section of a lily flower bud. Correlate the parts with similar structures shown in figure 19.1. Label all parts identified.

Consult the drawings in figure 19.2 of flower types, inflorescences, ovary position, and kinds of placentation, and apply as much as possible of this information to the flowers provided for study.

Using the outline above, examine other types of flowers as directed by the instructor. Make diagrammatic sketches showing vertical and cross sections of each flower studied.

B. The Stamen, Microscopic Structure

Correlate the terms *microsporophyll, microsporangium,* and *microspore* with the terms printed in *italics* in the foregoing directions.

Examine sections of *Lilium* (lily) anther containing mature pollen, but in which the pollen chambers remain distinct. Identify the *pollen chambers, pollen grains, connective,* and *filament.*

When the above parts have been studied and identified, label the drawing of a lily anther (worksheet 19.1B).

Microsporogenesis and Microgametogenesis

The anthers of a flower develop masses of diploid pollen mother cells (microsporocytes), which undergo meiosis to form *quartets (tetrads)* of microspores, each containing the haploid number of chromosomes. The details of meiosis are studied in chapter 5. A diagram of the diploid microsporocyte is shown in worksheet 19.1C. After the first division of meiosis, two haploid secondary sporocytes (often called a dyad) are formed (worksheet 19.1D). After second division of meiosis, a tetrad of microspores is formed (worksheet 19.1E) each of which rounds up as an isolated cell contained within the mother cell wall. The mother cell wall disappears, the uninucleate microspores (worksheet 19.1F) enlarge and develop characteristically sculptured outer walls (worksheet 19.1G). Mitotic division within a pollen grain results in the formation of a large *tube cell,* and a smaller *generative cell* (worksheet 19.1H) producing a two-celled *male gametophyte,* or *pollen grain.* The generative cell again divides, and two *male gametes* (male cells) are then produced (worksheet 19.1I). This last division may occur while the pollen is still contained within the anther or more commonly after pollination within a growing *pollen tube* as it passes through the tissues of the pistil.

A pollen tube containing cytoplasm, the tube nucleus and two sperms (worksheet 19.1J) is the *mature male gametophyte.* A pollen tube growing through the pistil eventually reaches an *ovule,* which it enters by means of the *micropyle.* Further behavior of the pollen tube, and the events of fertilization are described elsewhere in this exercise.

C. Germinating Pollen

Examine prepared slides of germinating pollen of *Polygonum,* elderberry, tobacco, lemon, lily, or a similar plant. Locate a pollen tube containing a tube nucleus and two male cells. Does the pollen tube contain cytoplasm?

Study the drawing of the lily pollen tube and its contents. Label all structures shown on worksheet 19.1.

Examine slides of whole styles and stigmas of *Datura,* tobacco, lily, or a similar plant that have been pressed out flat and stained to show pollen tubes.

Make a diagram of the flattened stigma and style showing pollen tubes in position.

D. Kinds of Pollen

Mount on a slide and examine under the microscope each of the various kinds of pollen provided. Do any of these, other than ragweed and timothy, cause hay fever? Are hay-fever pollens carried by insects or are they wind-borne? List the characteristics of a hay-fever pollen such as ragweed or timothy. Do sticky pollens such as goldenrod and rose cause much hay fever? Would a hay-fever pollen in the air be considered a real pollutant?

Study the pollens provided, and check with the drawings (figs. 19.3, 19.4, and 19.5). What external features are useful in identifying pollens?

Optional Study: Carefully draw in perspective several kinds of pollen not shown by the drawings.

E. The Pistil, Microscopic Structure

Examine a prepared slide showing a cross section through the ovary of a lily. Note the thick walls and the three chambers (locules), each containing two rows of ovules.

Study the outline drawing of a cross section of a *Lilium* ovary (fig. 19.6). Label all parts.

Study a single ovule very carefully, noting the *integuments* (inner and outer) surrounding the *nucellus,* within which is the *embryo sac.* The small opening or passageway piercing the integuments is the *micropyle.*

Study the parts of the ovule in figure 19.7. After you have studied the stages in the development of the embryo sac (section F), draw in the second four-nucleate stage of the embryo sac in the proper place on the drawing of the ovule. Label all parts.

F. Meiosis, Megasporogenesis, and the Female Gametophyte

Each ovule within the ovary of a flower develops a single diploid *megaspore mother cell* (megasporocyte) that undergoes meiosis to form four haploid megaspores.

Figure 19.3 *Solidago* sp. (goldenrod)

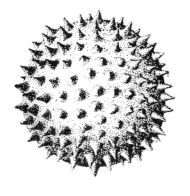

Figure 19.4 *Phleum pratense* (timothy)

Figure 19.5 *Ambrosia trifida* (giant ragweed)

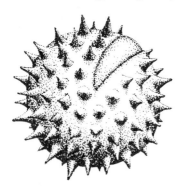

Figure 19.6 *Lilium* ovary, cross section

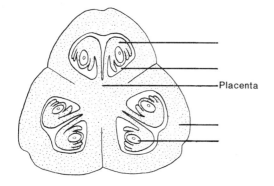

Placenta

Figure 19.7 *Lilium* ovule, longitudinal section

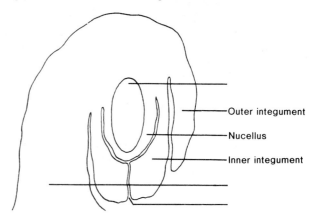

Outer integument

Nucellus

Inner integument

In typical angiosperm embryo sac (female gametophyte) development considered typical for angiosperms, a megaspore mother cell divides twice by meiotic divisions (divisions I and II) to produce a row of four haploid megaspores (linear tetrad). Three of these megaspores fail to develop further and disintegrate. The surviving megaspore then divides mitotically to form the two-nucleate stage of embryo sac development. The next division produces the four-nucleate stage and the following division results in the eight-nucleate stage. These eight nuclei become typically organized within the embryo sac to form one *egg*, two *synergids*, two *polar nuclei*, and three *antipodal* (or chalazal) nuclei. All of these nuclei are haploid. An eight-nucleate embryo sac, so organized, is the mature *female gametophyte*.

Although the development of its embryo sac differs markedly from the typical sequences just described, lily (*Lilium*) is more commonly studied for this purpose in beginning courses than any other plant. Reasons for this are as follows: (1) it is easily grown and available practically everywhere; (2) the ovary, ovules, and embryo sac are large and easily studied under the microscope; and (3) it is easy to section and stain; and (4) development stages are accurately determined by measuring the length of the flower bud.

In order to alleviate confusion often attending its use, a rather complete series of stages in the atypical embryo sac development of *Lilium* is shown in figure 19.8A–M to aid in the interpretation of this material from prepared slides.

Carefully study figures 19.8A–M showing the aforementioned series of stages in the development of the *Lilium* embryo sac. Examine (first using l.p., then h.p.) cross sections of lily ovaries showing similar stages, and identify each stage shown by the drawings.

A diploid megaspore mother cell or megasporocyte, (fig. 19.8A) of *Lilium* divides *meiotically* (fig. 19.8B) to form the two-nucleate embryo sac directly (fig. 19.8C). Each nucleus then divides equationally (fig. 19.8D) to produce four haploid nuclei. Meiosis is now complete (di-

Figure 19.8 Meiosis, development of the female gametophyte, double fertilization, early embryo and endosperm in *Lilium*

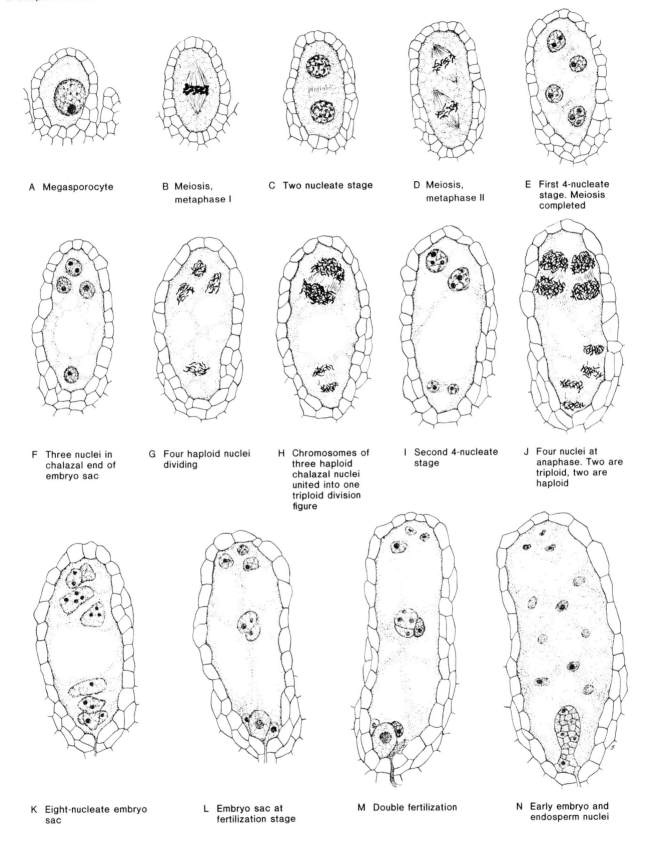

A Megasporocyte

B Meiosis, metaphase I

C Two nucleate stage

D Meiosis, metaphase II

E First 4-nucleate stage. Meiosis completed

F Three nuclei in chalazal end of embryo sac

G Four haploid nuclei dividing

H Chromosomes of three haploid chalazal nuclei united into one triploid division figure

I Second 4-nucleate stage

J Four nuclei at anaphase. Two are triploid, two are haploid

K Eight-nucleate embryo sac

L Embryo sac at fertilization stage

M Double fertilization

N Early embryo and endosperm nuclei

visions I and II), and the four nuclei lying free within the embryo sac correspond to the four megaspores of the typical embryo sac, except that a linear tetrad is not formed and none of the nuclei disintegrate. This is the first four-nucleate stage (fig. 19.8E) in the embryo sac development of *Lilium*. Three of these nuclei migrate to become grouped at the chalazal end (opposite the micropyle) of the embryo sac; the fourth nucleus remains near the *micropylar* end (fig. 19.8F). The three grouped nuclei begin division and commonly produce three division figures (fig. 19.8G). These eventually unite to form a single, large division figure containing the triploid number (3N) of chromosomes (fig. 19.8H). Concurrently, the single nucleus at the micropylar end of the embryo sac divides to form two haploid nuclei (fig. 19.8G and H). A second four-nucleate stage is thus formed that is composed of two large triploid nuclei, and two smaller haploid nuclei (fig. 19.8I). The nuclei of this stage divide (fig. 19.8J) to form the eight-nucleate embryo sac (fig. 19.8K). The eight nuclei then become organized to form a single haploid egg, two haploid synergids, two fusing polar nuclei (one triploid and one haploid), and three triploid antipodals (fig. 19.8L).

Fertilization (Syngamy)

A pollen tube containing cytoplasm, two sperms, and the tube nucleus enters the micropyle of an ovule and penetrates the embryo sac (fig. 19.8L). The pollen tube ruptures, releasing the two sperms into the cytoplasm of the embryo sac. One sperm nucleus fertilizes (unites with) the egg nucleus; the second sperm nucleus unites with the two polar nuclei, which may have fused or which are about to fuse (fig. 19.8M). The fusion of one sperm with the egg (syngamy) and of the second sperm with the polar nuclei (triple fusion) constitutes the double fertilization characteristic of the angiosperms. The antipodal nuclei are nonfunctional and disintegrate within the embryo sac.

After fertilization, an egg becomes a zygote, which undergoes a series of repeated divisions to develop into a many-celled embryo (fig. 19.8N). After a seed germinates, the embryo develops into a mature lily plant (sporophyte).

In the lily, the union of the second sperm with the two polar nuclei (one haploid, one triploid) results in the formation of a *pentaploid* (5N) *primary endosperm nucleus,* which divides to produce free endosperm nuclei (fig. 19.8N). Cell walls later develop around these nuclei, and endosperm tissue is formed.

The longitudinal section of an ovary of a flower is shown diagrammatically (fig. 19.1). Indicate the pathway of the pollen tube by coloring this structure with a red pencil. Note the details of the embryo sac at the time of fertilization.

G. Development of the Embryo

Study prepared slides of young *Capsella* (shepherd's purse) seeds. With the aid of worksheet 19.2A to F, identify important developmental stages and embryo structures. A detailed study of embryo development is impractical in this course, but the following stages may be considered.

Zygote. When an egg is fertilized it becomes a zygote, and the surrounding membrane is soon replaced by a definite cell wall. This stage is ordinarily difficult to find, and if shown, it will be by a special demonstration slide. After the cell wall forms around the zygote, a series of cell divisions soon follow, eventually forming a mass of cells that develops into the rudimentary plant, or embryo.

Two-celled stage. Study a section in which the embryo consists of a large basal cell (at the micropylar end of the embryo sac), and a slender suspensor terminated by a two-celled proembryo (worksheet 19.2A). The embryo proper develops from this two-celled structure. Endosperm nuclei are found lining the embryo sac, and the antipodals have developed into a mass of cells. This antipodal tissue persists through later stages (worksheet 19.2 A–D), but disappears as the seed approaches maturity.

Many-celled embryos. The two-celled proembryo soon divides, and a series of many-celled stages in the development of the embryo quickly follow. Only 4 of these (worksheet 19.2 B–F), are illustrated but many intermediate stages may be found. The endosperm nuclei persist in these early stages. Are the repeated divisions of endosperm nuclei accompanied by the formation of cell walls? As the number of cells increase in the developing embryo, various characteristic regions appear. The cotyledons are first apparent as rounded mounds of tissue (worksheet 19.2D) which continue to enlarge until they fill a considerable portion of the seed (worksheet 19.2E). Embryonic root tissues begin to differentiate near the point where the embryo is attached to the suspensor (worksheet 19.2C–D), and later enlarge to form the structure shown in worksheet 19.2E. Further development of the root occurs when the seed germinates.

Matured embryo. The embryo of a nearly matured seed (worksheet 19.2F) has the cotyledons fully developed, bent back, and nearly filling a large portion of the embryo sac. The *stem tip* (plumule) is well formed and appears as a pointed mound of tissue between the bases of the cotyledons. The *root region* (radicle) at the opposite end has already been described. The *stem region* (hypocotyl) between these two points is clearly defined. The *seed coats* have developed from the integuments of the ovule, and adjacent to the inner integuments, a layer of cells, the nucellus is found. The endosperm has vanished, and all reserve food is stored within the cotyledons. The basal cell and the suspensor are still present. The micropyle is apparent in all stages of seed development and is present in the matured seed.

After identifying the embryo structures outlined, check the legends and labels of worksheet 19.2 A–F. Note the early embryo and endosperm nuclei in the lily (fig. 19.8N). Add all labels needed.

Questions

1. What are the parts of a complete flower?
2. What are the essential organs of a flower?
3. What are the functions of a flower, and how is it adapted for these functions?
4. In what ways can you determine the number of carpels in a compound ovary?
5. What are the characteristics of a hay-fever pollen?
6. Name pollens causing hay fever in the order of their toxicity.
7. What are the parts of the ovule?
8. Name structures of a seed derived from these parts.
9. What are the contents of the mature embryo sac? of the pollen tube?
10. What is the range in size of flowers from smallest to largest?
11. Name the parts of the pistil and the stamen.
12. What is a carpel?
13. What is the male gametophyte of an angiosperm? the female gametophyte?
14. Define a flower and an inflorescence.
15. Diagram and name several types of inflorescences.
16. Illustrate several types of placentation that occur in flowers.
17. How do the sperms enter the embryo sac? With what do they unite? What are the results from these fusions?
18. Why are stamens and pistils so important in the identification of plants?

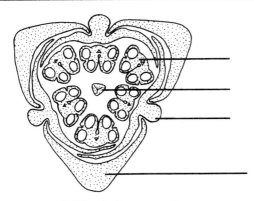

A Lilium bud, cross section

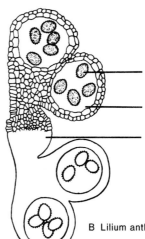

B Lilium anther, cross section

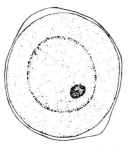

C Microsporocyte (2n)

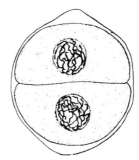

D Secondary sporocytes
(diad)

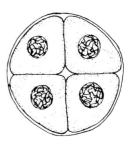

E Quartet of microspores:
meiosis completed (tetrad)

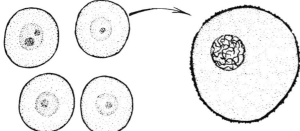

F Developing
microspores (n)

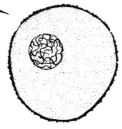

G Uninucleate microspore
(mitosis prophase)

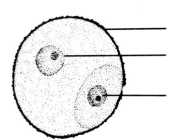

H Generative cell
formed in pollen grain
(male gametophyte)

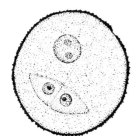

I Pollen grain with
two male gametes

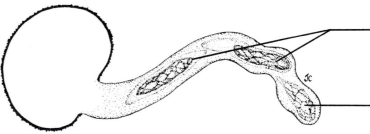

J Pollen tube containing two sperms and tube nucleus

Embryo Development in Capsella *(Shepherd's Purse) Seed*

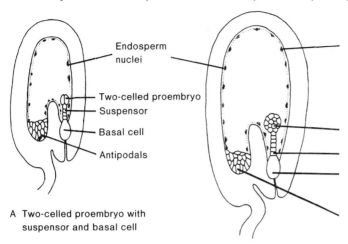

Endosperm nuclei

Two-celled proembryo
Suspensor
Basal cell
Antipodals

A Two-celled proembryo with
   suspensor and basal cell

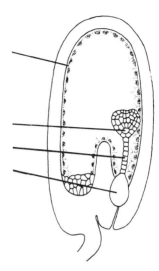

B Many-celled embryo with
   suspensor and basal cell

C Many-celled embryo showing
   differentiation. Suspensor elongated and
   basal cell enlarged.

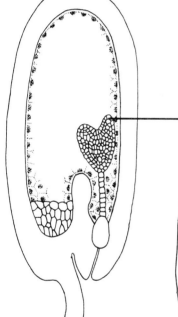

D Many-celled embryo developing
   cotyledons. Suspensor and
   basal cell unchanged.

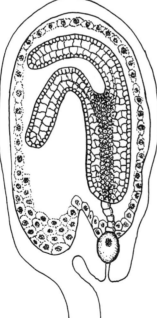

E Many-celled embryo developing cotyledons.
   Embryonic root tissues differentiate
   near suspensor.

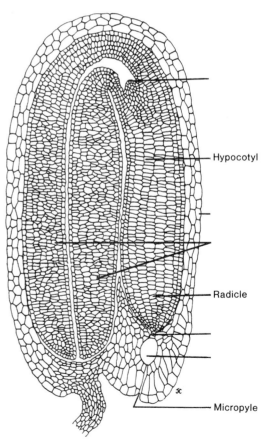

Hypocotyl

Radicle

Micropyle

F Many-celled embryo developed into mature cotyledons,
   hypocotyl, radicle, and stem tip. Suspensor much
   shortened; basal cell unchanged.

20 Fruits and Seeds

Plant Materials

Materials needed are fruits (fresh, if possible) as follows: pea or bean, milkweed, *Iris* or *Datura,* buckwheat or sunflower, dandelion, *Clematis,* or goatsbeard; maple or ash; acorn, filbert, or hazelnut; caryopsis of corn; tomato, cranberry, or grape; orange, grapefruit, or lemon; gourd, cucumber, or squash; peach, plum, or olive; apple, quince, or pear; basswood; strawberries; pineapple; ear of corn (dried) and magnolia (dried).

Equipment

You will need a paring knife, single-edged safety razor blades, and dissecting needles.

Introduction

The stimuli of pollination and fertilization initiate changes in the ovary of a flower that result in the formation of a fruit. A fruit may be defined as the ripened ovary (or ovaries), with contents, of a flower, and often including closely associated parts. There are numerous kinds of fruit, ranging from small, dry, seedlike fruits to the larger, fleshy types. The correct botanical classification of a fruit may at first be disturbing, for instance, the fact that a tomato is really a berry. There can be no argument about what is a fruit and what is a vegetable; if it is derived from the ovary of a flower, it is a fruit.

The parts of a fruit are the ripened ovary wall, or pericarp (which may be differentiated into outer exocarp, inner endocarp, and intermediate mesocarp); seeds; placental tissues; partitions; receptacle; and axis of the stem.

I. *Simple fruits.* The following are simple fruits, each derived from a single ovary:
   A. *Fleshy fruits* (pericarp fleshy): berry, drupe, pome, pepo
   B. *Dry fruits* (pericarp dry):
      1. Dehiscent (splitting open when ripe): legume, follicle, capsule, silique
      2. Indehiscent (not splitting open when ripe): achene, caryopsis (grain), nut, samara
II. *Aggregate fruits.* The following are aggregate fruits, derived from a number of ovaries belonging to a single flower, massed on or scattered over a single receptacle, and later uniting into a single fruit: strawberry, raspberry, and blackberry.
III. *Multiple fruits.* The following are multiple fruits, derived from the ovaries of several flowers, more or less united into one mass: mulberry, pineapple, and fig.

Types of Fruits and Their Seeds

1. *Legume.* Examine the pod of a pea (fig. 20.1A) or a bean. Along how many sides does this fruit split? Identify the floral structures that are represented. The pod is composed of one carpel. The fact that this carpel may represent a modified leaf is more apparent in the pea than in many fruits, since the venation is not obscured.

   Remove one of the peas and examine the hilum, or scar of the seed stalk, and close by it the micropyle, a tiny opening through which the pollen tube entered the ovule and which admits water as a preliminary to germination. Remove the seed coats, noting the relative position of the micropyle and the radicle of the embryo. This relation is true for all seeds. Is there an endosperm? The fleshy halves of the cotyledons are attached by slender connectives to the axis of the embryo. The primordial root is known as a radicle, and the embryonic shoot bud as the plumule. Locate the hypocotyl and the epicotyl of the stem.

2. *Follicle.* A follicle (fig. 20.1D) differs from a legume in that it splits along one side only. Examine the follicles of milkweed and peony. In the milkweed each seed has a large tuft of hairs by which it may be carried by air currents. From what ovule structure are these hairs derived?

3. *Capsule.* Examine capsules of mullein, castor bean, *Ludvigia,* or *Iris* (fig. 20.1B and C). How do these differ from follicles and legumes? How many carpels are there in the *Iris* capsule?

Figure 20.1 Fruit types

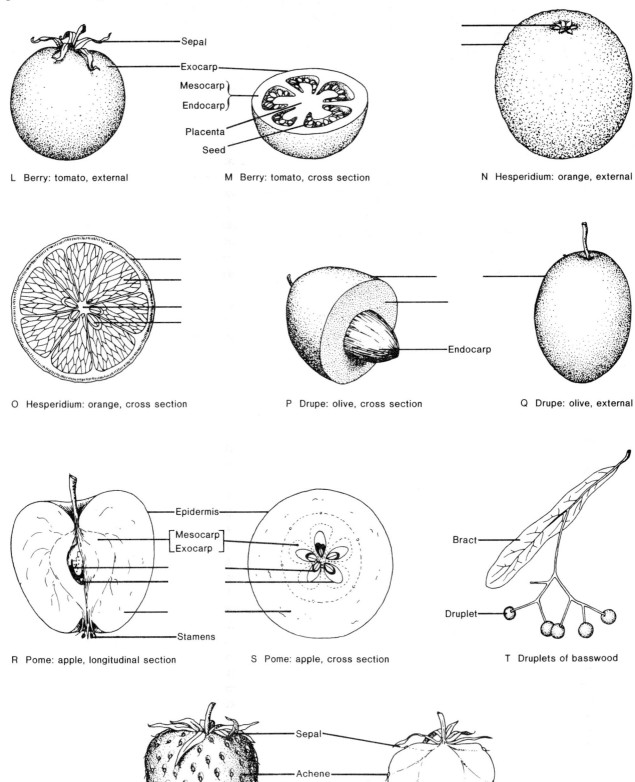

L Berry: tomato, external

Sepal
Exocarp
Mesocarp
Endocarp
Placenta
Seed

M Berry: tomato, cross section

N Hesperidium: orange, external

O Hesperidium: orange, cross section

P Drupe: olive, cross section

Endocarp

Q Drupe: olive, external

Epidermis
Mesocarp
Exocarp

Stamens

R Pome: apple, longitudinal section

S Pome: apple, cross section

Bract

Druplet

T Druplets of basswood

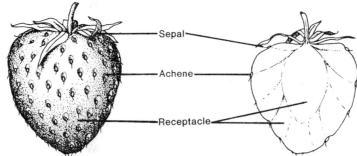

Sepal
Achene
Receptacle

U Aggregate fruit: strawberry, external

V Aggregate fruit: strawberry, longitudinal section

Figure 20.1 continued Fruit types

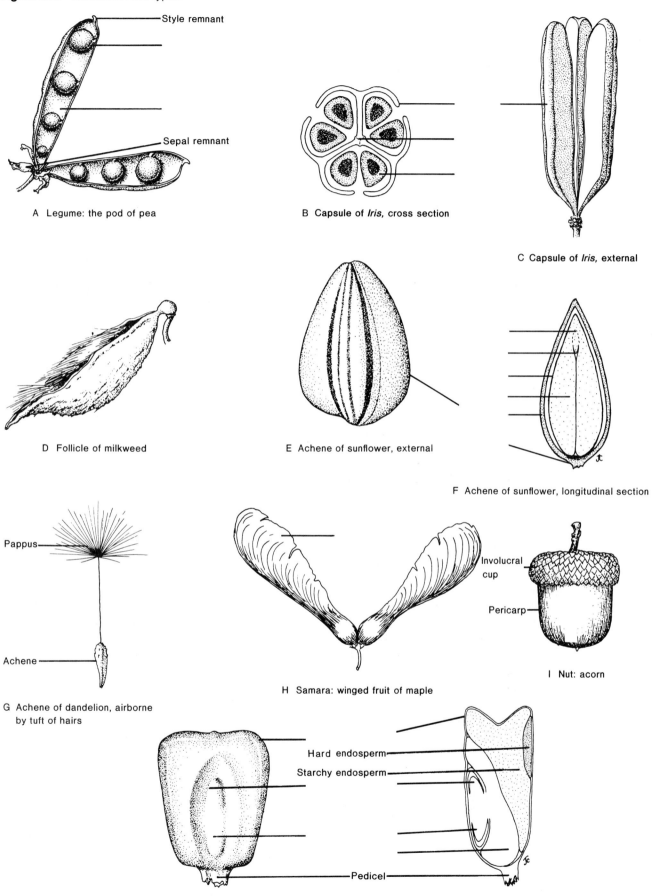

Style remnant

Sepal remnant

A Legume: the pod of pea

B Capsule of *Iris*, cross section

C Capsule of *Iris*, external

D Follicle of milkweed

E Achene of sunflower, external

F Achene of sunflower, longitudinal section

Pappus

Achene

G Achene of dandelion, airborne
by tuft of hairs

H Samara: winged fruit of maple

Involucral
cup

Pericarp

I Nut: acorn

Hard endosperm

Starchy endosperm

Pedicel

J Caryopsis: a grain of corn, external

K Caryopsis: a grain of corn, longitudinal section

4. *Achene*. Examine achenes of buckwheat or sunflower (fig. 20.1E, and F). Crack the outer coat and remove the seed. Are the seed coats attached to any part of the pericarp? Peel off the seed coats and remove the embryo. Are these plants monocotyledons or dicotyledons? Explain.

   Winged achenes are found in many plants, such as dandelions (fig. 20.1G), lettuce, and *Clematis*. From what flower structure is the parachute of the dandelion fruit derived?

5. *Samara*. The broad-winged fruits of ash, elm and maple (fig. 20.1H) are known as samaras or key fruits. From what flower structure are the wings derived? Drop one of these fruits from the height of six feet. Explain how the behavior of this fruit as it falls might benefit the plant.

6. *Nuts*. Acorns (fig. 20.1I), filberts, and hazelnuts are examples of true nuts, and are not to be confused with such commercial "nuts" as almonds, walnuts, and hickory nuts, which are really like the stones of drupes, or with pine nuts and Brazil nuts, which are hard-walled seeds. The pericarp is stony in a true nut. Examine an acorn, note the involucre (cup) at the base. Open the shell and remove the seed, noting the abortive ovule. Is this the seed of a dicotyledon or of a monocotyledon?

7. *Caryopsis*. The caryopsis (fig. 20.1J and K), is the typical fruit of the grasses. Examine a grain of corn (one of the largest grasses), and find the embryo or germ. Section the grain longitudinally, perpendicular to the flat sides. Identify the pericarp, the large endosperm (divided into hard and starchy portions), and the embryo. The latter is composed of a single cotyledon (scutellum), which is the structure in contact with the endosperm. Note the plumule, radicle, and hypocotyl. What is the coleoptile? the coleorhiza? How does this fruit differ from an achene?

8. *Berry*. Examine the fruit of cranberry, grape, or tomato (fig. 20.1L, and M). Cut it into sections, and determine the number of carpels and the arrangement of seeds. Such a fruit is a true berry.

The *hesperidium* is a type of berry with a leathery rind. The orange (fig. 20.1N, and O) and the other citrus fruits fall into this category. From what is the pulp derived?

Pepo. Study a cucumber, squash, pumpkin, melon, or gourd. Cut it into sections, and observe the arrangement of the seeds. A fruit of this type is developed from a flower with an inferior ovary, so the fruit wall and rind are composed in part of tissues from the receptacle. The flesh is mostly mesocarp and endocarp, but the placental tissues may also be well developed (especially in watermelon), which forms much of the pulp. This fruit, peculiar to the melon family, is a modified berry.

9. *Drupe*. Cut longitudinally through a cherry, peach, plum, or olive (fig. 20.1P and Q). Remove the flesh from one side, leaving the stone in place. Identify the exocarp or skin, the fleshy mesocarp, and the bony endocarp. Remove and crack the stone, exposing the seed. Vestiges of an abortive ovule may be present, or rarely, two seeds.

10. *Pome*. Examine an apple (fig. 20.1R and S) cut longitudinally and another cut transversely. Identify the sepals, ripened ovary, receptacle (fused floral tube) tissues, and vestiges of stamens. How many carpels are there? Was the ovary inferior or superior? Pears and quinces have similar structural features. Haws are similar, but differ in having bony ovary walls instead of papery ones as in a pome.

11. Note the fruits (druplets) of basswood (fig. 20.1T) attached to a leaflike bract. Drop one of these fruits from a height of six feet. What happens? Would this behavior serve any useful purpose to the plant?

12. The strawberry (fig. 20.1U and V) is an aggregate fruit in which the fleshy part consists of the enlarged receptacle. The small, seedlike structures (fruitlets) scattered over the surface of the receptacle are small achenes.

Completely label all diagrams in fig. 20.1 A to V.

Questions

1. What is a fruit?
2. Distinguish between a caryopsis and an achene.
3. Why is the tomato fruit a berry?
4. What are the three layers of the pericarp?
5. What part of the pericarp is eaten when you eat olives? cucumbers? oranges? tomatoes? plums? bananas?
6. What is the fleshy part of the apple? the strawberry?
7. What is the stone in a drupe?
8. What is the commercial importance of the caryopsis type of fruit?
9. List ways in which fruits and seeds may be naturally disseminated.
10. Comment on the value of fruits in the life of a plant.

Exercise 21

Seed Germination and Seedling Development

Plant Materials

Materials needed are lima beans, peas, peanuts, squash seeds, corn grains, onion seeds; seedlings grown in flats as follows: beans, peas, peanuts, squash, corn, onions. You will also need seedlings of at least four developmental stages (i.e., grown from seeds planted a week apart), ranging from germinated seeds with roots about 2 cm long, to the largest seedling 15 to 20 cm tall.

Equipment

Obtain single-edged razor blades, petri dishes, and filter paper.

Reagents

You will need iodine potassium iodide solution (diluted to a light amber color) and tetrazolium chloride.

Introduction

A seed may be defined as a matured (ripened) ovule. Each typical seed consists essentially of protective seed coat(s), some form of stored food, and an embryo. When a seed germinates, the embryo enlarges (grows), the seed coat(s) bursts, and the young plant emerges. Early growth is dependent on food stored usually within an endosperm or, if there is no endosperm, within the cotyledons. There are two distinct types of seedling development: (1) those in which the cotyledons are carried above ground by the elongation of the hypocotyl (*epigean*), and (2) those in which the cotyledons remain beneath the soil (*hypogean*). When the cotyledons are carried above ground they may serve temporarily as photosynthetic organs. In the germination of seeds the primary root arises from the radicle (root primordium) and is the first embryo structure to emerge. Lateral branches soon appear on the primary root. The young stem, arising from the stem tip of the plumule, follows the root in emerging from the seed. Young leaves are soon formed, and the seedling plant develops rapidly from this point.

The region of a seedling below the cotyledons, which gradually merges into the radicle or root, is the hypocotyl; the region above the cotyledons is the epicotyl.

Dicotyledonous Seeds and Seedlings

A. Bean (Epigean Development)

Review the description of a legume seed given in the exercise on fruits. Peel off the seed coat from a bean seed that has been soaked in water overnight, and locate the cotyledons, plumule, epicotyl, hypocotyl, and radicle. Scrape off a small amount of material from a cotyledon, and test with iodine. What substance is present in the cotyledon?

Examine lima bean seedlings in various stages of development. Do the cotyledons appear to perform any function other than storage? Which organ first emerges from the seed, the plumule or the radicle? Of what advantage is this to the young plant? Describe the process of germination in the bean.

Check the series of drawings (fig. 21.1) showing stages in the development of a bean seedling. Note the soil line in each drawing. Complete labeling.

B. Pea (Hypogean Development)

Identify the parts of a pea seed. Does it differ essentially from the seed of a lima bean? Examine pea seedlings in various stages of development. How do they differ from a bean seedling in their germination?

Check the series of drawings (fig. 21.2) showing stages in the development of a pea seedling. Note the soil line in each drawing. Complete labels as needed.

C. Peanut (Epigean Development)

Examine seeds of the peanut. How do they differ from the seeds of bean and pea? What is the thin, brown, paperlike covering of the peanut seeds? Study stages in the development of peanut seedlings. Is this development epigean or hypogean?

Check with the series of drawings (fig. 21.3) showing stages in the development of a peanut seedling. Note the soil line in each drawing. Complete labels.

Figure 21.1 Bean

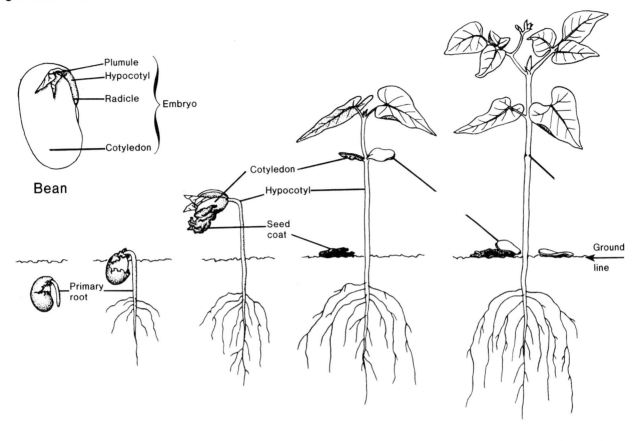

Bean

Plumule
Hypocotyl
Radicle
Cotyledon
Embryo

Bean

Cotyledon
Hypocotyl
Seed coat

Ground line

Primary root

Figure 21.2 Pea

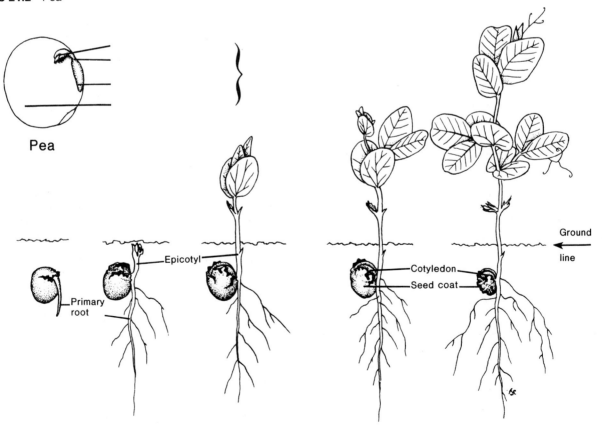

Pea

Pea

Ground line

Epicotyl

Cotyledon
Seed coat

Primary root

Seed Germination and Seedling Development   151

Figure 21.3 Peanut

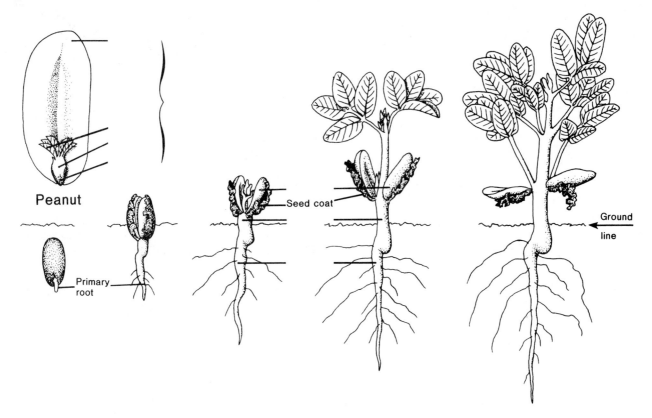

Peanut

Primary root

Seed coat

Ground line

D. Squash (Epigean Development)

Study germinating squash seeds, noting differences in the seed coats from those of bean and pea. The root emerges first, and a small shelf or peg of tissue develops, which serves as a point of anchorage for the seedling to pull itself free from the seed coats. What happens to the cotyledons of a squash seedling?

Draw and label a series of stages in the development of the squash seedling. Indicate the soil line in each drawing.

Monocotyledonous Seeds and Seedlings

A. Corn (Hypogean Development)

Review the corn grain (caryopsis) as studied in the exercise on fruits. Compare the parts of the corn grain with the parts of a bean or pea seed. What are the outstanding differences? Remove the embryo (germ) of a corn grain and identify the parts. The primary roots of corn do not persist and are soon replaced by adventitious roots developed from the stem. Examine seedlings in various stages of development, and identify the aforementioned structures. The early stages in the germination of wheat, oats, and rice are similar to those of corn.

Check the drawings (fig. 21.4) of a series of stages in the development of a corn seedling. Note the soil line in each drawing. Complete the labels.

B. Onion (Epigean Development)

Note the shape and size of a seed. Cut a seed parallel to the flat surface, and interpret what is exposed. Study seedlings in various stages of germination. Does the onion in its germination more nearly resemble the bean or the pea? Locate the cotyledon of an onion seedling.

Testing Seed Viability

Soak 40–50 corn kernels ("seeds") overnight in tap water, and divide into two equal lots. Kill the embryos of one lot by immersing in boiling water for 15–20 minutes.

A. Tetrazolium Test

Section several living (unboiled) corn kernels by placing each one flat with the scutellum of the embryo uppermost and slicing lengthwise with a razor blade to get median longitudinal views of the embryo. Immerse all segments in a petri dish (without filter paper) of 0.1% tetrazolium chloride. Observe after 30 minutes, and again after one hour.

Figure 21.4 Corn

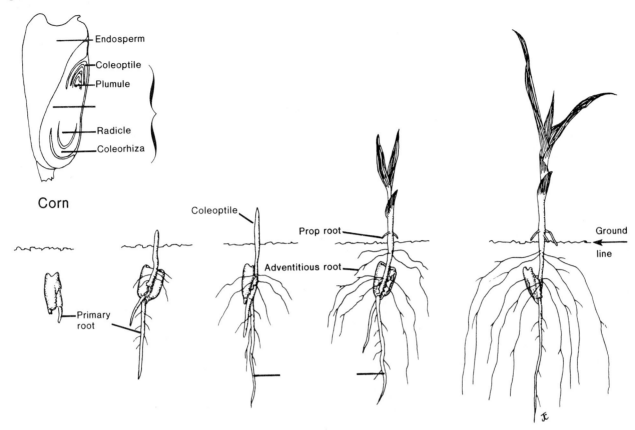

Corn

Questions

Similarly section several dead (boiled) kernels, and immerse in tetrazolium chloride. Did the embryos of the living or dead (boiled) seeds change color in the tetrazolium?

A carmine red color appearing in the embryo indicates that the kernel ("seed") is living (viable) and capable of germination. Respiring cells of the living embryo reduce the colorless tetrazolium to produce the carmine red color. However, the embryos of dead (nonviable) seeds do not respire and hence produce no color change in the tetrazolium.

B. Germination Test

Place 10–15 living (unboiled) corn kernels on wet filter paper in a petri dish, and set aside in a dark place to germinate.

Repeat this procedure using 10–15 seeds that have been killed by boiling.

Observe daily until the primary root is well formed on the germinating seeds. Did any of the killed (boiled) seeds germinate? What percentage of the unboiled (living) seeds germinated? Explain why one would not expect 100% germination from any given lot of viable seeds.

Consult standard texts of botany for a description of various seeds, their germination, and seedling development.

Questions

1. What are the parts of the complete embryo of a dicot seed? a monocot seed?
2. What functions do these parts serve?
3. Contrast the germination of bean with pea and of corn with onion.
4. What is unusual in the behavior of a peanut plant after the flowers have been pollinated?
5. How does water enter a seed previous to germination?
6. What happens to the primary root system of a corn plant? a bean plant?
7. What is the difference between epigean and hypogean development of seedlings?
8. What is vegetable ivory?
9. What is a radicle? plumule? cotyledon? hypocotyl? hypocotyl arch?
10. What are viable seeds? dormant seeds?
11. Comment on the economic importance of seeds.
12. Distinguish between fruits and seeds.

22

The Procaryotes: Bacteria and Blue-Green Algae (Cyanophyta)

The most ancient organisms to appear in the fossil record were the structurally simple, unicellular organisms represented in the world today by the living procaryotes. Usually classified in the Kingdom Monera, these microscopic organisms—lacking a nucleus, mitochondria, and other subcellular organelles—show incredible biochemical and physiological diversity. Largely unnoticed (except when they cause a disease), they nevertheless are the most numerous of living things, cosmopolitan in distribution, and through their recycling and transformation of organic compounds to nutrients, essential for the maintenance of the biosphere.

Recent progress in nucleic-acid technology has had a significant impact on procaryote classification. Distinctive forms of ribosomal RNA confirm the separateness of a group called the Archaebacteria from the more commonly known Eubacteria. The results of these studies agree with the theory that plant chloroplasts were derived from the blue-green algae (also called Cyanobacteria) or related primitive forms and that the separation between the cyanophytes and the gram negative and gram positive bacteria is also very ancient. Because procaryotes reproduce by binary fission, some classifications had placed them all in a single division (Schizophyta). Because of their distinctness from the eucaryotic organisms, they are grouped together in this exercise but in such a manner that they may be studied separately. Only Eubacteria and Cyanophyta will be examined.

Bacteria

Plant Materials

Materials needed are infusions of bean, hay, hamburger, and potato; cultures of common bacteria on agar plates; agar slants of *Serratia marcescens, Micrococcus (Staphylococcus) alba, M. aureus, Pseudomonas aeruginosa, Sarcina lutea, Bacillus subtilus, Chromobacterium violaceum, Streptococcus viridans,* and *S. hemolyticus* on blood agar.

Prepared slides showing bacterial types, spores, and pathological forms are also needed.

Equipment

A compound microscope with an oil-immersion lens; immersion oil; cotton plugs, test tubes of sterile nutrient agar, sterile petri dishes, 1,000-ml glass beakers, hot plates, medicine droppers, Syracuse watch glasses, Difco discs, and a fine-pointed curved forceps are needed.

Reagents

You will need strong solutions of phenol, silver nitrate, mercuric chloride (**These are DANGEROUS, use only as directed by your laboratory instructor**); hexachlorophene, potassium permanganate, Lavoris, Micrin, Cepacol, Bactine, Sucrets gargle, Listerine, or other disinfectants; and hydrogen peroxide 3% solution, crystal violet, iodine solution, ether-acetone solution, 0.5% safranin.

Introduction

Bacteria (singular, *bacterium*) are distinguished by being the simplest in structure, smallest in size, most abundant, and most widely distributed of all plants. Bacteria are procaryotic, one-celled organisms lacking chlorophyll. They often cohere and form visible aggregates (*colonies*) that may be red, yellow, purple, green, or other shades of color. Bacteria reproduce by simple (binary) fission. Bacteria are mostly parasites or saprophytes, but some forms are *autophytic* or *symbiotic* in habit. Most bacteria are useful to man. They are used commercially in the manufacture of acetic acid, lactic acid, butyl alcohol, and acetone. Other forms are the causal agents of some of the deadly diseases of man. Bacteria are abundant in soils; one gram of fertile garden soil may contain over one billion individuals. Some drinking water and all untreated sewage abound with various forms of bacteria. Bacteria in the root nodules of leguminous plants are known universally for their ability to fix free nitrogen from the air, converting it into soluble salts that the plant is able to use.

A. Living Bacteria

Mount some of the whitish scum from the bean, hay, or potato infusions provided, and focus very carefully under h.p. Note the numerous, colorless, variously shaped bodies in the mount. Are they all separate or are they connected?

If the latter, describe the connection. What different shapes are present? Are any of the bacteria in motion? If so, describe the motion.

In outline, draw bacteria of several different shapes.

B. Prepared Slides

Examine prepared slides of spherical (coccus), rod-shaped (bacillus), and spiral (spirillum) forms. Note especially those that are of economic importance.

Spores. Examine, under demonstration microscopes, prepared slides of bacteria showing spores (endospores). These are not spores in the ordinary sense in which the term is used, meaning reproductive cells, but are ordinary bacterial cells in which the contents have become agglutinated; thus, they serve as resistant resting cells.

Label one of the drawings showing bacterial spores in worksheet 22.1.

C. Growth of Bacterial Colonies

Bacteria are so minute and often so much alike that it is frequently difficult to tell much about them by looking at them through a microscope; hence, bacteriologists depend very much on nonmorphological characters for their classification. Among these are the production and nonproduction of gas in certain nutrient solutions and the manner of growth and appearance of the colonies on solid medium (nutrient agar).

Examine the agar plates (petri dishes) on which cultures of bacteria are growing. Compare the colonies as to color, surface, and margin. Do they all grow on the surface? Note the same bacteria as they grow on agar slants in test tubes.

The instructor will expose sterile plates of nutrient agar to the air of the laboratory. Reserve a place in your notes to describe, in the next laboratory period, the appearance of these plates as compared with the appearance of an unexposed (control) plate. Devise other experiments (such as letting a housefly or cockroach walk on a plate of sterile agar), using various means to contaminate agar plates. Observe the results in the next laboratory period.

Some bacteria are *chromogenic* (color forming) and when grown in colonies exhibit various colors. Examine agar slants or plates of nutrient medium on which cultures of the following bacteria are growing: *Serratia marcescens, Micrococcus (Staphylococcus) alba, M. aureus, Pseudomonas aeruginosa, Sarcina lutea, Bacillus subtilis,* and *Chromobacter violaceum.* What color are the colonies of each of these species of bacteria? Do the individual bacterial cells appear colored when viewed under the microscope? If the bacterial cells appear colorless under the microscope, why then are the colonies colored?

Draw several tubes showing the colored colonies of bacteria. Indicate the color of each colony by a label, or by using colored pencils.

Examine the sealed petri dishes containing streak cultures of *Streptococcus viridans* and *S. hemolyticus* growing on blood agar. Note the colonies of these bacteria on the surface of the medium. What has happened to the color of the blood agar on each side of the streaks of bacterial colonies? Is this area the same color for each of the species named? Define hemolysis, and explain its importance in bacterial infections of humans. The instructor will inoculate sterile plates of blood agar with material from a sore throat or cough from a person having a sore throat. View these plates after incubation and state why certain of the colonies that may appear on the medium probably belong to the genus *Streptococcus.*

Make properly colored sketches to show hemolysis in the demonstration and experimental materials described.

D. Effectiveness of Common Disinfectants

In this experiment one may test the effectiveness of various disinfectants on two common bacteria, *Serratia marcescens* (bloodred colonies), and *Micrococcus aureus* (yellow colonies).

Sterile nutrient agar (20 ml) in cotton-plugged tubes is melted in beakers of hot water on electric hot plates. Air cool a tube until it can be held under the jawbone three to five seconds without undue discomfort, then have your instructor inoculate it quickly with 1 to 2 ml (using a medicine dropper) of an active broth culture of *Serratia marcescens.* Briskly rotate the tube between your palms several times to mix the bacteria and agar. Using a sterile (and warm) petri dish, lift one edge of the cover and quickly pour in the still-melted contents of the inoculated tube as previously demonstrated by your instructor. Set it aside to cool and harden. It is necessary to proceed quickly with these operations in order to obtain smoothly poured agar plates.

Various disinfectants have been placed in Syracuse watch glasses, and two Difco discs (or filter paper discs cut with cork borers) placed in each to soak. For use as a control, two sterile discs have been placed in sterile distilled water. Place fine-pointed forceps (tweezers) in each dish; do not use any forceps for more than one disinfectant.

Lift one side of a petri dish cover, and with a forceps, place one wet (not dripping) disc from a disinfectant on the center of an agar plate inoculated with *Serratia marcescens.* Repeat this process for all disinfectants and the control. Properly label each dish to show the name of bacterium and disinfectant used.

Repeat this procedure to make a similar complete series using agar plates inoculated with *Micrococcus aureus.*

Allow the two series to incubate several days, or until a good growth of bacterial colonies has formed around the paper discs.

Note: Serratia marcescens must be incubated at room temperature of not more than 20 to 22°C, or the characteristic bloodred color of its colonies will not develop.

The effectiveness of each disinfectant is indicated by the width of the inhibition zone (i.e., no bacterial growth) around each paper disc. Indicate the degree of inhibition as directed in worksheet 22.2.

Disinfectants that may be used include phenol, silver nitrate, tincture of iodine, mercuric chloride, hexachlorophene, Lavoris, Cepacol, Bactine, Clorox, Mercurochrome, Listerine, Sucrets gargle, potassium permanganate, hydrogen peroxide, Micrin, or others as provided. Use dilutions as recommended by your instructor.

This experiment may be repeated using discs containing various antibiotics, or antibiotic discs may be used instead of certain disinfectants in this series.

E. Pathogens

Examine the demonstration slides of various *pathogenic* (disease-producing) bacteria. Note the scientific names of these bacteria, and check with the drawings (worksheet 22.1) for comparison. What magnification is used with the demonstration microscopes? What is an oil-immersion lens?

F. Staining Procedures (Optional)

Further study of the bacteria examined in part A may be done by staining smears of the cultures and reexamining them. The bacteria are transferred to the slide with a toothpick or inoculating loop using a circular motion to smear them in a thin film on the slide. The drop is allowed to air dry. The bacteria are then fixed by passing the slide through the flame of an alcohol lamp or Bunsen burner several times.

Simple stains. Place the slide over a watch glass or small beaker and add several drops of the stain. Crystal violet will give the darkest stain, but others such as methylene blue may be used. Let the stain dry for one minute, and then wash the slide with a gentle stream of water as from an eye dropper. Carefully blot (do not rub) dry. Add a drop of water and a coverslip and observe.

Gram stain. One method for this procedure is as follows. Cover the fixed smear with a 1 percent solution of crystal violet and immediately add 3 to 5 drops of a 5-percent sodium bicarbonate solution, and using a toothpick, mix this with the dye. Stain for one minute. Wash quickly with water and then cover the smear with iodine solution for one minute. Wash quickly with water. With the slide held at an angle over a beaker, wash with an ether-acetone mixture (one part petroleum ether to three parts acetone). Continue until the wash fluid becomes colorless. Drain the slide and wash with water once more. Counterstain with a 0.5% safranin solution for 10 seconds. Wash quickly, blot, dry, and examine. Gram-positive bacteria should stain blue and gram-negative bacteria will be pink to red.

Record your observations as directed by your instructor. It is important not to spill any of the stain and to wash the lab table with a disinfectant at the end of the exercise.

Root Nodules of Leguminous Plants

Plant Materials

Materials needed are young roots of clover, alfalfa, soybeans, or other legume with bacterial galls, and prepared slides of root nodules with bacteria.

Equipment

A compound microscope, blank slides, and cover glasses are needed.

Reagents

Eosin, 1% aqueous, is the required reagent.

Introduction

The most important natural factor in adding nitrogen to the soil is the action of certain bacteria that are able to fix free nitrogen from the air; that is, to use it in the synthesis of nitrogenous compounds (nitrates), which the higher plants are able to use as a source of nitrogen. Some of these bacteria live free in the soil (*Azotobacter*). The most important (species of *Rhizobium*) grow in connection with leguminous plants. They are restricted to the roots, forming galls (also called tubercles or nodules) in which they live in great masses, obtaining carbohydrates from the host plant and nitrogen from the air. Nitrogen is thus made available to the living roots. More nitrogen is released into the soil when the roots eventually die and decay.

A. External Appearance of Nodules

Study the root nodules in the small bottles. Does the root run through the center, or are the galls lateral or terminal?

Add labels to the drawing of a root with root nodules (worksheet 22.3A).

B. Internal Structure of Nodules

Examine prepared slides showing cross sections of the nodule. Note the cortex, vascular bundles, and cells filled with bacteria. The large cells in the central portion of the galls are filled with masses of stained bacteria. Is a nucleus present in these cells? Suggest how the bacteria originally entered the root.

Label the diagram (worksheet 22.3B) of a cross section of a root nodule (gall). Indicate by neat shading, the portion of the nodule occupied by bacteria-filled cells.

C. The Bacteria of the Nodules

Crush a small piece of a tubercle on a slide, and mix with a drop of eosin. Cover and examine with h.p. Note the numerous, minute, rod-shaped bacteria, also L-shaped, T-shaped, or other irregular forms (bacteroids) that may be present. These are all forms assumed by the bacteria in the nodule. The bacteria are more regular in shape when grown in pure cultures.

Draw three or four bacteria, illustrating some of the forms seen.

Questions

1. How do bacteria differ from the algae?
2. What are the three common shapes of bacteria?
3. Where are bacteria distributed?
4. Name locations where bacteria will not be found.
5. What are the economic uses of bacteria?
6. How do bacteria of the root nodules first obtain entrance into the root?
7. In what form must nitrogen be for assimilation by the plant?
8. Name the bacterium found in the root nodules of leguminous plants.
9. Give the scientific names of three or four bacteria that cause human diseases.
10. What is a pure culture?
11. How do bacteria move? Are all bacteria capable of movement?
12. Why were bacteria considered to be plants?
13. Comment on the importance of root nodule bacteria in a typical crop rotation program.
14. What is a disinfectant? a bacteriocide (germicide)? an antiseptic?
15. List precautions necessary when handling bacteria, especially pathogenic forms.
16. Why is *Serratia marcescens* said to be the cause of red milk and bloody bread?

Blue-Green Algae

Plant Materials

Materials needed are living or preserved *Gloeocapsa, Nostoc, Oscillatoria, Gloeotrichia, Lyngbya, Cylindrospermum, Merismopedia, Microcoleus, Spirulina,* or other blue-green algae.

Equipment

Obtain a compound microscope, blank slides and cover glasses, pipette, medicine dropper, and dissecting needles; also, glass jars for algal cultures.

Introduction

The blue-green algae are the simplest and most primitive organisms able to carry out photosynthesis with the evolution of oxygen. They possess chlorophyll a, a trait shared with the plants and plantlike protists. They also have phycobilin pigments, the blue *phycocyanin* and the red *phycoerythrin* that impart the characteristic blue-green color present in about one-half the members of this group. Other blue-greens range in color from a light chocolate brown to olive green. These algae are regarded as primitive because reproduction is always by *fission* or by *hormogonia* (fragmentation), and never sexual.

All blue-green algae are procaryotic organisms. They have no clearly delimited nucleus, typical chloroplasts, mitochondria, Golgi apparatus, or endoplasmic reticulum. Electron micrographs reveal, however, an assemblage of parallel photosynthetic membranes functioning as a chloroplast. Glycoproteins and cyanophycean starch are stored in the cells instead of true starch.

The cell walls are gelatinized, and a surrounding sheath or matrix of this material is usually present. The blue-greens are able to grow in practically any wet or moist habitat, hot springs, cold ponds, and polluted streams.

With the other algae and the land plants, they are the producers that form the basis of the food chain that sustains all life. They seem to be noticed most, however, because of their nuisance value. Most of the disagreeable tastes and odors in water supplies due to algae are caused by blue-greens. Considerable numbers of these algae live in the soil or are contained in other plants, and some of them are able to fix nitrogen from the air. This nitrogen-fixing ability sustains the growth of paddy rice and makes it the most efficient food-producing system used by humankind.

A. *Gloeocapsa*

Mount a small quantity of the living or preserved *Gloeocapsa* material on a slide, cover with a coverslip, and spread out by tapping gently with a pencil point. Examine under l.p. You may see a variety of microscopic plants and animals. Find a part of the field where there are a number of *globose cells* surrounded by ringlike, concentric, gelatinous sheaths. These cells may occur singly or in groups (colonies). Examine under h.p. disregarding, except as may be directed later, other organisms in the mount. What is the color of the living cell? Do not describe it merely as green but compare it with the color of other green plants. What is it that holds the cells together? Small, colorless, rod-shaped, or spiral bodies (bacteria), many of them in motion, may be present on the outside of the gelatinous sheath. What does their presence suggest as a possible function of the sheath? What other functions could the sheath perform? Is there any suggestion of a definite cell wall? What is the character of the cell contents? Is there any differentiation into nucleus and cytoplasm?

Begin with a somewhat elongated cell and look for a series of cells in which division is taking place. What is the first indication of fission? What follows?

After careful study of the plants, label the drawings of *Gloeocapsa* (worksheet 22.4B).

B. *Nostoc*

Nostoc is an example of an aggregate form. The gelatinous clumps (macrocolonies) are comprised of numerous filaments adhering to one another by means of their swollen, gelatinous sheaths. The color, originally dull green, may have been removed by the preservative (formalin).

Make a water mount of a small portion of the colony, and note the beadlike arrangement of the cells in the filament. How do these cells compare with those of the form previously studied? Note the occasional, large, and apparently empty cells with thick walls *(heterocysts)*. They function to fix nitrogen.

Label the drawings of *Nostoc* (worksheet 22.4D).

C. *Anabaena*

Make a water mount of living or preserved *Anabaena*. The beadlike filaments of this alga resemble *Nostoc*, but they are not contained in gelatinous balls, the heterocyst is different, and elongated akinetes (spores) are formed. Water blooms frequently consist of practically pure cultures of *Anabaena*. Under favorable conditions *Anabaena* may become so concentrated that livestock (hogs, chickens, and ducks) may be poisoned when they drink the water. The chemical nature of this quick-acting poison has not been determined.

Crush a small piece of *Azolla* (a water fern) in a drop of water under a cover glass, and observe under the microscope. Note the filaments of *Anabaena* mixed with *Azolla* fragments in the mount. With careful dissection *Anabaena* filaments may be seen massed in small pockets in the *Azolla* tissue. The heterocysts function to fix nitrogen.

Label the drawings of *Anabaena* filaments (worksheet 22.4C).

D. *Gloeotrichia*

Make a water mount of a small portion of preserved *Gloeotrichia*. This is a blue-green alga possessing a long, tapering filament terminating at the large end in an elongated akinete (spore), which is terminated by a heterocyst

(fixes nitrogen). The gelatinous sheath extends skirtlike from the heterocyst some distance down the filament. These plants grow in spherical colonies with the heterocysts toward the center.

Label the drawings of *Gloeotrichia* (worksheet 22.4F).

E. *Oscillatoria*

Examine cultures of living *Oscillatoria*, noting the deep blue-green color. Note the swampy odor of these cultures. Make a water mount of this material and search for long, bluish green filaments. How does their color compare with that of *Gloeocapsa*? What is the shape of the individual cells? How are they arranged in the filament? What of the cell contents? Is there any movement of the filament as a whole? If so, indicate it diagrammatically by small arrows in connection with the drawing. Note the numerous short filaments composed of only a few cells, the *hormogonia* (singular, *hormogonium*). Are there any in the process of formation?

Label the drawings of *Oscillatoria* (worksheet 22.4H).

F. *Lyngbya*

The filaments of *Lyngbya* cells are enclosed in a thick, tubular, gelatinous sheath but are otherwise similar to those of *Oscillatoria*. Make a water mount of living or preserved *Lyngbya*, noting the features. It is often found in marine habitats.

Label the drawing of *Lyngbya* (worksheet 22.4G).

G. *Microcystis (Micrococcus)*

Make a water mount from living or preserved plankton. Note the masses of cells loosely arranged in an irregular pattern within a diffuse gelatinous mass.

Label the drawing of *Microcystis* (worksheet 22.4A).

H. *Merismopedia*

Make a water mount of living or preserved *Merismopedia* material. The cells of *Merismopedia* divide into two directions in one plane only, resulting in the formation of a flat, square, one-cell thick colony embedded in a gelatinous sheath.

Label the drawing of *Merismopedia* (worksheet 22.4E).

I. Others

Examine some water bloom or *Cylindrosperum, Spirulina, Stigeonema,* and such other forms as are available. Draw as many as time permits, carefully indicating differences between these genera and those previously studied.

Questions

1. What range in form occurs in the blue-green algae?
2. Why are they called blue-green?
3. Compare a hormogonium with an akinete.
4. What are the advantages of the gelatinous sheath?
5. Be able to comment on the pollution of water supplies by blue-greens.
6. How may these algae be removed from drinking water supplies?
7. What is a heterocyst?
8. What is an algacide?
9. What range of habitats do you find among the blue-greens?
10. Are all blue-green algae blue-green in color? Explain.
11. What is a water bloom?

Name _____

Different Bacterial Forms

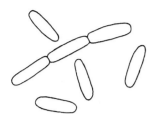

Bacillus subtilis

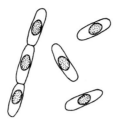

B. subtilis, spores

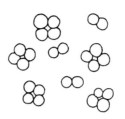

Sarcina lutea

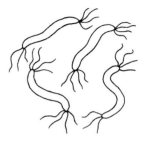

Spirillum volutans

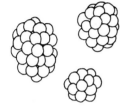

Micrococcus aureus

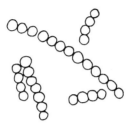

Streptococcus viridans

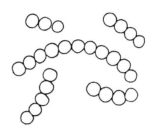

Streptococcus lactis

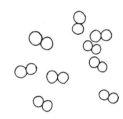

Diplococcus pneumoniae
(syn. *Streptococcus pneumoniae*)

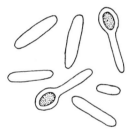

Clostridium tetani

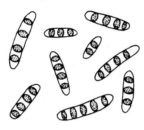

Corynebacterium diphtheriae

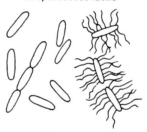

Salmonella typhosa
(syn. *Eberthella typhi*)

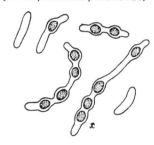

Mycobacterium tuberculosis

Effectiveness of Disinfectants

Disinfectant	Amount of inhibition Indicate by O, +, + +, + + +, + + + +, or by sketches	
	Serratia marcescens	*Micrococcus aureus*

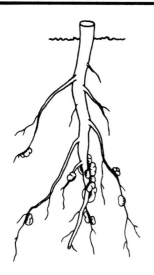

A Root with bacterial tubercles

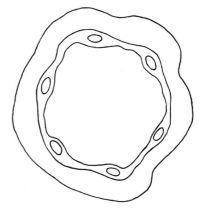

B Cross section of root tubercle

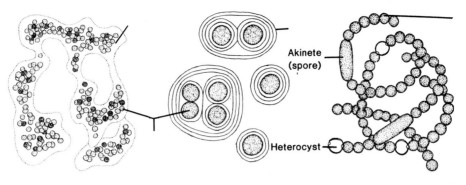

A *Microcystis*   B *Gloeocapsa*   C *Anabaena*

Akinete
(spore)

Heterocyst

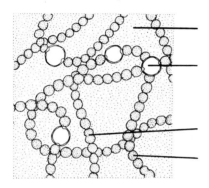
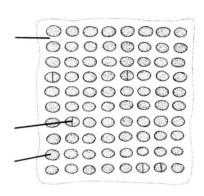

D *Nostoc*   E *Merismopedia*

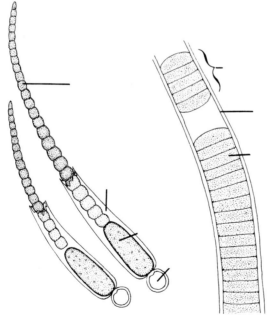

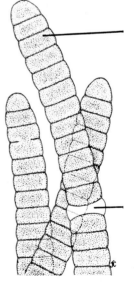

F *Gloeotrichia*   G *Lyngbya*   H *Oscillatoria*

23

Green Algae (Chlorophyta)

Plant Materials

Materials needed are living or preserved *Protococcus, Ulothrix, Oedogonium,* and *Spirogyra,* and prepared slides of *Ulothrix, Oedogonium, Spirogyra,* or other green algae.

Equipment

A compound microscope, blank slides and cover glasses, teasing needles, sharp-pointed forceps, and glass jars for algal cultures are needed.

Introduction

The chlorophyta are the most common, and most widely distributed, of all the algae and embrace a wide variety of sizes, forms, and types of life history. Green algae live in clear, cool, and often running water. They do not tolerate pollution. All are eucaryotic organisms. Their cells have chloroplasts usually with pyrenoids; a nucleus with a nuclear membrane; mitochondria; Golgi apparatus; and endoplasmic reticulum. Reproduction is by simple fission in some forms, by gametes and zoospores in others. Food is stored as starch in them. *Ulothrix,* having morphologically similar gametes, illustrates the most primitive type of sexual reproduction. A more advanced type of sexual reproduction, involving heterogametes, is found in *Oedogonium.* The present study must be limited to a very few representative forms of this group. Consult the text and references for descriptions of other forms.

A. *Ulothrix*

This alga will usually be studied from prepared slides or preserved material, hence, it may have lost its green color; otherwise, there is little difference between its present appearance and that when collected.

Note the cylindrical cells attached end-to-end to form a separate filament. A basal holdfast may be seen in some filaments. Study the flat, collar-shaped chloroplast containing pyrenoids (centers of starch accumulation). Cytoplasm and a central nucleus are surrounded by the chloroplast.

Label the drawing of a *Ulothrix* vegetative filament (fig. 23.1A).

Treat the plants with iodine. What happens?

Asexual Phase

Find a cell in which the contents have divided to form two to four rounded bodies, each a developing zoospore (fig. 23.1B). The escaped mature zoospores (fig. 23.1C), each with four flagella and a colored eyespot, are able to develop into a new vegetative filament.

This completes the asexual phase in the life history of *Ulothrix.*

Sexual Phase

Find cells (gametangia) in which the contents have divided into eight, sixteen, or smaller bodies; these are isogametes (morphologically identical but physiologically different from each other). Find gametangia (fig. 23.1D and F) with young gametes. In preserved material it may be difficult to find mature, escaped isogametes (fig. 23.1E and G), each with two flagella and a colored eyespot. Two isogametes meet and conjugate (fuse) (fig. 23.1H) to form a zygote (fig. 23.1I). The 2N zygote undergoes meiosis to produce four young haploid zoospores (fig. 23.1J). The escaped zoospores (fig. 23.1K), each with four flagella and a colored eyespot, develop into new vegetative filaments.

This completes the sexual phase in the life history of *Ulothrix.*

Because its sexual reproduction involves fusion of like gametes (isogametes), *Ulothrix* is called an isogamous alga.

Completely label the drawings of *Ulothrix,* figure 23.1B to K, inclusive.

Ulothrix may be considered typical of aquatic colonial green algae.

B. *Protococcus (Pleurococcus)*

A second type of colonial growth is found in the irregularly clustered cells of the reduced terrestrial form *Protococcus.* As you examine this alga try to determine why it can grow on tree bark while *Ulothrix* must be completely immersed in water to stay alive.

Note the velvety green material on pieces of tree bark. These green patches are due to the growth of a single-celled plant, *Protococcus.* Lightly scrape off a small amount of this green growth, being especially careful not to include bark scrapings. Mount in water and examine, first under l.p., then h.p. After careful study of a number

Figure 23.1 *Ulothrix*

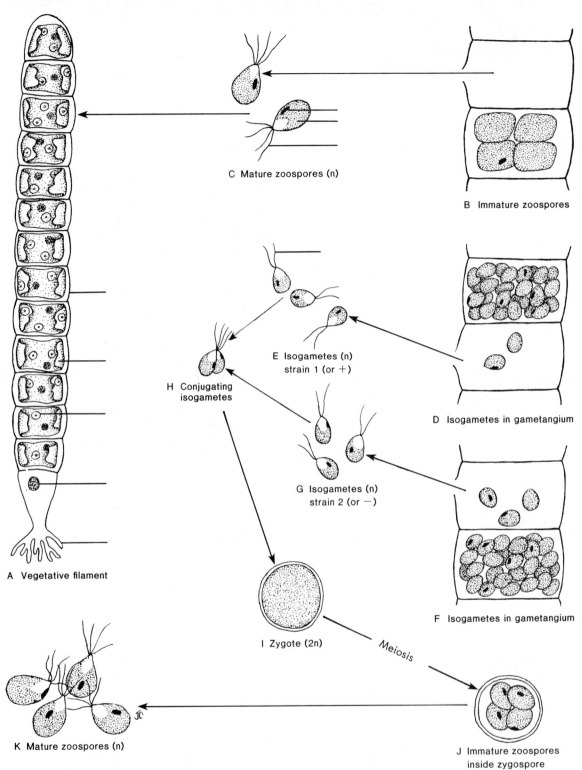

C Mature zoospores (n)

B Immature zoospores

H Conjugating
isogametes

E Isogametes (n)
strain 1 (or +)

D Isogametes in gametangium

G Isogametes (n)
strain 2 (or −)

F Isogametes in gametangium

A Vegetative filament

I Zygote (2n)

Meiosis

K Mature zoospores (n)

J Immature zoospores
inside zygospore

of cells, consider the following general characteristics of this plant:

1. Appearance on bark: color, surface, thickness of layer
2. Color of single cell seen under the microscope
3. Cell wall: note thickness
4. Cell contents (protoplast)
   a. Chloroplast: number, shape
   b. Nucleus: easily seen or indefinite
5. Reproduction: simple cell division (fission); note variation in the number of cells in the clusters

Label the drawings of *Protococcus* cells (worksheet 23.1A).

How many of the processes necessary to the life of higher plants are carried on by this one-celled plant? Make a list of them. Stain plants with iodine or mount in a 0.1% solution of neutral red to make the contents more apparent. What substance is formed in these cells in the light?

Outdoor Observations

Look for *Protococcus* on the bark of trees, sides of buildings, and stone walls. Green-stained patches found in these localities are frequently growths of *Protococcus*. Under what environmental conditions does this plant occur most abundantly? What conditions probably determine its distribution? Suggest ways in which this plant may be spread from place to place. Might the relative abundance of this plant suggest local climatic conditions?

C. *Oedogonium*

Oedogonium will usually be studied from slides or preserved material. Mount a small quantity on a slide, spread out the filaments by teasing them with needles or by dropping water on them. Cover with a coverslip, draining off the excess water.

Find a typical vegetative cell free from attached growths, and focus carefully under h.p. Note the cell wall, the net-shaped chloroplast with its numerous pyrenoids, and the single nucleus. The ring-like structures found on the cells of *Oedogonium* are the characteristic mark of this genus and are not found on other algae.

Optional. Make a labeled drawing of a vegetative cell showing in detail the structures previously mentioned.

Sexual Phase Involving Heterogametes

Note the dark-colored, globoid, swollen cells in some filaments. Each is an *oogonium* (plural, *oogonia*) containing a single large egg or female gamete, in which fertilization (fig. 23.2C) takes place.

Some vegetative cells divide to produce a number of short, disc-shaped, male sex cells, the *antheridia* (singular, *antheridium*) (fig. 23.2A). Each small antheridium develops two motile sperms (male gametes). Each re-leased sperm (fig. 23.2B) has a circle or crown of flagella encircling the small (anterior) end. Try to find antheridia in which the sperms have formed, or are in the process of formation. Locate empty antheridial cells from which the sperms have been discharged, and attempt to determine how they escaped.

After fertilization (fig. 23.2C), the egg becomes a *zygote* (fig. 23.2D) (i.e., a spore formed as the result of the fertilization of an egg by a male gamete). If the mass inside an oogonium is not surrounded by a definite independent wall, it has not been fertilized and is still an egg. If it has been fertilized, there will be a thick independent wall surrounding it.

This completes the sexual phase involving heterogametes in the life history of *Oedogonium*.

Asexual Phase Involving Microzoospores

The zygote (fig. 23.2D) undergoes meiosis to produce four *zoospores* (fig. 23.2E). These mature zoospores are much smaller than the single large zoospore formed under different conditions and are thus called *microzoospores*.

Each microzoospore has many flagella arranged in a circle or crown around the smaller (anterior) end (fig. 23.2F). Microzoospores settle down flagellate-end first, then develop into new filaments (fig. 23.2G and H).

This completes the asexual phase involving microzoospores in the life history of *Oedogonium*.

Asexual Phase Involving Macrozoospores

The contents of some vegetative cells may round up individually as a developmental stage in zoospore formation (fig. 23.2I). The filament breaks open (fig. 23.2J) to release a single zoospore that, because of its large size, is called a *macrozoospore* (fig. 23.2K). Each macrozoospore has many flagella arranged in a circle or crown around its smaller (anterior) end. A macrozoospore settles down flagellate-end first to develop into a new vegetative filament (fig. 23.2G and H).

This completes the asexual phase involving macrozoospores in the life cycle of *Oedogonium*.

Because its sexual reproduction involves fusion of two unlike gametes (a large nonmotile egg and a small motile sperm), *Oedogonium* is a heterogamous alga. This pattern is called *oogamy*.

Compare material studied to the drawings of *Oedogonium*, figure 23.2A–K, inclusive. Complete labels as needed.

D. *Spirogyra*

Spirogyra (green silk) is usually found in clear, cool, running water. The filaments have a characteristic slippery feel to the touch. A cylindrical vegetative cell contains one or more (depending upon the species) spirally shaped chloroplasts, each with several pyrenoids. The nucleus and cytoplasm are easily seen in this alga.

Figure 23.2 *Oedogonium*

Sexual Phase with Microzoospores

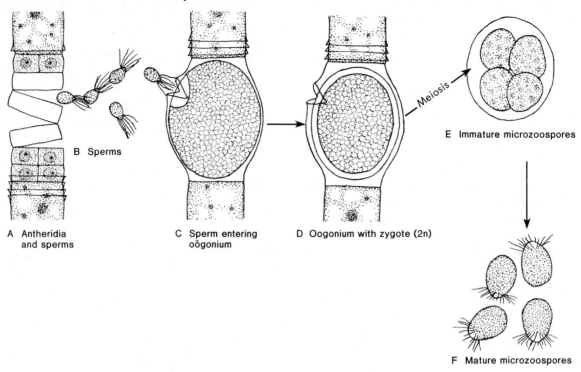

B Sperms

A Antheridia
and sperms

C Sperm entering
oögonium

D Oogonium with zygote (2n)

Meiosis

E Immature microzoospores

F Mature microzoospores

Asexual Phase with Macrozoospores

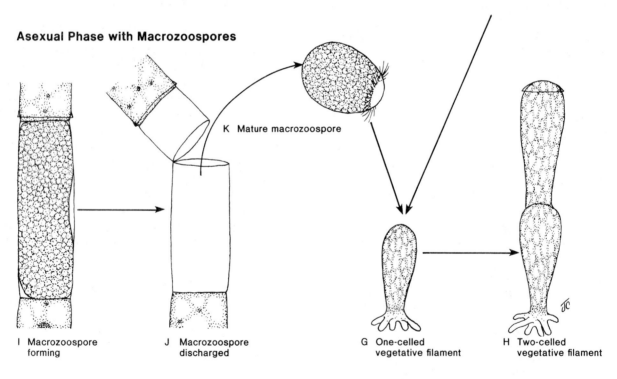

K Mature macrozoospore

I Macrozoospore
forming

J Macrozoospore
discharged

G One-celled
vegetative filament

H Two-celled
vegetative filament

Zoospores are not formed here, and sexual reproduction is by means of nonciliated isogametes. This process is called *conjugation*. During sexual reproduction, two apparently identical filaments (designated as + and −) are closely placed side by side. Tubes push out from each filament, meet, fuse, and form a short connecting passageway between the two cells. The contents of one cell (a gamete) move through this conjugation tube into the cell of the adjacent filament, fusing with its contents to form a zygote (zygospore). Then a zygote forms a hard shell, becomes a zygospore, and is released as the parent cell wall disintegrates. Meiosis occurs to produce four haploid (N) nuclei. Three disintegrate, and the remaining fourth nucleus enters into the new vegetative filament growing from the old zygospore at germination.

Compare with the drawings of a vegetative cell and two conjugating filaments (worksheet 23.2) of *Spirogyra*. Label all structures.

E. Other Green Algae

Carefully examine any other green algae provided. Identify the parts of the cell, if possible, and determine the growth form of the plant.

Make a labeled drawing of forms observed. Some typical greens are shown on worksheet 23.1. Add labels to the diagrams of those seen.

Questions

1. What pigments are present in the green algae?
2. What is the range of their distribution in the world?
3. What are heterogametes? isogametes?
4. How is *Protococcus* spread from place to place?
5. Define oogonium, antheridium, zygote, sperm, and egg.
6. What is a vegetative cell?
7. What are pyrenoids?
8. How, and in what plant part, are the gametes formed in *Ulothrix? Oedogonium? Spirogyra?*
9. How do the green algae differ from the blue-greens?
10. Make a life cycle in the form of an illustrated circle for *Ulothrix, Oedogonium,* and *Spirogyra.*
11. Contrast the habitats of the green and blue-green algae.

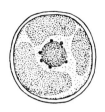
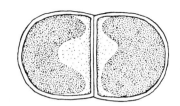
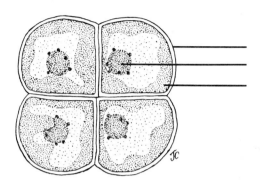

A *Protococcus* cells

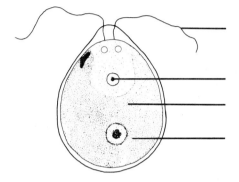

B *Chlamydomonas*

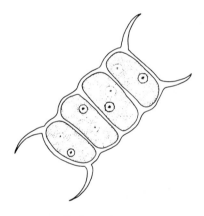

C *Scenedesmus*

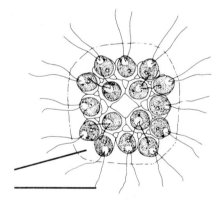

D *Pandorina*

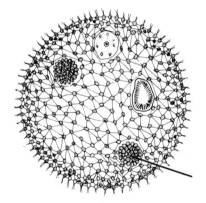

E *Volvox*

F *Enteromorpha*

Thalloid Forms

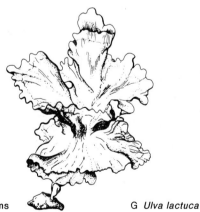

G *Ulva lactuca*

Spirogyra

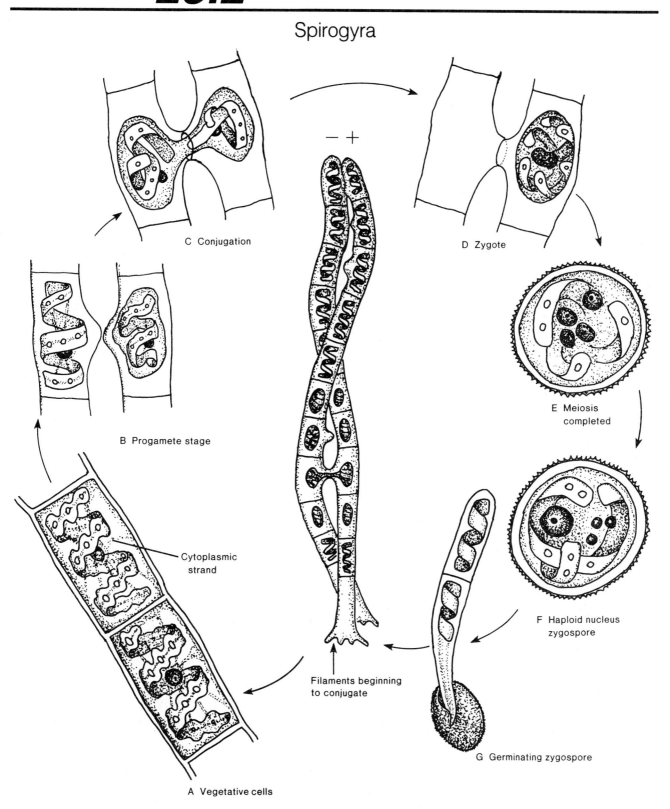

C Conjugation

D Zygote

E Meiosis completed

B Progamete stage

F Haploid nucleus zygospore

Cytoplasmic strand

Filaments beginning to conjugate

G Germinating zygospore

A Vegetative cells

24 Plankton: Diatoms and Dinoflagellates

Plant Materials

Materials needed are living and preserved diatoms, diatomaceous earth, plankton samples from various locations, and cultures of such representative genera as *Ceratium, Gymnodinium, Vaucheria,* and *Euglena.*

Equipment

Obtain a compound microscope, blank slides and cover glasses, teasing needles, sharp-pointed curved forceps, and glass jars for cultures.

Introduction

Plankton is the name given, collectively, to the unattached, free-floating, usually microscopic, aquatic plants and animals. They are carried about by wind and current since they lack strength of locomotion, although many of them possess it to a limited degree. Plants of the plankton mass are called *phytoplankton;* the animals, *zooplankton.*

The contamination of water supplies by plankton organisms may become a serious problem in any community. Filter plants remove all sediments, bacteria, and plankton organisms, but the objectionable odors and tastes caused by these organisms frequently remain in the purified water. These tastes and odors do not cause diseases but simply make the water unpalatable. Only very small amounts of the by-products of these organisms are required to be noticeable in water. *Synedra* (a diatom) oil is recognizable in one part in twenty-five million; *Asterionella* (a diatom) oil in one part in two million. The iodoform, or medicine-like, odors that may be present (from phenols and cresols and their compounds) are noticeable in the extremely small concentration of one part in one thousand million.

Plankton organisms furnish much of the food for aquatic animals such as fishes, whales, and oysters. The high vitamin A content of cod and shark livers is due to the carotene obtained from the plankton organisms that these animals feed upon.

Phytoplankton are grouped within the Kingdom Protista. Representatives of several major divisions will be examined. The Chrysophyta (golden algae) include the diatoms. The Xanthophyta (yellow-green algae) often are classified in the Chrysophyta. Dinoflagellates are members of the Pyrrhophyta (fire algae), and the *Euglenas* are bright green members of the division Euglenophyta.

A. Diatoms *(Chrysophyta)*

Diatoms are single-celled, yellow-brown, microscopic algae of world-wide distribution, are numerous in both saltwater and freshwater areas (especially in cool or temperate regions), and exhibit many diverse forms. Diatoms are of great economic importance because they release much oxygen into their environment through photosynthesis. They are sensitive indicators of pollution and do not thrive in contaminated waters. Oil is stored in them, but not starch. There are two great groups of diatoms, with many intermediate forms.

1. *Pennate.* These diatoms are commonly motile and elongated, cigar-, boat-, or needle-shaped, with lines of minute, pinnately-arranged markings along each side of their longitudinal axis. They are bilaterally symmetrical in valve view and thrive predominately in fresh water (see fig. 24.1).
2. *Centric.* These diatoms are usually nonmotile, and are round, disc-, drum-, or cylinder-shaped, with straight rows of markings in radial lines, and have radial symmetry in the valve view (see fig. 24.2).

A diatom has a highly silicified (glassy) wall made up of two overlapping parts or valves that fit together like the halves of a petri dish or a candy box. The wall is often beautifully and minutely sculptured and ornamented. This glass case remains unaltered when the protoplasmic contents die and decay. Great numbers of these empty shells may accumulate on the bottoms of oceans and lakes. Fossil diatoms thus deposited form *diatomaceous earth* (Kieselguhr). Diatomaceous earth is used commercially to filter liquids (especially in sugar refineries), to insulate the walls of high-temperature furnaces (superior to asbestos in this respect), to act as an absorbent in metal polishes and abrasive soaps, and to test the resolving power of lenses. The diet of many aquatic animals consists in a large part of living diatoms.

Examine a sample of living, freshwater, diatom plankton. It is composed of various elements: unicellular, filamentous, colonial green, and blue-green algae; microscopic animals; and especially, numerous isolated or co-

Figure 24.1 *Cymbella,* a pennate diatom (Courtesy of H. L. Dean)

Figure 24.2 *Arachnodiscus,* a centric diatom (Courtesy of H. L. Dean)

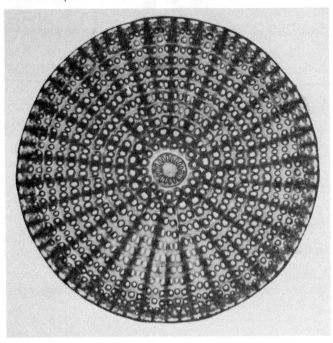

lonial unicellular forms of definite shape; with golden brown *chromatophores*—the diatoms. Do diatoms have the power of locomotion? Describe any movements observed.

Find a part of the field in which there are several somewhat boat-shaped forms as seen from the top or bottom, the *valve view* (worksheet 24.1A). When viewed from the side, the *girdle view* (worksheet 24.1B), the same organisms appear rectangular. These are diatoms belonging to the genus *Navicula.* If you watch a moving cell for a few minutes, you can usually see it in both positions.

Examine a plant in the valve view. Note the position, appearance, and markings of the shell; the two long chromatophores, one on each side; and the single nucleus in the center. Oil globules may be present in the cells.

Examine a plant in girdle view. Note the overlapping transparent shells or valves and the appearance and size of the chromatophore as seen in this position.

After careful study of the material, fill in details of cell contents and wall markings, using the outline drawings furnished (worksheet 24.1A and B). Examine any other diatoms provided. Draw as directed by your lab instructor. Label all structures.

B. Diatomaceous Earth

Mount a very small amount of diatomaceous earth in water and examine, first using 1.p., and later with h.p. Note the variety of shells; some broken, others entire. List the commercial uses of diatomaceous earth.

Draw two or three unbroken shells.

C. *Vaucheria (Xanthophyta)*

Mount a sample of *Vaucheria* in water and examine, or study a prepared slide. Note the nonseptate nature of the long tubular filament. Heterogametes are formed in gametangia cut off from short-side branches. Food is stored as an oil.

Add labels to the diagram on worksheet 24.1C.

D. Dinoflagellates *(Pyrrhophyta)*

Mount a sample in water and examine, or study a prepared slide of *Ceratium, Gymnodinium,* or other dinoflagellates. Note the golden-brown color of the chloroplasts in each flagellated motile cell. Identify the two flagella: one trailing towards the posterior and the other usually in a lateral groove encircling the middle of the cell. The cell wall may be absent or divided into interlocking plates.

Add labels to the diagrams of worksheet 24.1 (D and E).

E. *Euglena (Euglenophyta)*

These bright green, motile flagellates with a single, emergent, anterior flagellum and a single, reddish eyespot are not grouped with the chlorophyta because their stored food is not starch but paramylon and because they have a flexible, noncellulose cell wall. There is an anterior gullet into which a contractile vacuole discharges. Observe the varying shapes of the cell from a sample mounted in water.

Add labels to the diagram of worksheet 24.1F.

F. Plankton

Examine each of the samples of living and preserved plankton provided, noting where each was found and the time of the year it was collected. Thoroughly examine each mount, because some forms are found only occasionally and might otherwise be overlooked. Note the relative frequency of each form. Be able to comment on the periodic appearance and disappearance of phytoplankton forms. Do other algal forms exhibit such periodicity?

When examining plankton, mount a small portion on a slide, and draw each kind of organism found. Divide these organisms primarily into animals and plants. Divide the latter group again into bacteria, blue-green algae, green algae, dinoflagellates, euglenas, and diatoms. How many kinds of each can be found? If their names cannot be determined, then indicate them as Blue-green A, B, C, etc.; Diatom A, B, C, etc., using an outline sketch to show their general appearance and relative size.

Are any of the animals feeding on any of the other organisms present? Give details. What is the source of nourishment that supports the bacteria?

Bass, northern pike, walleyes, and other game fish feed largely on smaller fish. These in turn eat small animal forms, and the latter eat minute crustaceans and algae. Most saltwater fish such as cod have habits similar to those of the bass. On the other hand, carp, in fresh water, mostly feed directly on plant life. Outline a few typical food chains of various animals, including humans.

G. Field Trip (Optional)

A field trip will be made to a local water-filtration plant to demonstrate how impurities, including plankton organisms, are removed from the water supplies of a city. Fill in the answers to the questions in worksheet 24.2 and be prepared to comment briefly on the important problem of water supplies and their purification. How are water supplies purified for an army in the field? for summer camps?

Questions

1. What are two unique features of diatoms?
2. What is the economic importance of diatoms?
3. What is Kieselguhr?
4. What animals use diatoms as food?
5. What is phytoplankton?
6. How are diatoms used to test lenses?
7. Be able to name and describe a number of the forms found in the examination of plankton.
8. Fish livers are rich sources of vitamin A. Comment on the importance of plankton organisms in the diet of fish and as a source of this vitamin.
9. What is the relation between carotene and vitamin A? vitamin A and visual purple (rhodopsin)?

Name _____

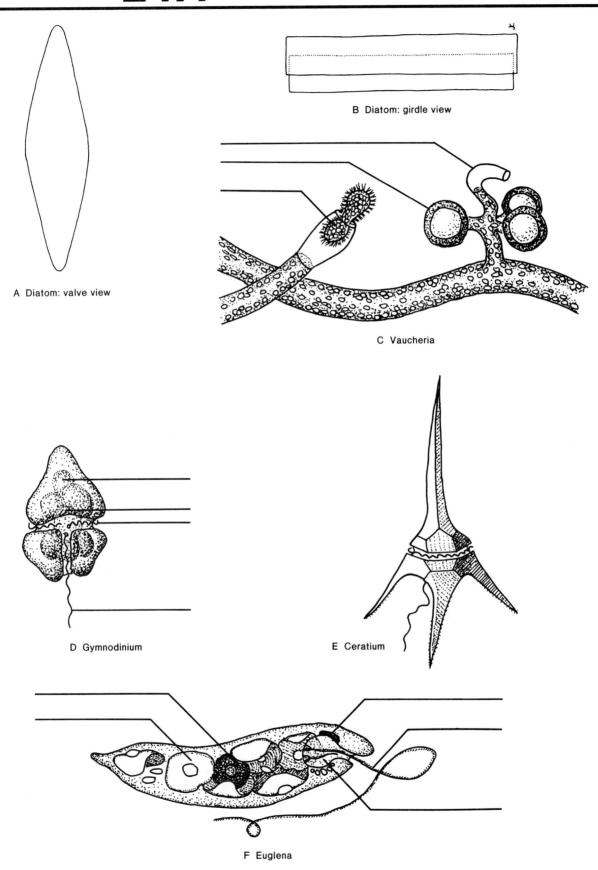

A Diatom: valve view

B Diatom: girdle view

C Vaucheria

D Gymnodinium

E Ceratium

F Euglena

Trip to a City Water Plant

1. Intake: Where is it?

   What is the daily capacity of the intake pumps?

2. Aeration: How is it done?

   Why?

3. Settling tank: What settles out here?

   What chemicals are added at this stage?

   What does each do?

4. Filtration: How is the filter made and of what material does it consist?

   How often must it be cleaned?

5. Chlorination: What is the purpose of chlorination?

   How is it done?

   Is pure chlorine gas put in the water?

6. What is the bacterial count in city tap water?

7. Demand for water: What is the estimated daily consumption per capita in your city?

8. What auxiliary sources of water are there?

9. What organisms cause objectionable odors and tastes?

10. What are the troublesome products from these organisms?

11. What are troublesome inorganic materials?

12. Is the water supply of your city fluoridated? What is the purpose of fluoridation? What are objections to this practice?

13. Miscellaneous notes:

Exercise 25 Brown Algae (Phaeophyta) and Red Algae (Rhodophyta)

Plant Materials

Materials needed are fresh or preserved *Fucus, Nereocystis, Sargassum, Laminaria, Chorda, Postelsia, Alaria, Macrocystis, Chondrus, Corallina, Polysiphonia,* and *Grinnellia;* prepared slides with male and female conceptacles of *Fucus;* demonstration of algin, agar, and carrageenin.

Equipment

A compound microscope is needed, along with slides of *Polysiphonia* to show antheridia, tetraspores, and cystocarps.

Introduction

The brown algae are almost exclusively marine plants and are most abundant along the rocky shores of cooler seas. Their dark color is due to a brown pigment, *fucoxanthin.* Chlorophylls a and c and related pigments are present, but their color is masked by the fucoxanthin. The largest algal forms in the world are found among the Phaeophyta. The larger forms, commonly called kelps, contain commercially important amounts of iodine, potassium, and sodium. Processed in various ways, the algae are utilized as algin (sodium alginate) from brown algae and carrageenin from the red algae in the manufacture of ice cream, salad dressings, cake icings, chocolate milk, shaving creams, face and hand lotions, jellies, cosmetics, many pharmaceutical products, candies, sizings for industrial purposes, and many other products. Some agar is obtained from the brown algae, but the best grade comes from the red algae.

Fucus is one of the best known and most common of the temperate benthic brown algae and will be studied in some detail.

A. *Fucus* (Rockweed)

Examine a *Fucus* branch. Note the flat *thallus,* branching dichotomously; the air bladders, or *floats;* and the swollen fruiting tips, or *receptacles,* bearing numerous small projections on their surfaces. These latter are the papillate mouths of the *conceptacles,* or chambers, in which are borne the oogonium containing eggs in the female plants, and the antheridium, containing sperms in the male plants.

At the base of a demonstration plant, note the strong, cuplike *holdfast,* which holds the plant to the rock on which it grows. These plants grow between high- and low-tide limits on rocky ocean shores. What adaptations to the conditions of their intertidal habitat can be observed? In what ways do the holdfasts resemble roots? In what ways are they different?

Identify the parts described and then add proper labels to the drawing of a *Fucus* plant (worksheet 25.1A). The holdfast is shown.

Examine prepared slides of cross sections of male and female receptacles. Locate the conceptacles.

Label the parts of the cross section of a receptacle (worksheet 25.1B).

Male conceptacle. Find a conceptacle in which the section shows the opening (ostiole) to the exterior. Note the sterile hairs, the *paraphyses* (singular *paraphysis*) and the branched antheridial stalks bearing many *antheridia.* The antheridia contain numerous sperms (male gametes).

Identify the parts of a male conceptacle of *Fucus,* add proper labels to the drawing of this structure and to the cluster of antheridia drawn separately on a larger scale (worksheet 25.1C and D).

Female conceptacle. Find a female conceptacle in which the pore is shown. Note the *oogonia,* each containing, when mature, eight large eggs. How many eggs appear in the oogonium section containing the largest number? Where are the others? Are paraphyses present in this conceptacle?

Identify the parts of the female conceptacle of *Fucus.* Add proper labels to the drawing of this structure and to the oogonium drawn separately on a larger scale (worksheet 25.1E and F).

B. The Kelps and Other Brown Algae (Demonstration)

Study preserved specimens of common brown algae: *Nereocystis* (worksheet 25.2A), *Sargassum* (worksheet 25.2B), *Fucus* (worksheet 25.2C), and *Laminaria* (worksheet 25.2D). Add proper labels to these drawings. Notice the branched holdfasts of the kelps.

Examine other forms as available: *Chorda, Postelsia, Alaria,* and *Macrocystis.* Write brief descriptions, and make quick sketches of these additional forms. Before leaving the laboratory, carefully study the photographs showing the habit relations of some of these larger kelps.

C. Red Algae (Rhodophyta)

The red algae are almost exclusively marine plants, are most abundant in the warmer ocean waters, and as a rule, grow more deeply submerged than the brown and green algae. No species will be intensely studied, but members of the class should examine Polysiphonia and the slides mounted under the demonstration microscope, as well as the plants mounted on paper and the photographs. What is the economic importance of the red algae?

Demonstration

Red algae of economic importance on display include *Chondrus* (worksheet 25.2E), *Corallina* (worksheet 25.2F), and *Grinnellia* (worksheet 25.2G). Other forms of red algae will be studied if available. Add labels to these drawings and those on worksheet 25.3A to D.

Questions

1. How does the life history of *Fucus* differ from that of *Ulothrix? Oedogonium? Protococcus? Oscillatoria?*
2. How is *Fucus* adapted to withstand drying while exposed during low tide?
3. Define receptacle, conceptacle, paraphysis, thallus, and holdfast.
4. What is the economic importance of the brown algae?
5. Name and describe four or five of the kelps from the display in the laboratory.
6. What is the largest brown algae?
7. Where do the red algae grow? What is their economic importance?
8. Diagram in the form of an illustrated circle the life cycle of *Fucus*.
9. Comment on the economic importance of algin and carrageenin.

Fucus

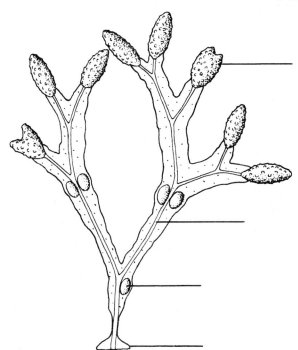

A *Fucus* plant with receptacles and air bladders

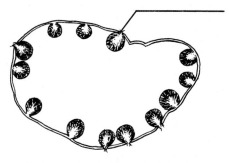

B Cross section of receptacle and conceptacles

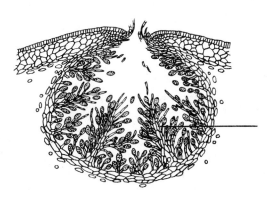

C Male conceptacle with antheridia

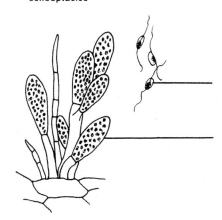

D Antheridia and sperms

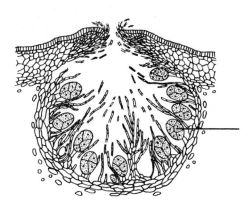

E Female conceptacle with oogonia

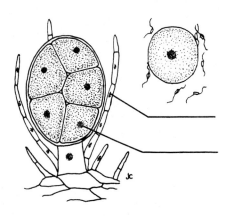

F Oogonium and eggs

Name _____

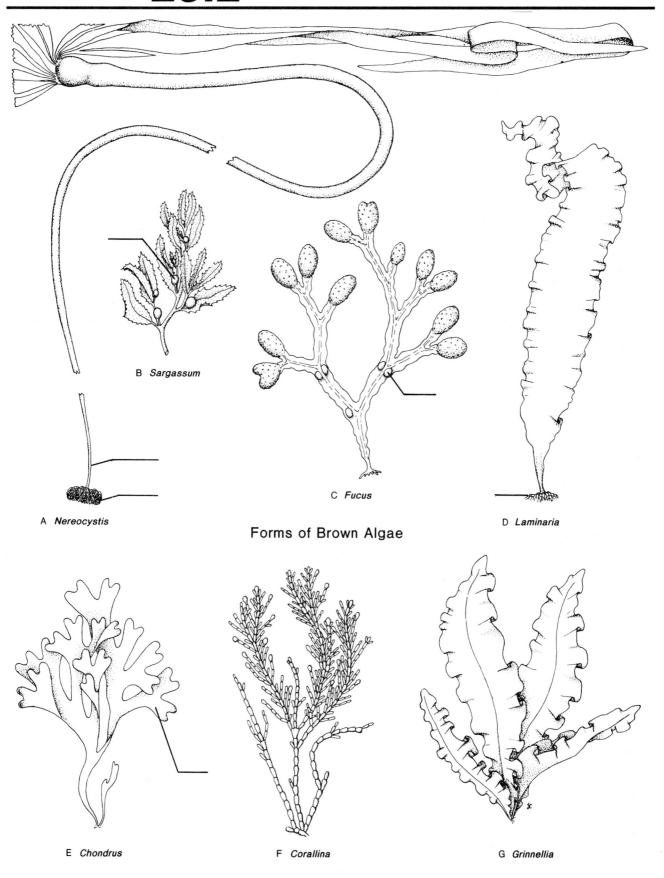

B *Sargassum*

C *Fucus*

A *Nereocystis*

D *Laminaria*

Forms of Brown Algae

E *Chondrus*

F *Corallina*

G *Grinnellia*

Forms of Red Algae

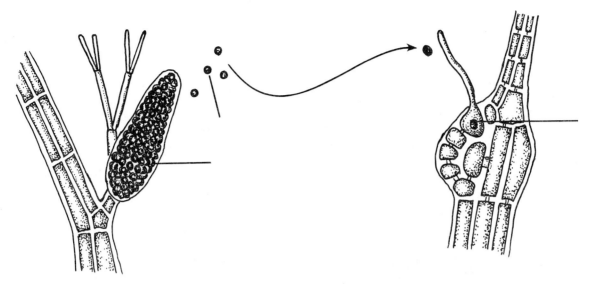

A Male gametophyte of
   Polysiphonia with spermatogonial
   branch

B Female gametophyte of Polysiphonia
   with carpogonial branch. Fusion
   of gametes produces the cystocarp

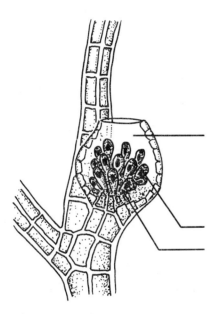

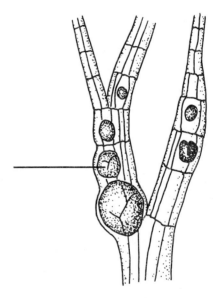

C Female gametophyte with
   mature cystocarp showing
   carposporangia and carpospores.
   Carpospores produce the tetrasporophyte

D Tetrasporophyte with the
   tetraspores formed by meiosis.
   These haploid spores will
   produce the gametophytes.

Exercise 26 Slime Molds (Myxomycota)

Plant Materials

Materials needed are plasmodia of *Physarum, Hematrichia,* or other slime molds growing on Knop's agar in petri dishes. Fruiting *Stemonitis, Physarum, Hematrichia, Fuligo, Enteridium, Reticularia, Lycogala,* or other slime molds.

Equipment

A compound microscope, blank slides, cover glasses, petri dishes, test tubes with cotton plugs, pipettes, and medicine droppers are needed.

Reagents

Reagents needed are Norit, 75% ethanol, iodine potassium iodide solution, Knop's agar, and 2% plain agar.

Introduction

The myxomycetes (mycetozoa) are a relatively small group of unusual organisms possessing certain characteristics of both plants and animals. Since they lack chlorophyll, they are usually included in the fungi, but also may be classified with the Protista.

Myxomycetes are commonly found on the surface of the soil, in the dead plant litter covering it, and on the bark of trees. Within such substrata, they occur in the form of plasmodia, which are extensive, netlike or fan-shaped, naked, protoplasmic masses containing innumerable nuclei but without cell walls. The bright yellow plasmodium of certain species may often be found in the summer on the hymenium of gill fungi. Plasmodia may be secured at any time of the year by bringing small pieces of rotten wood, bark, clusters of twigs, dead leaves or grass into the laboratory, placing them in petri dishes, wetting with distilled water, and keeping in subdued light. Plasmodia will usually appear within a few days. If wanted for further study or demonstration, a piece of the material bearing a plasmodium may be placed on the surface of hardened Knop's agar in another petri dish. In a few hours the plasmodium will leave the opaque substratum and crawl onto the clear agar, where it may be readily examined. (Knop's agar is prepared by diluting 67 ml of stock Knop's solu-tion to 1 liter with distilled water, adding 15 grams of agar-agar, and sterilizing.) Under appropriate conditions the plasmodium becomes transformed into a fructification.

A. The Plasmodium

Examine a well-developed plasmodium growing in a petri dish of Knop's agar (fig. 26.1). What is its color? its shape? Does it change shape or move during the period? Describe. How can one determine in which direction the plasmodium is moving?

Place the dish upside down under 1.p. of the microscope, and focus on a small plasmodial vein until the moving stream of particles becomes visible. What is this flowing material? How fast is the movement? Does it always flow in the same direction? Study carefully for several minutes and note how long the material flows in each direction.

Record your results, and compare with those obtained by others.

Draw in detail a portion of a small plasmodial vein as seen under 1.p., indicating protoplasm by stippling.

Figure 26.1 Slime mold plasmodium growing in Petri dish of Knop's agar (Courtesy of H. L. Dean)

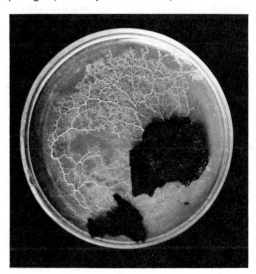

B. The Fructifications

Fructifications are of three principal types, not always sharply distinguishable from one another.

1. *Plasmodiocarp.* The simplest type is the plasmodiocarp, in which the protoplasm becomes aggregated into a few of the larger plasmodial veins and there becomes transformed as a continuous or broken network into a mass of spores surrounded by a firm outer membrane. Sterile hairs of the capillitium bearing characteristic markings are interspersed among the spores.

2. *Sporangium.* The strands of the plasmodium network become broken up into fairly uniform, but not particularly elongated spore-bearing units, each being a sporangium. Sporangia may be stalked or sessile.

3. *Aethalium.* The entire mass of the plasmodium may fruit by the transformation of the heaped veins into a fairly solid cake, the aethalium.

Sporangiate Fructification: Stemonitis

Examine the clusters of featherlike sporangia formed on wood or other substratum (worksheet 26.1A). How large is a sporangium? What is its color? Carefully remove a single stalk from a cluster of sporangia, selecting one from which most of the spores have fallen. Place it on a slide, wet with alcohol, drain the alcohol, then add a drop of water and a coverslip. The basketlike structure cradling the spores is the capillitium. What is the color of the spores? Do they have a thick or a thin wall? Are there any surface markings?

In the space provided on worksheet 26.1C and D, sketch a portion of the capillitium as it appears under l.p., showing a few spores in position. Draw separately a single spore under high power, carefully noting the spines and reticulations. Examine other sporangiate forms as directed. Make notes and quick sketches of this material.

Plasmodiocarp: Physarum, Hemitrichia

Examine the typical plasmodiocarp of *Physarum Serpula, Hemitrichia Serpula,* or other available forms.

Draw a somewhat enlarged, typical plasmodiocarp of the species provided.

Aethalium: Fuligo *or* Enteridium

Examine the aethalium of *Fuligo septica, Enteridium Roseanum,* or other species available.

Draw a typical aethalium of the species provided, enlarged if necessary.

C. Swarm Cells

Boil 0.5 gram activated charcoal (Norit) in 200 ml of pond, river, or distilled water for two to five minutes, and allow to settle overnight. Use the supernatant liquid to thoroughly wet (by continued rubbing) mature spores of *Reticularia Lycoperdon, Enteridium Roseanum, Fuligo septica,* or other genera. Then pipette enough of this liquid to make a thin film on 2% plain agar in a petri dish. Swarm cells of these genera should be evident within two to three hours at room temperature. Spores of other genera may require several days to produce swarm cells. Not all spores or culture attempts will provide swarm cells.

Examine them under h.p. and note the characteristic movements. Are there any vacuoles? If so, what is peculiar about their behavior? Remove the cover glass, kill the cells with iodine, replace the cover and tap gently to help extend the flagella. Are cell contents and flagella more apparent after this treatment? What part do swarm cells play in the life history of a myxomycete?

Carefully draw one or two swarm cells in the space provided on worksheet 26.1G showing nucleus, cytoplasm, flagella, and contractile vacuole.

Questions

1. Why are these organisms called myxomycota or slime molds? mycetozoa?

2. What is the plasmodium? Why is a plasmodium considered good material for the study of protoplasm?

3. Comment on the flow of material in the veins of the plasmodium. Could this movement serve any useful purpose?

4. What are the three types of myxomycete fructifications? Name and give examples of each.

5. What are swarm cells? Of what importance are they in the life history of a myxomycete?

6. What is the food of a plasmodium?

7. What are plantlike characteristics of a myxomycete? animallike characteristics?

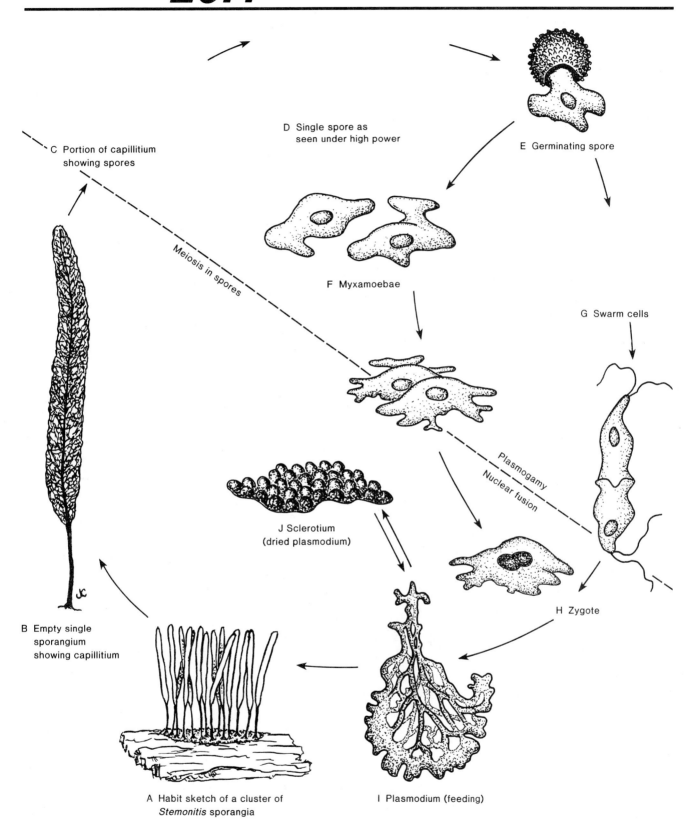

D Single spore as
    seen under high power

C Portion of capillitium
    showing spores

E Germinating spore

Meiosis in spores

F Myxamoebae

G Swarm cells

Plasmogamy
Nuclear fusion

J Sclerotium
(dried plasmodium)

H Zygote

B Empty single
    sporangium
    showing capillitium

A Habit sketch of a cluster of
    Stemonitis sporangia

I Plasmodium (feeding)

Exercise 27 — The Lower Fungi (Algalike Fungi)

Fungal and Other Materials

Materials needed are moist chambers containing *Rhizopus* growing on stale bread, orange peel, filter paper soaked in orange juice, or on one-half strength cornmeal agar in petri dishes; *Saprolegnia* or *Achlya* growing on a dead housefly, bee, grasshopper, cockroach, or cracked hemp seed; and living or preserved specimens or their photographs of lower fungi causing plant diseases.

Equipment

You will need compound microscopes, blank slides and cover glasses, curved sharp-pointed forceps, and prepared slides of *Rhizopus* zygospores.

Reagents

Reagents needed are 10% glycerine, 0.1% neutral red, or phloxine.

Introduction

The true *fungi* (singular, *fungus*) are nongreen (i.e., lacking chlorophyll) organisms previously classified as plants. Now, however, botanists consider the fungi to be a separate evolutionary line, parallel with green plants, and thus forming a distinctly different group. Fungi are very numerous and include a great variety of forms. Some are commercially valuable; for instance, yeast in the preparation of bread and in the production of industrial alcohol by fermentation.

The fungi, however, cause most of the plant diseases, with accompanying losses amounting to millions of dollars annually. In addition, millions of bushels of fruits and vegetables in storage are ruined yearly by fungi. Some serious human diseases are caused by fungi.

The fruiting (reproductive) body is the conspicuous part of most fungi and is important in the classification of these organisms. The vegetative (assimilative) body is usually hidden from view under leaves, in the soil, under bark, or within the plant it is living upon. The entire vegetative body is the *mycelium* (plural, *mycelia*) of the fungus. Each individual strand of the mycelium is a *hypha* (plural, *hyphae*).

Only a few forms of the fungi can be studied in this course. Consult the instructor for additional information and further details. The biological study devoted to the fungi is known as *mycology*.

The Lower Fungi *(Algalike Fungi)*

The fungi formerly classified as Phycomycetes are now placed into distinct divisions including the Chytridiomycota, the Oomycota, and the Zygomycota, based upon their considerably different structures and reproductive habits.

In this exercise selected common representatives of the lower fungi will be studied. They are characterized by a generally nonseptate (i.e., no cross walls) mycelium containing many nuclei (coenocytic). They are called algalike fungi because they resemble certain green algae in their structures and reproductive habits.

A. Water Mold, *Achlya*, *Saprolegnia*—an Oomycota

The water molds are fungi that live in water or moist soil. Dead fish, insects, animals, or decaying vegetation may be completely covered and penetrated by slimy masses of colorless water mold hyphae. Species of these fungi may parasitize living mature fish, growing on the gills or abraded skin surfaces to cause serious harm; they are destructive also to fish eggs and young fry.

The following directions are for living material, but the essential features may be studied, if necessary, using preserved material or prepared slides.

Note the small insect (housefly, bee, grasshopper, or cockroach) or cracked hemp seed in the water (from pond or ditch) surrounded by radiating filaments or hyphae of the fungus, composing the external mycelium and bearing the fruiting structures. Within the substratum are other hyphae, which absorb nutrients and pass them on to those outside.

Make a habit sketch, x2, of the fungus as it appears on the substrate.

Very carefully, so as not to bend or crush them, cut off a few of the external hyphae, and by means of a pipette, transfer from the water in the dish to a slide. Place a coverslip on the mount and examine, using l.p. The fruiting hyphae are of two sorts: zoosporangia, clublike structures at the ends of branches, which contain zoospores, and globose oogonia, which contain eggs.

Find a zoosporangium in which the contents appear to be divided into segments. These are the zoospores. Find

Figure 27.1 *Saprolegnia*, zoosporangia

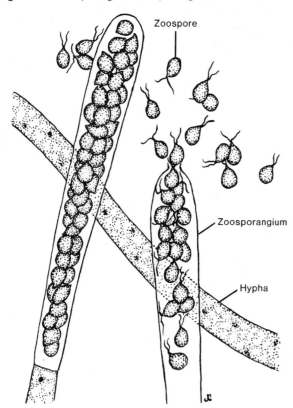

Zoospore

Zoosporangium

Hypha

a sporangium in which a good deal of motion is apparent, and watch it for a few moments to see whether the zoospores escape. Find an empty sporangium. Are there any signs of renewed growth? What is the relation of the new growth to the old?

Draw a zoosporangium containing zoospores, or a cluster of zoosporangia showing, if possible, various stages in the development and escape of zoospores. Compare with figure 27.1.

In an older culture, find an oogonium in which the contents are homogeneous. Is this an old or young stage? Find another in which there are several eggs, each surrounded by a definite wall. Locate the long slender hypha growing partly around the oogonium. This is the antheridial branch. Where does it originate? Is the wall of the oogonium smooth or marked in any way?

Draw an oogonium showing eggs. Notice the penetration of the antheridium into the oogonium to ensure the fusion of the gametes. Label all structures.

B. *Rhizopus* (Bread Mold, Zygomycota)

A zygomycete, *Rhizopus,* or black mold, is widely distributed over the world, being readily spread from place to place by means of light, airborne spores. *Rhizopus* has been commonly called bread mold because of its favorable growth on bread. *Rhizopus* also grows well on fruits and vegetables, and a number of damaging rots are due to this

fungus. Some rots due to *Rhizopus* are the soft rot of sweet potatoes, the watery rot of strawberries, the storage or transportation rot of pome fruits, and the soft rot of tomatoes. Seeds and seedlings in germinators may also be attacked by this fungus.

Examine *Rhizopus* as it grows on bread, orange peel, or other media in the culture dish. Note the white mycelium and the numerous black fruiting heads, and the mature *sporangia* (singular, *sporangium*). Also note the date when each culture was started.

Take a small portion of mycelium from the edge of a culture growing in a petri dish on filter paper soaked in orange juice. Cover it with a drop of water to which a wetting agent has been added and coverslip, and press gently so as to spread it out slightly. Examine, first using l.p., then h.p. Are there any branches? cross walls? nuclei? vacuoles? Is there movement (streaming) in the protoplasm? Streaming is more easily seen if the mycelium is mounted in a 10% solution of glycerine. Protoplasmic details are more apparent if the mycelium is mounted in a 0.1% solution of neutral red or phloxine.

Draw in detail a small portion of the mycelium, indicating branching, vacuoles, and protoplasm.

Mount a small portion of a culture from a place where the sporangia are still white. Note the rhizoids, the stolons, and the sporangiophores (in groups), each bearing at the top a globose sporangium containing numerous spores.

When all the parts named have been identified, add labels to the drawing (worksheet 27.1A) of a cluster of sporangiophores. Label also the drawings showing the development of a single sporangium (worksheet 27.1B–F).

In the formation of zygotes (sexual spores), two hyphae lie in contact parallel to each other; a short tubelike extension develops from each; these tubes meet, and gametangia are cut off by the formation of cross walls. The contents of the gametangia fuse, and the resulting structure is the zygote (zygospore). Formation of zygotes occurs only when two separate kinds (or strains) of *Rhizopus* are placed together. The hyphae of these strains are alike in appearance but probably differ physiologically. For convenience they are designated as plus (+) and minus (−) strains. This process is easily demonstrated in the laboratory but is more difficult to see in the natural habit of these fungi.

Note: A fungus needing hyphae of two kinds (+ and −) for sexual reproduction is termed *heterothallic.* When only a single kind of hypha is needed for sexual reproduction a fungus is termed *homothallic.*

Examine, using l.p., prepared slides (also living or preserved material if available) of *Rhizopus* zygospores. Study the rough, heavy-walled zygospores (zygotes); locate the suspensors, gametangia, and hyphae.

After the parts have been identified, label the drawings (worksheet 27.1G–J) representing stages in the development of the zygospore of *Rhizopus.*

C. Pathogenic Fungi

Examine the demonstrations of various plant diseases caused by the lower fungi. Make brief notes and quick sketches of these forms.

Questions

1. What are the characteristics of the lower fungi?
2. Why are they called algalike fungi? Is this a good term?
3. What is a hypha?
4. Define mycelium.
5. How is *Rhizopus* spread so readily?
6. With so many spores of bread mold in the air, why does it not cover everything exposed?
7. What is a coenocyte?
8. Name plant diseases caused by the lower fungi.
9. What are water molds? What is their economic importance?
10. Compare *Rhizopus* with a water mold (*Achlya* or *Saprolegnia*) with reference to habit, sexual reproduction, and asexual reproduction.

Rhizopus Nigricans

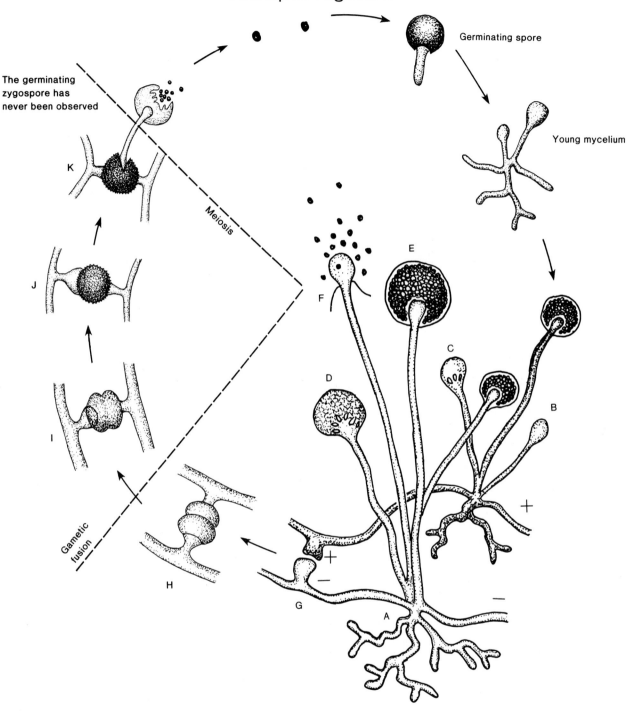

Germinating spore

Young mycelium

The germinating zygospore has never been observed

Meiosis

Gametic fusion

Exercise

28 Ascus-bearing Fungi (Ascomycota)

Fungal and Other Materials

Materials needed are a moist yeast cake, dry yeast cake, apples, oranges; *Penicillium, Sordaria,* and *Aspergillus* cultures on orange peel or nutrient agar; prepared slides of *Penicillium, Aspergillus* (whole mounts), and yeast spores; *Peziza* fruiting body, fresh or preserved; photographs and illustrated descriptive leaflets concerning *Penicillium;* various living or preserved specimens or photographs of plant diseases caused by Ascomycetes; Morchella fruiting bodies, and other available ascomycetes to show the range of variation.

Equipment

A compound microscope, blank slides, cover glasses, incubator, large moist chamber, dissecting needles, and beakers (100 and 50 ml) are required.

Reagents

Reagents needed are an iodine potassium iodide solution, 1% phloxine, and a 10% glucose solution.

Introduction

The ascomycota are characterized by a septate mycelium, and the formation of spores (ascospores) in a specialized cell, the *ascus* (plural, *asci*). The ascus is ordinarily a cylindrical or saclike structure, usually containing eight spores (ascospores). Yeast is a unicellular ascomycete important in baking and in the production of alcohol. Numerous plant diseases are caused by ascomycetes, including fruit rots, mildews, cankers, leaf spots, blights, and Dutch elm disease.

Ergot of rye (*Claviceps*) is the source of useful and powerful drugs. Only two representatives of the ascomycetes will be emphasized in the laboratory: yeast, because of its industrial importance, and *Peziza,* to demonstrate certain typical ascomycete characteristics.

A. Yeast (*Saccharomyces*)

Mount a little material from a 10% glucose solution to which a portion of a moist yeast cake has been added (and thoroughly mixed) a few hours previously. Examine under

h.p., and describe the form, size, color, and content of the yeast cells. Examine cells that are budding. How does budding differ from binary fission?

Make a water mount using a very small quantity of dry yeast cake, and examine under h.p. How does the preparation differ from the moist cake? Draw part of a drop of iodine potassium iodide under the cover glass and observe under the microscope. What substance changed color? Why include starch in a dry yeast cake?

After careful study, add labels to the drawing of yeast cells and buds (worksheet 28.1A).

Under adverse conditions, the contents of the individual cells round up to form (in this case) four *ascospores*. Find such a cell (ascus) in the material provided, or examine demonstration mounts of prepared slides showing stained spores.

Compare with the outline drawing (worksheet 28.1B) of a cell (ascus) of yeast containing ascospores. Complete labels.

Note: See exercise 8 for directions in the study of yeast fermentation and its important products. Wild yeast can be cultured by crushing grapes or raisins in the glucose solution for 2 to 3 days prior to the lab.

B. Living Ascomycete Mycelium

In several places of a ripe sweet apple, such as a Delicious or Jonathan, or an orange, make about a 1.5-cm-deep puncture with a blunted pencil tip. Inoculate the wounds deeply and thoroughly with masses of spores or mycelium from a living culture of *Penicillium*. Incubate in a moist chamber 5 to 10 days, or until definite rot appears in and around the wounds.

Mount a small amount of the nearly rotten apple or orange in 1% aqueous phloxine, tease apart with needles, add a cover glass, and gently tap to spread the tissue. Examine it under l.p. and h.p., noting the *hyphae, conidiophores,* and *spores* dispersed among the cells. Do hyphae grow between the cells or penetrate into them? Are the hyphae septate? coenocytic?

Draw several apple cells showing the associated hyphae and spores.

Figure 28.1 Nuclear history in a magnified section through the apothecium in the life cycle of a heterothallic ascomycete (From L. W. Sharp, *Fundamentals of Cytology,* McGraw-Hill Book Co., 1943. Used by permission)

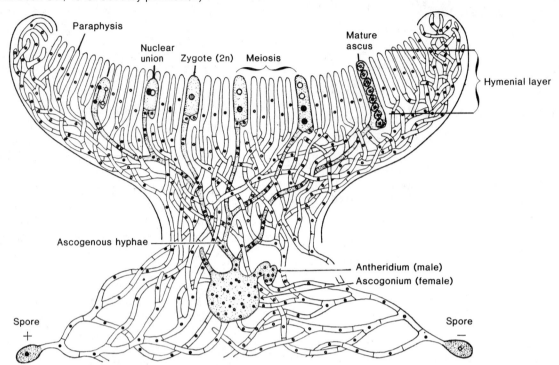

C. Asexual Spore Formation (*Penicillium* and *Aspergillus*)

Penicillium and *Aspergillus* are Ascomycetes formerly classified as Deuteromycetes (*Fungi Imperfecti*). They are blue and green (however, some *Aspergillus* species are sooty black) molds that grow profusely in humid atmospheres on leather, fruits, jams, jellies, paper, and ensilage. The color of these molds is due to immense numbers of tiny *conidia* (singular, *conidium*) or spores produced in chains at the tips of sterigmata borne on the conidiophores (worksheet 28.1C and D).

Study the cultures growing on oranges in moist chambers, or on nutrient agar, and the prepared slides of *Aspergillus* and *Penicillium. Aspergillus glaucus* and *A. niger* are common laboratory pests that frequently contaminate cultures of other organisms; *A. niger* may sometimes affect humans. *Penicillium Roquefortii* is necessary for the manufacture of Roquefort cheese. Penicillin is obtained by the growth of *Penicillium chrysogenum.* Examine the descriptive leaflets, photographs, and colored plates showing cultures of this fungus, and be able to comment briefly on the commercial production of penicillin. What are the uses of penicillin? What is an antibiotic? Are similar substances produced by other fungi? Explain.

Compare the side-by-side sketches of the conidiophores and conidia of *Penicillium* and *Aspergillus* (worksheet 28.1C and D) with specimens observed. Label the diagrams.

D. Gametic Reproduction and Sporocarp Formation

Nuclear History of an Apothecium

Shown diagrammatically (fig. 28.1) are the sexual apparatus (ascogonium and antheridium), dicaryotic cells (contain paired nuclei in ascogenous hyphae), nuclear fusion, and meiosis of ascospore formation in an Ascomycete fruiting body (sporocarp or apothecium), as seen in *Peziza, Morchella,* and other genera.

On the left side of the diagram, plus (+) nuclei in spore and hyphae are represented by black dots (•). On the right side, minus (−) nuclei of the spore and hyphae are represented by small circles (o). Early stages of development are shown in the lower portion of the diagram; later stages in the upper portion.

A hypha from the (−) spore (male) forms an antheridium containing (−) nuclei. A hypha from the (+) spore (female) forms an ascogonium containing (+) nuclei (see lower center of diagram). The smaller antheridium becomes attached to the larger ascogonium and a number of (−) male nuclei pass from it into the ascogonium. In the resulting mixture, (+) and (−) nuclei become paired (but do not fuse) in the ascogonium. Ascogenous hyphae (shaded gray), containing paired (+) and (−) nuclei (here called a dicaryon) in their cells, grow upward into the hymenial layer. Further events within an ascogenous hyphal tip result in fusion of a pair of (+) and (−) nuclei (each n) to produce a zygote (2n). This 2n nucleus of the zygote divides meiotically, resulting in four haploid (n) nuclei in an elongated ascogenous hyphal tip (the young ascus). The four nuclei then divide mitotically forming eight nuclei that eventually produce eight ascospores enclosed in a mature ascus. When an ascus ruptures the ascospores are released.

Note: The diagram, for clarity, shows only a few representatives of the hundreds of similar structures included in an apothecium.

A mature apothecium is composed of (1) dicaryotic (containing paired (+) and (−) nuclei) ascogenous hyphae entering into ascospore formation, and (2) monocaryotic hyphae (containing either (+) or (−) nuclei, but not both) combining to form the apothecium. Paraphyses develop in the hymenium from many interspersed monocaryotic hyphal tips.

Peziza (Cup Fungus)

Examine the fruiting body of the cup fungus provided. This is an *apothecium* (plural, *apothecia*). Where would one look for the mycelium of *Peziza?* Why is the fruiting body called an apothecium?

See the habit sketch of *Peziza* fruiting structures (worksheet 28.2A). Complete labels.

Examine a specimen cut in half longitudinally. Note the stalk or point of attachment, the waxy lower portion of the cup, and especially the fruiting layer, the hymenium.

Label the parts of an apothecium section as shown in the diagram (worksheet 28.2B).

Make a water mount of a very small portion of the hymenium on a slide, and crush by tapping gently with your pencil. Examine, using h.p., and note the cylindrical asci and the slender paraphyses. How many spores in an ascus? Is the number always the same? Find an empty ascus and determine how the spores have escaped.

Label the parts shown in the drawing of a group of hymenial elements of *Peziza* (worksheet 28.2C).

E. Morchella

The edible morel or "sponge mushroom" (worksheet 28.2D) is one of the easiest Ascomycetes to identify and the safest to eat of all fungi. The hollow fruiting body (ascocarp) of this Ascomycete is a short stem bearing an enlarged terminal portion covered with irregular ridges and furrows in which the hymenium develops. It cannot be grown in culture (like true mushrooms) to produce typical ascocarps. Examine material provided.

F. Pathogenic Ascomycetes

Examine infected heads of rye or other grass, bearing long, dark-colored *sclerotia* of ergot. Sclerotia are masses of hard mycelium that have replaced the grain of the rye. The active principle of the drug ergot is contained in the sclerotia. Label sclerotia on worksheet 28.2E.

Examine the demonstration of other various diseases caused by Ascomycetes. Take brief notes and make quick sketches of these forms. Many pathogenic fungi are known only from their conidial (asexual or imperfect) stage.

Questions

1. What is an ascus?
2. In what ways may Ascomycetes be distinguished from the lower fungi?
3. What is the hymenium of an Ascomycete?
4. Define apothecium.
5. What is a dicaryon?
6. How does budding differ from fission?
7. Name several plant diseases caused by Ascomycetes.
8. What are antibiotics? Comment briefly on the production of these substances by *Penicillium* and other fungi.
9. Does an apothecium contain only heterothallic or homothallic mycelia, or both?

Worksheet 28.1

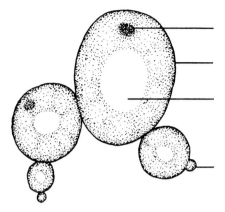

A Colony of yeast showing buds

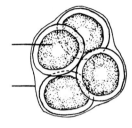

B Yeast ascospores in an ascus

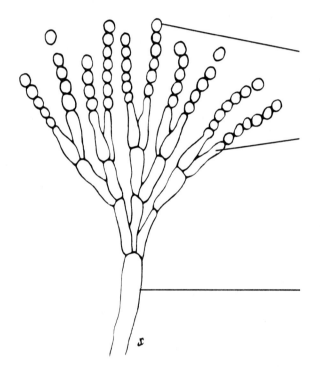

C Penicillium conidia on conidiophore

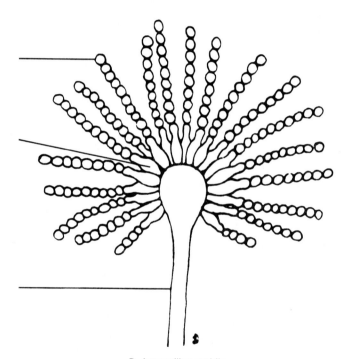

D Aspergillus conidia on conidiophore

A *Peziza*. Habit sketch

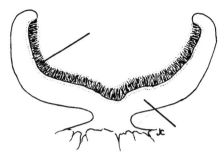

B *Peziza*. Longitudinal section of apothecium with hymenial layer

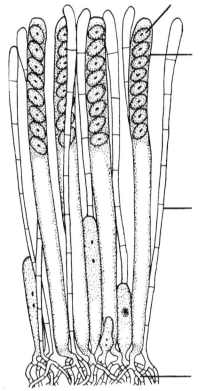

C *Peziza*. Hymenial elements (asci and paraphyses)

D *Morchella*

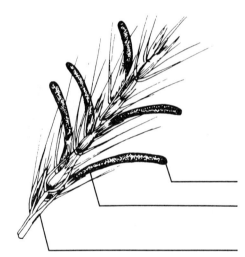

E Sclerotia of ergot

Exercise 29 Lichens

Lichen and Other Materials

You will need specimens of *Parmelia, Physcia, Peltigera, Lecanora, Rhizocarpon, Lecidea, Cladonia, Usnea, Umbilicaria, Stenocybe, Ramalina, Cetraria,* and *Haematomma;* prepared slides with cross sections of *Physcia* thallus and apothecium; dry orcein, cudbear, and litmus; filtered aqueous solution of cudbear; and litmus paper.

Equipment

A compound microscope, dissecting needles, blank slides, and cover glasses are required.

Introduction

Lichens are dual organisms composed of a fungus and an alga growing in intimate association, the combination producing a distinctive plant structure. This association has been termed *symbiotic,* but it is more probable that the fungus is parasitic on the alga. The algae are common single-celled forms capable of living alone under certain conditions but not, as a rule, in the situations in which lichens occur. The thallus of a lichen is built up of fungus tissue in which the algal cells are embedded, usually in definite groups or layers. The thallus may be *crustose* (closely appressed to the substratum), *foliose* (when it has leaflike lobes), or *fruticose* (when it forms erect or pendant branching structures). The *fructifications* are those characteristic of the fungus and may be either apothecia or perithecia. *Orcein* (a cytological dye), *litmus* (a dye used as an indicator in volumetric analysis), and *cudbear* (a coloring agent for medicines and foods) are obtained from lichens. Other lichens are the source of demulcent agents used in medicine. Reindeer moss, a lichen, provides food for reindeer and caribou in the Arctic regions. The scriptural manna was probably a form of lichen. Lichens are still used as food by the natives of southwestern Asia during periods of famine. Lichens are also important as soil-forming agents.

In addition to the fungus spores, some lichens form *soredia.* Soredia are small dustlike pieces of a lichen containing algal cells and fungus hyphae. Soredia are carried by the wind and develop into new lichens under favorable conditions.

A. *Physcia:* A Foliose Lichen

Examine the thallus of *Physcia* growing on pieces of bark or twigs. Is it the same color above and below? Are there fruiting bodies (apothecia)? Are soredia present? Explain. What color is this lichen? Inspect specimens of this same lichen that have been soaked in water and have become soft and pliable. Could a lichen of this type withstand long periods of dryness?

Add proper labels to the drawing of *Physcia* (worksheet 29.1A).

Examine prepared slides of a cross section of a *Physcia* thallus. Note the apothecia, fungal hyphae, and algal cells. Where are the algae distributed in the thallus and apothecium?

Under h.p. note the algal cells enmeshed in the fungal hyphae (worksheet 29.1C).

After study of the slides, check with labels to the drawing of a section of lichen thallus and apothecium (worksheet 29.1E).

Living material. Place a small portion of *Physcia* thallus on a slide in a drop of 1% phloxine and tease it into tiny pieces with dissecting needles. Add a cover glass, and under the microscope note the green algal cells surrounded by the normally colorless (may be stained) fungal mycelial strands (worksheet 29.1C).

B. Crustose Lichens

Study samples of crustose lichens. Why have they been termed crustose? Is it always easy to distinguish clearly between the rock and the lichen? These forms may become partially embedded in the rock substratum by the slowly corrosive action of weak acids produced by the lichen. Can this be considered an early step in the process of soil formation? Explain.

Add labels to the drawing of a crustose lichen (worksheet 29.1B).

C. Fruticose Forms

Examine samples of fruticose lichens. In what ways do they differ from the forms previously described? Do fruticose lichens have any economic value? Explain. Locate the fruiting structures.

Add labels to the drawing of a fruticose lichen, *Usnea* (worksheet 29.1D).

D. Coloring Matter from Lichens

Inspect the dry pigments and the filtered solutions made from them of cudbear, litmus, and orcein. Cudbear is a harmless food and drug coloring matter.

E. Forms of Lichens

Examine lichens named in the display of the following categories and which have been soaked in water to give them a lifelike appearance. (1) Foliose: *Physcia* (already studied); *Parmelia, Peltigera,* and *Umbilicaria;* (2) Crustose: *Lecanora, Rhizocarpon, Stenocybe,* and *Haematomma;* and (3) Fruticose: *Cladonia* (reindeer moss), *Usnea, Ramalina,* and *Cetraria.*

Sketch and describe several of the previously named forms.

Questions

1. What are lichens?
2. Where do lichens grow?
3. What are the three common forms of lichens?
4. What is the economic importance of lichens?
5. How do lichens reproduce?
6. Why is a lichen said to be an example of symbiosis?
7. To what group of fungi does the fungus belong in *Physcia?*
8. To what group of algae does the alga belong?
9. Explain how lichens may be important in the formation of new soil.
10. How are lichens important in detecting air pollution?

Name _____

Lichen

A Foliose lichen (*Physcia*)

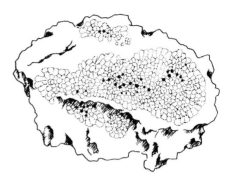

B Crustose lichen

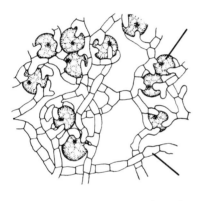

C Agal, fungal cells (detail)

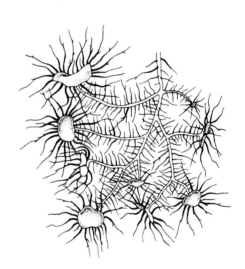

D Fruticose lichen (*Usnea*)

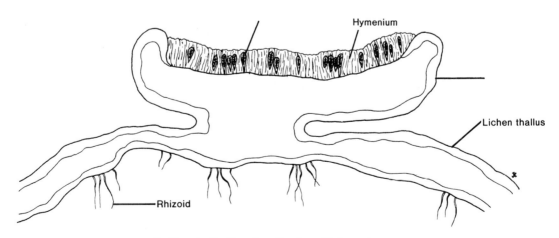

E *Physcia*. Section of apothecium with hymenium

Exercise 30

The Club Fungi (Basidiomycota)

Fungal and Other Materials

Materials needed are fresh edible mushrooms, a fresh or preserved *Amanita* or other poisonous mushroom, a kit for growing fresh edible mushrooms; specimens or the photographs of various other mushrooms from them; prepared slides of mushroom gills, whole mounts of smut spores, fresh, preserved, or dried specimens, or the photographs of Basidiomycota pathogenic to plants and/or humans; fresh or dried wheat or oat stems with sheathing leaf bases and infected leaves bearing, variously, uredinia and telia of grain rust; fresh or pressed leaves of the common barberry bearing mature pycnia and aecia of grain rust; fresh or pressed leaves of the common barberry and the Japanese barberry, both with fruit; prepared slides of wheat stem and leaf base cross sections showing, variously, mature urediniospores and teliospores; prepared slides of common barberry leaf cross sections showing, variously, mature pycnia and aecia; fresh, preserved, or dried specimens of corn smut.

Equipment

Compound microscope, dissecting microscope or 10× hand lens, dissecting needles, blank slides and cover glasses, colored pencils or crayons.

Introduction

The Basidiomycota have a septate mycelium that often bears specialized structures: the clamp connections. The spores are borne externally on a specialized cell, the *basidium* (plural, *basidia*). Each basidiospore is produced at the tip of a delicate projection of the basidium, the *sterigma* (plural, *sterigmata*). Typically, four basidiospores are borne on each basidium. The common mushroom of the marketplace is a Basidiomycete; numerous other members of this class are also edible. Some mushrooms (and other Basidiomycota) are extremely poisonous, and unknown or doubtful forms of these fungi should not be eaten. Many destructive plant diseases are included in this group of fungi. Some of these are corn smut, wheat rust, smuts and rusts of various grains and vegetables, wood rots, and potato scab. There are many interesting Basidiomycota, but only a few of these fungi will be studied.

Consult the text for additional information.

A. Common Edible Mushroom or Gill Fungus: Psalliota *(Agaricus)*

Examine the fruiting bodies (basidiocarps) of the common cultivated mushroom. Note the expanded cap, or *pileus,* bearing on its lower surface the *gills;* the whole structure is raised above the ground by a stalk, or *stipe.* Note the ring, or *annulus,* on the stipe. By examining a young mushroom (button), determine the origin of the annulus. Why is a mushroom called a gill fungus? Why are some mushrooms called toadstools? Is this a good term? Explain.

Label the habit sketches of the fruiting body (fig. 30.1).

Very carefully cut a mushroom in half lengthwise, so as to split the stipe in the exact center, or use a specimen that has already been cut. How are the gills attached to the stipe? What is the texture of the inside of the stipe? These are important taxonomic characters. How many spores are on each basidium of a cultivated mushroom?

Draw the longitudinal section and label.

Examine prepared slides showing cuts through the gills of a mushroom. Note the central tissue of the gill, bearing on each side the hymenial layer, which is composed essentially of basidia and paraphyses. How does this hymenium differ from that of *Peziza?*

Study the diagrammatic drawing (fig. 30.2) of the hymenium showing basidia in various stages, sterigmata, basidiospores, and subhymenial layer. Complete labeling of this drawing.

B. Nuclear History of a Mushroom

Shown diagrammatically (fig. 30.3) is the fusion of uninucleate primary hyphal strands (primary mycelium) to form binucleate (containing paired nuclei) secondary mycelium; nuclear fusion; meiosis; and the formation of basidiospores.

On the left of the diagram (+) nuclei of spore and hyphae are represented by black dots (·). On the right side minus (−) nuclei and hyphae are represented by small circles (o). Early stages of development are shown in the lower portion of the diagram; later stages in the upper portion.

The mycelium resulting from the development of either a (−) or a (+) spore is called a primary mycelium.

Figure 30.1   Common mushroom

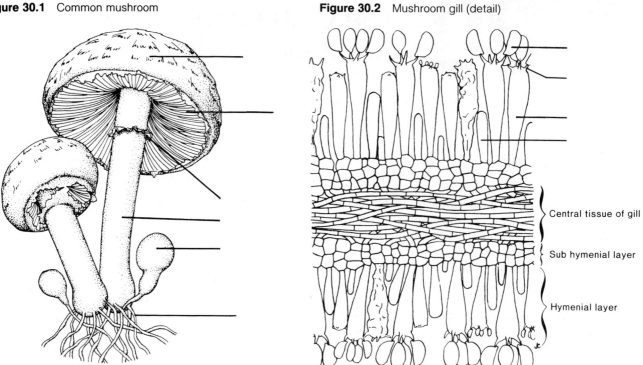

Figure 30.2   Mushroom gill (detail)

Central tissue of gill

Sub hymenial layer

Hymenial layer

Figure 30.3   Nuclear history in the life cycle of a heterothallic basidiomycete, a mushroom (From L. W. Sharp, *Fundamentals of Cytology*, McGraw-Hill Book Co., 1943. Used by permission)

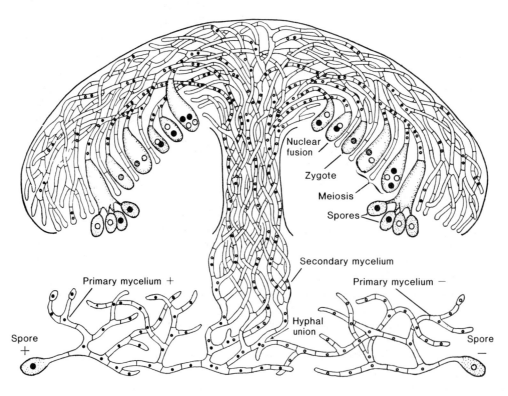

Nuclear fusion

Zygote

Meiosis

Spores

Secondary mycelium

Primary mycelium +

Primary mycelium −

Spore +

Hyphal union

Spore −

When a uninucleate (+) hypha fuses with a minus (−) hypha, the resulting dicaryotic hyphal mass is called secondary mycelium. Cells of the secondary mycelium contain paired but not fused (+) and (−) nuclei. Each pair of (+) and (−) nuclei in the cells is called a dicaryon and the dicaryotic mycelium containing them is the dicaryophase. The entire fruiting body (sporophore or basidiocarp) of a mushroom is composed entirely of secondary mycelium.

At the surface of the mushroom gills many of the hyphal tips (containing paired (+) and (−) nuclei) enlarge to become basidia. The (+) and (−) nuclei in a young basidium fuse to form a zygote nucleus (2n). This 2n nucleus divides meiotically, resulting in four haploid (n) nuclei; two containing (+) nuclei and two containing (−) nuclei. Each nucleus migrates into one of the four small protuberances, the sterigmata (developed on the basidium tip), where they develop into basidiospores. Basidiospores are shot from the basidia when mature and fall from between the gills.

C. A Poisonous Mushroom (Amanita)

Note the jars on the demonstration table containing mushrooms belonging to the genus *Amanita*. The mushrooms belonging to this genus (figs. 30.4, 30.5) have white spores and are characterized by a volva (a cuplike or bulbous structure at the base of the stipe), in addition to a large annulus. A few of the species are edible; others are among the most poisonous plants known, and the great majority of the cases of serious (often fatal) mushroom poisoning are caused by representatives of this genus.

D. Growing Fresh Mushrooms in the Laboratory

Activate the contents of a mushroom-growing kit by watering according to the accompanying directions. Mushrooms should be available for study about 30 days after the first watering and will continue to appear for several weeks. Mushroom kits are available from Carolina Biological Supply Company, General Biological Supply House, Ward's Natural Science Establishment, and others. (See appendix E.)

E. Wheat Rust (Puccinia gramminis Pers.)

The Uredinia

Examine leaves or stems of wheat or other small grain bearing reddish pustules, *uredinia* (singular, *uredinium*) of rust on the surface. Describe the appearance of such a pustule. Is it elongated? If so, in what direction? These reddish, rustlike pustules are responsible for the term *rust* that has been applied to this and similar plant diseases.

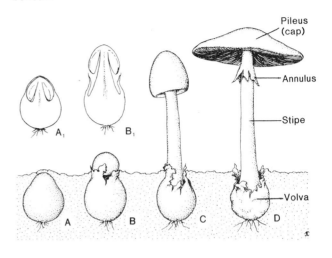

Figure 30.4 Diagrams showing development of a poisonous mushroom (*Amanita*) from the young stage (button or egg) to a mature sporophore. A_1 and B_1 are sections of similar stages, A and B, shown immediately beneath

Figure 30.5 *Amanita verna* (Courtesy of H. L. Dean)

Figure 30.6 Wheat rust. Rusty summer spores on wheat

Figure 30.7 Uredinium in cross section of wheat leaf

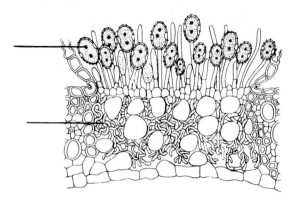

Label the drawing (fig. 30.6) of uredinia in position on a portion of wheat stem. Shade the pustules lightly or color by means of colored pencil.

Scrape off a few spores from the uredinia into a drop of water and mount on a slide. Examine, h.p., and describe. Note shape, color, thickness of wall. Are there any markings on the outside? How many nuclei does each spore contain?

These spores are the *urediniospores,* or summer spores, of the rust that spread the disease rapidly from one grain plant to another (repeating stage). Draw a urediniospore.

Examine prepared slides showing urediniospores in place in the pustules of the grain stem and leaves. Note the fungal hyphae at the base of the uredinium.

Add labels to the drawing of a uredinium shown in the cross section (fig. 30.7).

The Telia

Examine leaves or stems of wheat or other small grain bearing black pustules, *telia* (singular, *telium*), of the rust. These pustules are responsible for the term *black stem rust*. Describe the appearance of the telia.

Scrape off a few spores from a telium into a drop of water and examine, using h.p. Of how many cells is each spore composed? How many nuclei in each cell? How does the wall compare with that of the urediniospore as to thickness? as to color? These spores are the *teliospores.*

Draw a teliospore.

The teliospore is the resting spore, passing the winter in a dormant state and producing in spring a basidium (promycelium) bearing four basidiospores (sporidia) that cannot attack grain but are able to attack only the common barberry.

Examine prepared slides showing teliospores in place in the pustules of the grain stem and leaves. Note the fungal hyphae at the base of the pustule.

Add labels to the drawing of a telium shown in the cross section of a wheat leaf (fig. 30.8).

The Alternate Host, Common Barberry

Examine infected leaves of the common barberry, noting minute pustules on the upper surface and masses of crowded cuplike structures on the lower surfaces. These are the fruiting structures produced by the mycelium and originating from infection by the basidiospores. The small flasklike structures embedded in the upper surface are the *pycnia* (singular, *pycnium*) (spermagonia) producing very small pycniospores (spermatia) that serve as gametes. The cuplike structures on the lower surface are *aecia* (singular, *aecium*), or clustercups, which produce aeciospores that can attack only the grain.

Examine a cross section through an infected barberry leaf showing pycnia and aecia. Are fungal hyphae visible in the leaf tissues? How many nuclei are there in each aeciospore?

Fill in significant details of the pycnia and aecia shown on the diagram of the cross section of an infected barberry leaf (fig. 30.9).

Compare common barberry (*Berberis vulgaris*) with Japanese barberry. (*Berberis thunbergii*) as to length and size of branches, leaves, and berries; list differences noted. Is the common barberry plentiful today? Why is this plant usually difficult to find in many parts of the United States?

F. Corn Smut

Examine preserved and dried specimens of corn smut. What parts of the plant does this fungus attack? Describe the appearance of the smut lesions on the ear, the tassel, the stalk, and leaves. How do they differ? What is the economic importance of corn smut?

Mount a very small quantity of the smutted mass from a lesion, and examine under h.p. Of what is it composed?

Figure 30.8 Telia in cross section of wheat leaf

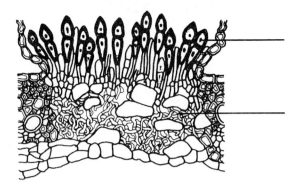

Figure 30.9 Pycnia and aecia in cross section of barberry leaf

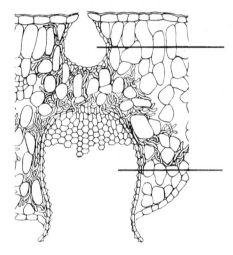

Describe the shape, size, and color of the spores. Are their surfaces smooth or roughened?

Label the diagrammatic habit sketch of the fungal lesion of the host (fig. 30.10).

Draw a single smut spore from suitable fresh material or prepared slides. Make the drawing about 3 cm in diameter, showing markings and the thickness of the wall.

G. Other Pathogenic Fungi

Examine the demonstrations of various plant diseases caused by Basidiomycetes. Take brief notes and make quick sketches of this material.

Examine the photographs showing the severe effects of various fungi that are pathogenic to humans. Take brief notes on the characteristics of several of these fungi. Comment briefly on the importance of medical mycology, especially for those living in tropical regions.

Figure 30.10 Corn smut

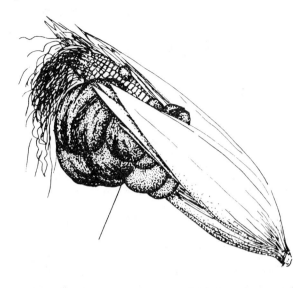

Questions

1. How does the hymenium of *Agaricus* differ from that of *Peziza*?
2. Why is a mushroom called a gill fungus?
3. What characters distinguish the poisonous *Amanita*?
4. What is the safest rule to follow if you do not know if a mushroom is poisonous?
5. Explain the popular conception of the terms *toadstool* and *mushroom.* What scientific objections can be raised against this distinction?
6. How are mushrooms grown commercially?
7. What is mushroom spawn?
8. Comment briefly on the gravity of mushroom poisoning.
9. Beginning with the basidiospore, list the five spore stages in the order they occur naturally in the life cycle of grain rust.
10. Why does it help to eradicate the common barberry?
11. List characteristics of the common barberry that contrast with those of the Japanese barberry.
12. Why may urediniospores blown to northern regions from the southern grain fields be dangerous to the northern wheat crop?
13. Make a life cycle of wheat rust in the form of an illustrated circle showing the spore stages, the seasons of the year, and the plants affected by each spore stage.
14. Where are fungal mycelia found in nature?
15. To what group do most of the fungi belong which are pathogenic to man?
16. Give the scientific name of several pathogenic (human) fungi and briefly characterize the symptoms of each disease.

31

Liverworts and Mosses (Bryophyta)

Plant Materials

Materials needed are living *Marchantia* plants with (variously) cupules, antheridiophores, archegoniophores, and mature sporophytes; living moss protonema, moss archegonial and antheridial plants, and plants with mature sporophytes; fresh, preserved, or dried *Sphagnum;* prepared slides of *Marchantia* thallus with cupules, antheriodiophores with antheridia, archegoniophores with archegonia, and mature sporophytes; cross sections of an antheriodiophore, of an archegoniophore: prepared slides of moss antheridial and archegonial tips, and longitudinal and cross sections of sporophytes.

Equipment

A compound microscope, blank slides and cover glasses, dissecting needles, and fine-pointed curved forceps are needed.

Introduction

Modern evidence indicates that the plants usually grouped as Bryophytes are really members of three separate divisions: the liverworts, the mosses, and the hornworts. Bryophytes are typically land plants but seldom attain a height of more than a few inches. They are widely distributed, occurring in practically all parts of the world. A well-defined alternation of generations is demonstrated in their life histories. The plant developed from the germination of a spore is the *gamete-bearing plant,* or *gametophyte* (containing the monoploid, or n number of chromosomes). Gametophytes of mosses and liverworts are independent plants and are the green structures commonly seen. The plant developed from the zygote is the *spore-bearing plant,* or *sporophyte* (containing the *diploid,* or 2n number of chromosomes). The sporophyte develops after fertilization of an egg inside an archegonium and is almost entirely parasitic on the gametophyte. Hornworts and liverworts have no true vascular tissue. Moss sporophytes have non-lignified vascular cells.

The bryophytes have little economic importance. Peat is derived from various mosses, the better grades containing *Sphagnum. Sphagnum* is also used as packing material, especially when objects must be kept moist. It has also been used as a filler in surgical dressings. The

dead, empty cells of the *Sphagnum* leaf absorb several times their weight in fluids.

Marchantia: A Thalloid Liverwort

A. Gametophyte

Examine the green, dichotomously branching, dorsiventral, gametophyte plant (*thallus*). With a hand lens study the dorsal (upper) surface, noting the raised polygonal areas, each with a centrally located white-rimmed pore. Suggest functions of the pore. Note the midrib. How does this differ from the true midrib of a leaf?

Cupules (gemma cups) on the dorsal surface contain small, green, asexual reproductive bodies called *gemmae* (singular, *gemma*). Mount several in water and observe under l.p. Identify the two lateral notches with their growing points, the terminal point of attachment of the stalk, and the colorless cells from which rhizoids will develop.

On the ventral (lower) surface of the thallus note the masses of unicellular rhizoids and the rows of multicellular scales. Detach and study a few rhizoids in a water mount, first under l.p., then h.p. How do the two kinds of rhizoids differ? How do *Marchantia* rhizoids compare with roots and root hairs in structure, size, and function? Do the scales serve any useful purpose?

Antheridiophore (antheridial branch). Examine male plants with antheridial receptacles composed of lobed, dislike structures borne at the top of slender antheridiophores, which arise from notches in the thallus. Study prepared slides, under l.p. and h.p., of longitudinal sections through an antheridial disc, noting cavities in the upper portion that each contain an *antheridium*. An *antheridium* has a short *stalk* and a uniseriate *jacket* of sterile cells enclosing blocks of cubical *sperm mother cells* or masses of sperms. Suggest a function for the canal connecting an antheridial chamber to the top of a disc.

Study the drawing of a thallus with antheridial receptacles (worksheet 31.1A), the longitudinal section of an antheridial receptacle (worksheet 31.1B), and of an antheridium (worksheet 31.1C). Label worksheet 31.1B and C.

Archegoniophore (archegonial branch). Examine female plants with archegonial receptacles composed of fingerlike projections radiating from a central disclike structure borne at the top of slender archegoniophores. Study prepared slides, under l.p. and h.p., of longitudinal sections through an archegonial receptacle. Identify flask-shaped *archegonia* of various ages on the lower receptacle surface. Find a mature archegonium and identify the stalk, neck, neck canal, venter, ventral canal cell, and egg. What has happened to the neck canal cells and the cap cells characteristic of young archegonia? Does the mucilaginous plug filling the neck canal serve any useful purpose?

Study the drawing of a thallus with archegonial receptacles (worksheet 31.1D), the longitudinal section of an archegonial receptacle (worksheet 31.1E), and of an archegonium (worksheet 31.1F). Label worksheet 31.1 D–F.

B. Sporophyte

The zygote produced when an egg is fertilized in an archegonium divides to form a simple *embryo*, which in turn soon develops into a *sporophyte*. Examine prepared slides, under l.p. and h.p., of longitudinal sections through an older archegonial receptacle, noting the mature sporophytes. Each sporophyte is composed of an ovoid *capsule* with a short stalk, or *seta*, attached to an absorptive and anchoring *foot* embedded in the gametophytic archegonial receptacle tissues. A mature sporophyte is closely enveloped by the calyptra (two to three cells thick), which in turn is enclosed by the perigynium (one-cell thick).

Diploid spore mother cells in a young capsule undergo meiosis and cytokinesis to produce monoploid spores. Among the spores of a mature capsule note the *elaters*, which appear as elongated narrow cells with spirally thickened walls. Elaters, by their twisting hygroscopic action, aid in spore dispersal.

Does a spore produce a gametophytic or sporophytic plant when it germinates? If gametophytic, state what percentage of these plants will be antheridial (male), and what percentage will be archegonial (female).

Label the drawing of a *Marchantia* sporophyte (worksheet 31.1G).

C. Thallus (Internal Structure)

Examine prepared slides, under l.p. and h.p., showing a *Marchantia* thallus in cross section and with the attached cupules cut longitudinally. Note *pores* on the dorsal surface opening into *air chambers* containing erect, branching rows of *photosynthetic cells*. Examine a cupule containing gemmae. Is a gemma best shown by a section, or by a whole mount? What is the character of the mid-thallus tissue? Determine how rhizoids and scales originate from the ventral surface.

Label the drawing of a cross section of *Marchantia* thallus (worksheet 31.1H).

D. Optional

Examine prepared slides, under l.p. and h.p., of cross sections through an archegoniophore and antheridiophore. Do these structures resemble the thallus in any way? Note the water-conducting system functioning wicklike by capillarity along a midrib and up an archegoniphore or antheridiophore. Is this a true vascular system?

Make neat sketches of the aforementioned structures, showing and labeling the parts described.

E. Other Liverworts

Examine live specimens or prepared slides of any other liverworts displayed. If so instructed, make habit sketches of the plants observed. Thalloid liverworts will look much like *Marchantia* while leafy liverworts will have a simple thallus without internal structure but often elaborately lobed in "leaflike" projections.

F. *Anthoceros*: A Hornwort

Examine live specimens or prepared slides of *Anthoceros*. The gametophyte thallus is simple and lobed. The sporophyte is elongated and tubular, splitting into two valves at maturity. The valves surround the spores and a long, thin, central columella. Spores are continually being produced by meiosis.

Identify the spore mother cells, diads, and tetrads as you move from the base to the apex of the sporophyte. Draw a portion of the sporophyte to show valves, columella, and spores in several stages of development.

A Common Moss

A. Gametophyte

A moss spore, when it germinates, produces a gametophytic structure called a *protonema* (plural, *protonemata*). Examine moss protonemata growing on the soil. Carefully remove a small portion with needles or fine-pointed forceps and immerse in water, agitating gently until it is free from sand. Mount it on a slide in water, and study it first under l.p., then under h.p. Does this stage of the moss resemble any plant previously studied? Note the arrangement of cells, method of branching, and chloroplasts. Search carefully for budlike structures.

Label the drawing of a moss protonema (worksheet 31.2A).

Mount a single leaf of a mature gametophyte on a slide and examine it under l.p. Note the shape, margin, and cell arrangement. How many cells thick is the blade? Is there a midrib? Do you find any stomata or stomatalike openings on the leaves?

Examine fresh or preserved material and prepared slides showing the tip of a leafy branch bearing *antheridia* (singular, *antheridium*). Study a single antheridium and describe the stalk, wall, sperm mother cells, and the surrounding leaves united into a flowerlike *involucre*.

Examine prepared slides showing the tip of a leafy branch bearing *archegonia* (singular, *archegonium*). Study a single archegonium and describe the stalk, the venter, the neck, the neck canal, the ventral canal cell, and the egg.

Add proper labels to the sketches of the archegonial and antheridial tips (worksheet 31.2B and C) of the leafy shoots of moss.

Label the parts of the drawings of archegonium and antheridium (worksheet 31.2D and E).

B. Sporophyte

When the egg inside the archegonium is fertilized, forming a zygote, it divides and grows into the *sporophyte*. As the sporophyte develops, the upper part of the archegonium also enlarges but is eventually torn off and carried up on top of the capsule (sporangium) to form the caplike *calyptra*. Beneath the calyptra is the swollen spore chamber, or capsule, borne on a long slender stalk (seta), the foot of which is buried in the top of the leafy branch of the gametophyte. Is the sporophyte dependent on the gametophyte for all its nourishment? For any of it? Explain.

Gently remove the calyptra and describe the sporophyte, carefully noting size, color, relation of parts to each other and of the whole to the gametophyte.

Note the capsule lid (*operculum*), and using the hand lens, describe its general appearance. Remove it carefully with forceps, and notice around the opening the ring of toothlike projections, the *peristome*. Breathe on the peristome and note any response. What, can you suggest, is the function of the peristome? Remove spores and examine them under h.p. What is their size, shape, and surface?

Study the drawing of a sporophyte of moss attached to the leafy gametophyte (worksheet 31.2F).

Check with labels to the exploded drawing showing calyptra, capsule, operculum, and peristome (worksheet 31.2G).

Examine prepared slides showing cross and longitudinal sections through the capsule of a moss. Note the tissue that will later develop into spores.

Label the parts of the drawing of a longitudinal section of a moss capsule (worksheet 31.2H).

C. *Sphagnum* (Peat Moss)

Examine fresh, preserved, and dried *Sphagnum* material, noting the long, leafy stems and the rounded capsules. In these forms the short stalk of the capsule is a gametophytic, not a sporophytic, structure.

Examine a single leaf of the living moss under the microscope, noting small, green, photosynthetic cells (living) and large, colorless, water-holding cells (dead). How does this type of leaf structure make *Sphagnum* ideal for florists' packing and for surgical dressings?

Optional: Make an outline drawing of a portion of *Sphagnum* leaf showing its cell structure.

D. Other Mosses

Examine fresh, preserved, or dried material of any other mosses provided. Note in particular the shape of the capsules and the length and number of perisome teeth.

Questions

1. Name the parts of *Marchantia* and moss sporophytes.
2. What constitutes the gametophyte of a moss? of a liverwort?
3. Is the calyptra of a moss capsule n or 2n?
4. Define archegonium, antheridium, foot, seta, gemma, cupule, operculum, thallus, rhizoids, elater, and protonema.
5. What is peat? What is the commercial value of peat?
6. What enables the *Sphagnum* leaf to absorb and hold so much water?
7. List the uses of *Sphagnum*.
8. Diagram the life cycles of *Marchantia* and a common moss in the form of illustrated circles, indicating structures as 2n (sporophytic), or n (gametophytic).
9. What is the importance of an archegonium to an individual plant and in the developmental history of land plants?
10. Compare the archegonium with the oogonium as to form, structure, function, and occurrence in the plant kingdom.
11. State which of the following are monoploid (1n, gametophytic), or diploid (2n, sporophytic) structures: egg, sperm, thallus, gemma, spore mother cell, spore, archegonium, antheridium, ventral canal cell, sporophyte, zygote, and calyptra.

Marchantia

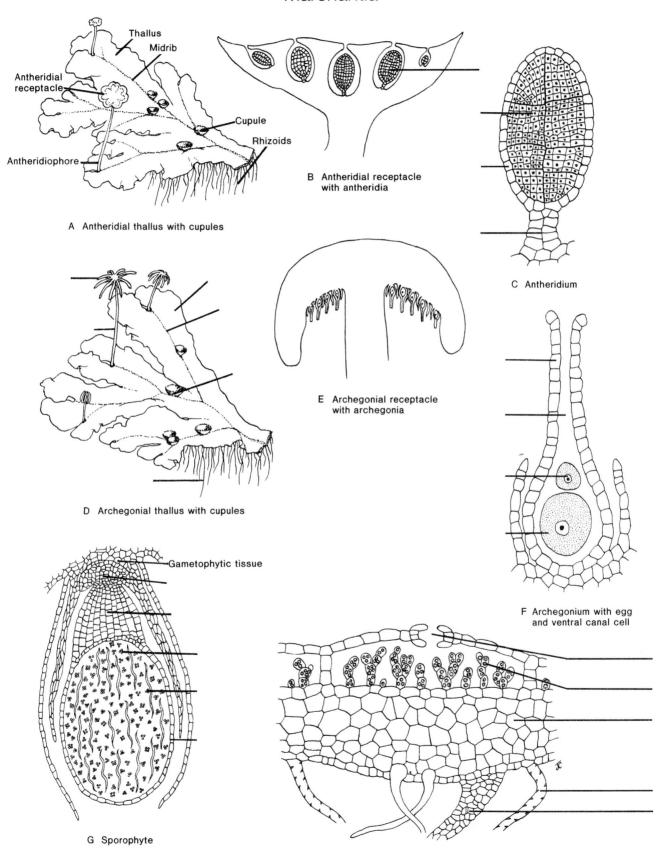

Thallus
Midrib
Antheridial receptacle
Cupule
Rhizoids
Antheridiophore

A Antheridial thallus with cupules

B Antheridial receptacle with antheridia

C Antheridium

D Archegonial thallus with cupules

E Archegonial receptacle with archegonia

F Archegonium with egg and ventral canal cell

Gametophytic tissue

G Sporophyte

H Thallus section showing structure

Moss

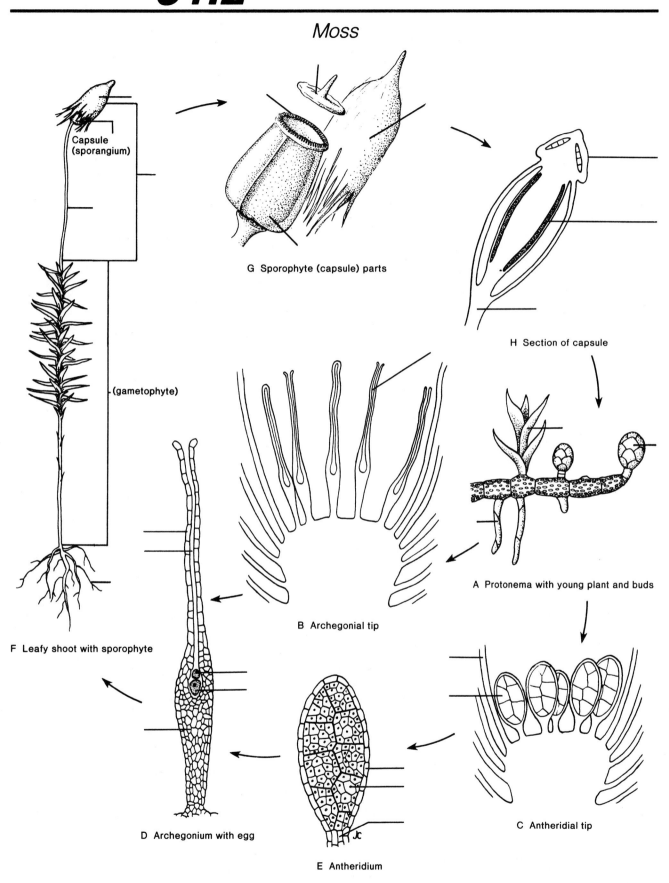

Capsule
(sporangium)

(gametophyte)

G Sporophyte (capsule) parts

H Section of capsule

A Protonema with young plant and buds

B Archegonial tip

F Leafy shoot with sporophyte

D Archegonium with egg

E Antheridium

C Antheridial tip

Club Mosses and Horsetails

Plant Materials

Materials needed are living or preserved, sterile and fertile shoots (with strobili) of *Equisetum arvense* with attached rhizomes; living, preserved, or dried specimens of *Lycopodium* and *Selaginella* species; spores of *Lycopodium;* resurrection plants (*Selaginella*); and *Psilotum.*

Equipment

A compound microscope, blank slides and cover glasses, dissecting needles, sharp-pointed curved forceps, and a hand lens (10x) are needed.

Introduction

The living, lower vascular plants (Lycophyta and Sphenophyta) are but insignificant modern representatives of the great and abundant forms that flourished during the Carboniferous geologic period (345 to 280 million years ago). In contrast to the Bryophyta, these plants have a dominant sporophyte generation with true roots and stems with xylem and phloem, tiny microphyll leaves, and sporangia often clustered into cones or strobili. *Equisetum* contains a large amount of silica in its stem, which helped give some species of these plants the name "scouring rushes." *Lycopodium* is used as an ornamental plant for Christmas greens; the spores (vegetable sulfur) once were used as a dry lubricant in the preparation of foot powders, to roll suppositories in to prevent their sticking together, and in the manufacture of fireworks. Extremely limited supplies restrict such uses today. *Selaginella* is studied only because in a few species it so very nearly approaches the seed habit of the higher plants (by retaining the megaspore within the megasporangium in such a way as to suggest a true seed). The common resurrection plants are species of *Selaginella*. These plants roll and unroll in response to moisture changes, even when they are dead.

Lycophyta

A. *Lycopodium:* A Homosporous Club Moss

Examine the living, preserved, or dried specimens of several species of *Lycopodium*. Describe the shape and size of the leaves and the method of branching of the stems.

Label the drawing of a *Lycopodium* plant (worksheet 32.1A).

Note the strobili, composed in this case of *sporophylls*. How are the sporophylls arranged on the stem? Mount a single sporophyll without using a cover glass, and examine it under the hand lens and l.p. Describe the location and shape of the sporangium.

Label the drawing of a *Lycopodium* sporophyll (worksheet 32.1B).

Crush a sporangium and examine the spores (worksheet 32.1C). What is the shape? the character of the outer coat? Examine *Lycopodium* spores (vegetable sulfur). Rub a small quantity between your fingers. Why is this material called a dry lubricant?

B. *Selaginella:* A Heterosporous Club Moss

Examine the living or preserved plants of *Selaginella*. Compare the leaves and strobili with those of *Lycopodium,* noting both resemblances and differences.

Label the drawing of a portion of a *Selaginella plant* (worksheet 32.1D).

Remove a sporophyll from the base and one from the tip of a strobilus; mount them without a cover glass side by side so as to show the sporangia; and examine, using the hand lens and l.p. Note and describe any differences. The sporangium containing a few (how many?) large spores is a megasporangium, and the large spores are megaspores. The sporangia bearing numerous small spores are microsporangia (often orange-red in color), and the small spores are microspores.

Compare with the drawings of a megasporophyll (worksheet 32.1E) and a microsporophyll (worksheet 32.1F) of *Selaginella.*

Crush the sporangia so as to liberate the spores. How do the megaspores (worksheet 32.1G) and microspores (worksheet 32.1H) compare as to color, shape, and surface markings? Calculate their relative size and comparative volume. How many megaspores are there in a megasporangium? How many microspores in a microsporangium?

Examine the dried and moist resurrection plants on display.

C. Other Lycophyta

Examine any specimens demonstrated, including fossil forms. Compare with those already studied.

Sphenophyta

D. *Equisetum*

The gametophytes of the horsetail closely resemble those of the ferns. The sporophyte of one species only (*Equisetum arvense*) will be studied.

Examine the underground stems (rhizomes), some of which have vegetative shoots (sterile) and others spore-bearing (fertile) shoots attached to them. In the case of the vegetative shoots, note the minute, scalelike leaves. How are they arranged on the stem? Of what value are they to the plants? What part of the plant performs photosynthesis? Feel the stems and describe the sensation they give to the touch. Does this suggest why some species of these plants are called scouring rushes?

Label the drawing of a vegetative shoot of *Equisetum* (worksheet 32.2A).

Examine a fertile shoot. Are there any functional leaves on this stem? Is there any provision for photosynthesis? Where is the food supply of this shoot? Note the spore-bearing portion at the top. What is its shape? Are the spores borne on leaves in this plant? The entire spore-bearing tip is called a *strobilus* (plural, *strobili*). Look this word up in the dictionary and learn what it means. Is the term appropriate?

Label the drawing of a fertile shoot of *Equisetum* (worksheet 32.2B).

The strobilus is composed of numerous *sporangiophores* (structures bearing *sporangia*). Remove a single sporangiophore, and examine it under the hand lens. What is its shape? How many sporangia does it bear?

Label the drawing of a sporangiophore of *Equisetum* (worksheet 32.2C).

With a needle, remove a few spores from a sporangium; mount in a drop of water; and examine, first using l.p., and then h.p. Note that the outer spore coat has de-veloped into two long bands (elaters) wound spirally about the spore and attached to the point where they cross each other. Allow the spores to dry on an uncovered slide. When dry, examine them under the microscope using l.p., then breathe very gently on the spores and observe their responses. What happens? How may this be explained? What purpose may it serve?

Label the drawing of an *Equisetum* spore (worksheet 32.2D).

E. Other Sphenophyta

Examine any specimens demonstrated including fossil forms. Compare with the *Equisetum* already studied.

F. Psilophyta

Today Psilophytes are represented by only two living genera. They are land plants with a dominant sporophyte generation having no roots, dichotomously branched stems, a primitive vascular system, and clustered sporangia not fused in cones. They have been classified with the most ancient vascular plants, but recent studies show characteristics in common with a primitive group of ferns, the grape-ferns.

Examine *Psilotum,* if available, and note the branching pattern of the upright stem, the lack of roots and leaves, and the lobed sporangia in the axils of small scale-like projections.

Questions

1. Why are the plants in the previous exercise sometimes called fern allies?
2. What function may the elaters of *Equisetum* serve?
3. Define sporangium, microsporangium, and megasporangium.
4. How nearly does *Selaginella* approach the seed habit?
5. Comment on the fossil record of the Pteridophytes.
6. What materials now used as fuel were formed during the Carboniferous period?
7. Why are *Lycopodium* spores called vegetable sulfur?

Worksheet 32.1

Name _____

Lycopodium *and* Selaginella

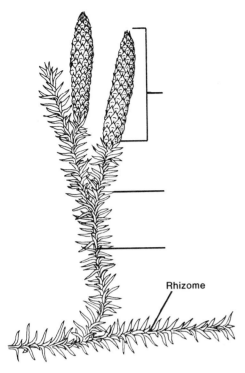

Rhizome

A *Lycopodium*

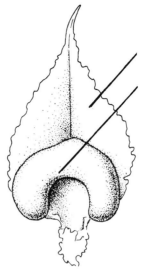

B Sporophyll
(*Lycopodium*)

C Spore
(*Lycopodium*)

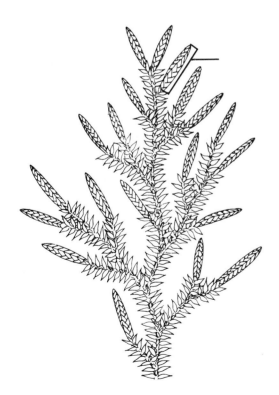

D *Selaginella*

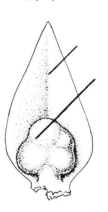

E Megasporophyll
(*Selaginella*)

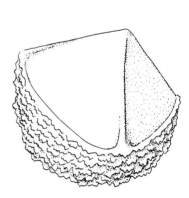

G Megaspore
(*Selaginella*)

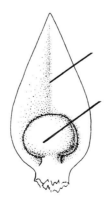

F Microsporophyll
(*Selaginella*)

H Microspore
(*Selaginella*)

231

Name _____

Equisetum

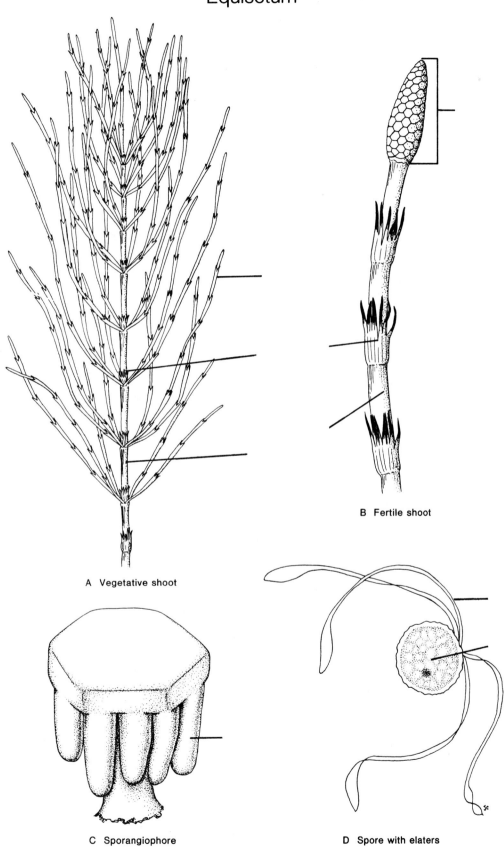

A Vegetative shoot

B Fertile shoot

C Sporangiophore

D Spore with elaters

Exercise 33 — Ferns (Pterophyta)

Plant Materials

Materials needed are living or preserved *Pteridium* rhizomes; living or dried fronds of *Cyrtomium, Aspidium, Polypodium* or other ferns with sori; section of tree fern stem; mature prothallia with antheridia and archegonia. Prepared slides of *Pteridium* rhizome, fern prothallia, and various living or mounted ferns for demonstration.

Equipment

A compound microscope, blank slides and cover glasses, and a hand lens (10×).

Reagents

You will need ethanol, 70%.

Introduction

It is the frond, or megaphyllous leaf, of the fern sporophyte that catches your eye. In a number of genera they are the largest and most complex leaves in the plant kingdom. Stems up to 50 feet tall in tropical ferns with complex vascular bundles are often reduced to rhizomes in common temperate ferns. Sporangia are numerous and borne on the leaves. Gametophytes are independent, small, and inconspicuous.

Ferns grow in a wide variety of habitats and vary greatly in size and form. Ferns were the dominant vegetation during the Carboniferous period approximately 300 million years ago, and many beautifully preserved fossils of these ancient forms may be studied. Commercially, ferns are used mainly for decorative purposes. The young rhizomes have been used for food by humans, some fern leaves in the making of teas and liquors, and one fern, *Aspidium*, has been used as a specific remedy for tapeworm.

A. The Sporophyte Structure

An aboveground leaf (frond) and its attached underground stem (rhizome) and roots constitute the sporophyte. Study a living or pressed specimen of *Polypodium* (worksheet 33.2A) or other common fern with a frond still attached to its rhizome. The rachis of the frond corresponds to the petiole and midrib of a flowering plant leaf. Brown "dots" on some leaf undersurfaces are the *sori* (singular, *sorus*) composed of a compact cluster of sporangia and are usually covered by a membrane called the *indusium* (plural, *indusia*) in other genera.

The ferns have, like the mosses, an alternation of distinct gametophyte and sporophyte generations. In the ferns, however, the sporophyte is larger and more conspicuous than the gametophyte and will be studied first.

Examine the rhizome of the common bracken fern, *Pteridium (Pteris)*. Note its shape in cross section, the lateral ridges, the places where leaves have been attached, and the method of branching.

Using the hand lens and l.p. of the microscope, examine a stained transverse section of the stem (rhizome) and identify the following tissues: the cortex and its outer region of thick-walled cells; sclerenchyma strands of masses of undifferentiated, dark-colored, thick-walled cells; vascular bundles of various shapes and sizes; and pith: the parenchyma tissues in which the sclerenchyma strands and vascular bundles are embedded.

Complete the diagram (worksheet 33.1A) of a cross section of the stem of *Pteridium*, labeling the tissues named.

Examine a single bundle under l.p. and h.p. Note the thick-walled xylem cells (tracheids) in the center, surrounded by phloem, and the whole bundle separated from the pith by an endodermis. The layer of cells just within the endodermis is the *pericycle*.

Label the outline drawing (worksheet 33.1B) of a single bundle, indicating xylem, phloem, endodermis, pericycle, and pith cells.

Examine the stem of a tree fern on display. How does it differ from the stem of *Pteridium*? Study the large photographs of tree ferns growing in their natural habit. Take brief notes, and make quick sketches of this material.

B. The Sporophyte: Spore Production

Examine leaves (fronds) of various species of ferns. Note the variation in shape, with the general tendency toward greatly dissected compound leaves. Describe the sporulating leaf and compare it with the sterile leaf of the same species in *Onoclea sensibilis* (the sensitive fern), *Polypodium virginianum* (the polypody), or other species as directed by the instructor.

Examine the *pinna* (plural, *pinnae*) or *pinnule* of a fern bearing clusters of sporangia or *sori* (singular, *sorus*).

Note the *indusium* (plural, *indusia*), if present, fastened at one side or in the center and almost completely covering the sporangia beneath.

Study the drawing (worksheet 33.2B) of pinnae bearing sori, and also the parts of an enlarged sorus shown separately in face view (worksheet 33.2C), and in longitudinal section (worksheet 33.2D).

Remove a few sporangia from a sorus, and place them on a slide in plenty of water. (If dry, first moisten with alcohol). Note the stalk and the helmetlike sporangium, with the annulus partially encircling it, and the mouth from which the spores are discharged. Notice also the spores themselves. Suggest a function of the annulus. What is the shape of the spores? Are they smooth or rough?

Label the drawing (worksheet 33.2E) of a fern sporangium. Draw several spores to proper scale beside this drawing.

C. The Gametophyte

The spore, on germination, does not grow directly into a leafy fern plant, such as that which produced it, but into a totally different structure, the gametophyte.

Examine the gametophyte, or *prothallium* (plural, *prothallia*) of a fern. What is its shape? Can a leaf, stem, or root be distinguished?

Using a hand lens and 1.p., study the upper and lower surfaces of a whole gametophyte mounted on a slide. Where are the rhizoids? What does the notch represent? Try to find sex organs (antheridia and archegonia) on the lower surface. If present, describe their appearance.

Label the outline drawing (worksheet 33.3C) of a fern gametophyte (prothallium).

Under the demonstration microscope, examine a cross section of a prothallium. How many cells thick is it in most parts? How thick is it at the portion where the sex organs are borne? Label all structures identified as shown on worksheet 33.3.

Study demonstration mounts showing antheridia and archegonia. How do these structures compare with similar organs of the bryophytes as to size and complexity? How do the sporophytes of the two groups compare?

D. Identification

Using the accompanying key, identify each of the mounted and numbered ferns on the supply table. Return all material to the proper place after using.

Questions

1. What are the advances of ferns over mosses?
2. Would a tree fern make good lumber?
3. What is a frond of a fern? a pinna? a pinnule?
4. What kind of venation is found in a fern leaf?
5. Diagram, in the form of an illustrated circle, the life history of a fern.
6. What structures or parts of a fern are useful in the identification of these plants?
7. Where do ferns grow naturally?

Key to Genera of Common Ferns

1. Leaves (fronds) undivided *Camptosorus*
1. Leaves (fronds) variously lobed or divided into numerous leaflets **2**
    2. Fronds not divided to the rachis **3**
    2. Fronds divided into distinct leaflets **5**
3. Spore-bearing fronds much reduced in size *Onoclea*
3. Spore-bearing fronds essentially like vegetative fronds **4**
    4. Divisions of the frond lobed *Phegopteris*
    4. Divisions of the frond simple *Polypodium*
5. Pinnae simple, at most toothed or notched **6**
5. Pinnae deeply lobed, notched, or divided into pinnules **7**
    6. Sori round, crowded on the reduced tip of the frond *Polystichum*
    6. Sori forming a continuous marginal band around each pinna *Pellaea*
7. Spore-bearing fronds or segments of fronds much different from sterile fronds **8**
7. Spore-bearing fronds and sterile fronds similar **9**
    8. Plants with only one much-divided leaf and one erect stalk, bearing a cluster of sporangia at the top *Botrychium*
    8. Plants with more than one leaf (large ferns) *Osmunda*
9. Sori distinctly at extreme margins of pinnules **10**
9. Sori not produced at margins of pinnules **13**
    10. Indusium produced as a continuation of the inrolled edge of the frond **11**
    10. Indusium shield shaped, fastened by a stalk near its center; not a continuation of the inrolled edge of the frond *Aspidium marginale*
11. Sori in a continuous band at edge of frond **12**
11. Sori distinct, not in a continuous band *Andiantum*
    12. Large ferns, growing in sandy soil *Pteridium*
    12. Small leathery ferns, growing in rock crevices *Pellaea*
13. Sori elongated *Asplenium Filix-femina*
13. Sori round **14**
    14. Indusium cup shaped when young, enclosing the sorus; later splitting into strips that are completely hidden by the sporangia *Woodsia*
    14. Indusium not cup shaped **15**
15. Indusium attached by its margin, soon disappearing *Cystopteris*
15. Indusium attached by its middle; a narrow cleft extending from one side to point of attachment *Aspidium*

Fern

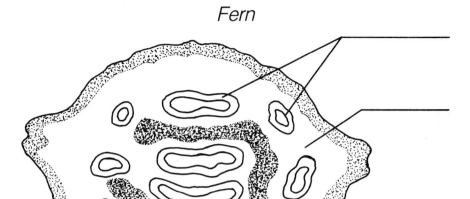

A *Pteridium.* Rhizome cross section

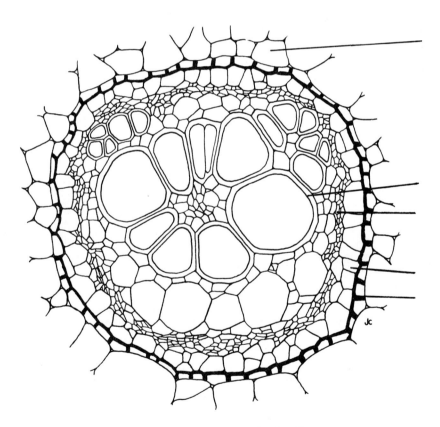

B *Pteridium* rhizome. Vascular bundle (detail)

Fern

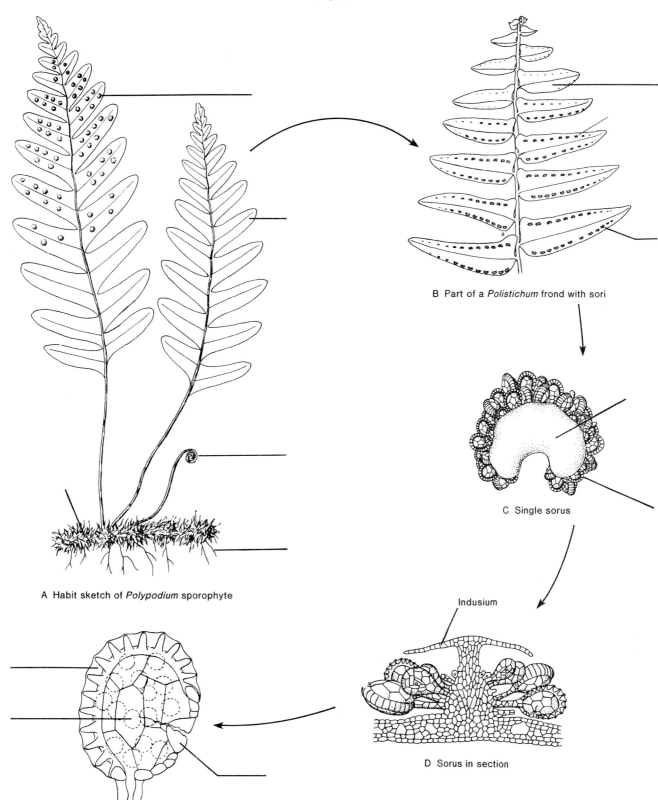

A Habit sketch of *Polypodium* sporophyte

B Part of a *Polistichum* frond with sori

C Single sorus

Indusium

D Sorus in section

E Sporangium

Fern Gametophyte

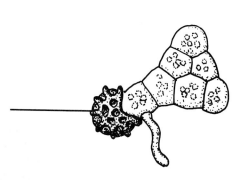

A Fern spore germinating

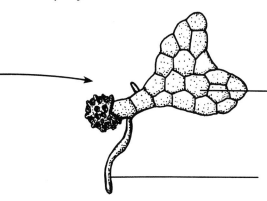

B Young prothallium

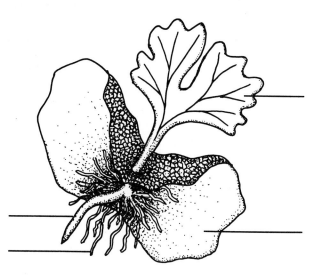

F Young sporophyte
attached to gametophyte

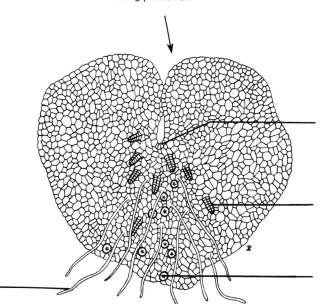

C Mature prothallium with archegonia and antheridia

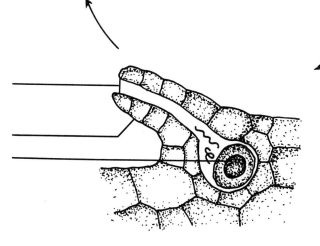

E Archegonium

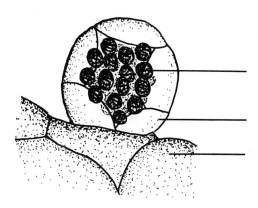

D Antheridium

Exercise 34

The Pine and Other Gymnosperms

Plant Materials

Materials needed are twigs of a common pine (*Pinus strobus, P. sylvatica, P. resinosa, P. ponderosa,* etc.) with attached leaves; dried, preserved, or living female and male pine cones; pine seeds; potted cycad plants, male and female strobili of cycads; *Ginkgo* stem with leaves; female cones of various coniferous trees; prepared slides of pine leaf cross sections, longitudinal sections of pine microsporophylls and microsporangia with pollen grains.

Equipment

A compound microscope, dissecting needles, sharp-pointed curved forceps, and a hand lens (10×) are needed.

Introduction

Seed plants, are divided into gymnosperms and angiosperms: the former group including the coniferous (cone-bearing) trees and their relatives; the latter, the plants bearing what are commonly recognized as true flowers. Several of the plant groups included among the gymnosperms were represented by numerous species during past geological ages but are now either wholly extinct or represented by a few remnants. The pines and their allies, however, still form extensive forests. One of the oldest living plants known is a gymnosperm, the bristlecone pine (4,600 years old). Coniferous trees are important sources of lumber and wood pulp and supply pine tar resins, and turpentine.

A. Pine Sporophyte (Coniferophyta)

Examine the twigs of pine showing the leaves and terminal bud. Where was the terminal bud last year? How can one tell? What is the gain in length during a year? Note that the leaves are borne in clusters surrounded by a sheath on dwarf branches. How many leaves are in a group? How are the dwarf branches arranged on the stem? Note the shape of the leaf, its length, and the shape and dimensions of its cross section. What is its superficial area? In what two conspicuous particulars is it different from an elm or a similar deciduous leaf? What qualities fit this

leaf to live as an evergreen? If material permits, determine how long a pine tree keeps its leaves.

Draw a single cluster of pine leaves in the space provided on worksheet 34.1B.

Examine prepared slides of cross sections of pine leaves. Locate the epidermis, the sclerenchyma layer underlying the epidermis, cutin, mesophyll, endodermis, vascular bundles, resin ducts, and sunken stomata. Note the peculiarly infolded cell walls of the mesophyll.

Label the diagram showing the leaf in cross section (worksheet 34.1C).

The stem and wood of this plant have already been studied (exercise 12). In what conspicuous respect does it differ in microscopic features from the stems of angiosperms?

B. Microstrobili (Staminate Cones)

Examine a cluster of "male" cones (microsporangiate strobili). How large are they? What time of year are they formed? What is their position on the branch? How are the individual sporophylls arranged in the strobilus (cone)? Remove a single microsporophyll. Note the stalk, the expanded tip, and the two microsporangia, or pollen sacs, extending lengthwise on the underside.

Label the drawing of the "male" cones of pine (worksheet 34.1D).

Label the drawing of a microsporophyll showing the two pollen sacs (worksheet 34.1E). Also label the diagram showing the longitudinal section of these structures (worksheet 34.1F).

Crush the contents of a sporangium on a slide, mount in water, and examine under h.p. Note the microspores, or pollen grains. These are two-celled structures, each with two winglike expansions formed by the growth of the outer coat. What purpose may these expansions serve?

Compare with the drawing of a pollen grain of pine (worksheet 34.1G). Label the drawing.

Have you been studying the sporophyte or the gametophyte? Give reasons for this answer. The alternate generation (gametophyte) of the gymnosperms will not be studied in the laboratory.

C. Megastrobili (Ovulate Cones)

Young "female" cones (megasporangiate strobili) are small (7 to 8 mm long) structures appearing in the spring. They are soft, green or reddish in color, and are composed of ovuliferous scales (modified branches) arranged spirally around a central axis to form a strobilus. The scales eventually separate, allowing pollen grains to fall between them, which results in pollination.

Examine living or preserved young "female" cones, note the aforementioned features, and check with the drawing (worksheet 34.2A).

An older (one year old) "female" cone is larger and harder than a young one, and its scales are also more tightly closed (worksheet 34.2B). Carefully remove a single ovuliferous scale from an older cone, and note the two young winged seeds lying exposed on its upper surface (worksheet 34.2C). Examine them under a hand lens, and describe their appearance. Look in the dictionary for the definition of the word *gymnosperm*. Why is it an appropriate term for these plants? Complete the labels.

Label the drawing of an ovuliferous scale showing winged seeds on its upper surface (worksheet 34.2C).

Examine a mature (two years old) female cone. Is this cone erect or pendant upon the tree? Note how the scales have separated allowing the seeds to escape. How does the pendant position of the cone aid in seed dissemination?

Examine a seed. Note the winglike extension of the seed coat. What function does it serve? Carefully remove both the seed coat and the embryo embedded in the female gametrophytic tissue. How many cotyledons are present? What function does the gametophyte tissue perform? Do gymnosperms produce fruit? Explain.

Label the drawing of a pine seed (worksheet 34.2D). Complete all labels on the worksheet.

D. Other Gymnosperms

Inspect the potted cycad plants (Division Cycadophyta), and describe their appearance. What group of pteridophytes do the cycads suggest and in what way? What group of plants do the pines and junipers suggest?

Examine the micro-and megastrobili of cycads contained in the demonstration jars.

All gymnosperms are not evergreen, nor do they all have needlelike leaves. Note the photograph of the maidenhair tree, or *Ginkgo* (Division Ginkgophyta), which is a native of eastern Asia but now commonly cultivated in the United States. In its habit of branching does it suggest a pine tree, a maple, or an oak? Examine the leaves and note the *venation*. The ferns previously studied have leaves with similar veins.

Draw a leaf of the *Ginkgo*, or maidenhair tree, ×2. Show several veins in detail (see fig. 2.2).

Examine the megasporangiate cones of other coniferous trees such as spruce, hemlock, redwood, juniper, or fir. Describe as many as time permits, comparing each with the mature pine cone that you have studied in detail.

Questions

1. What advances have pines made over ferns?
2. What are the seed plants?
3. What does the term *gymnosperm* mean?
4. In what ways does a pine leaf differ from that of an elm?
5. How long does it take for the life history of a pine to be completed?
6. What commercial uses are made of pines?
7. In what regions of North America are the great coniferous forests?
8. Compare the habit of growth of a pine with that of elm or maple. What terms have been applied to these types of branching?
9. How may the excurrent branching habit of a pine or spruce help in preventing injury to the tree by heavy loads of ice and snow?
10. Why is the *Ginkgo* sometimes called a living fossil?
11. Fossil pollens are found in many peat bogs. Explain how pine pollen may be identified in such mixtures.
12. List ways in which gymnosperms differ from angiosperms.

Name _____

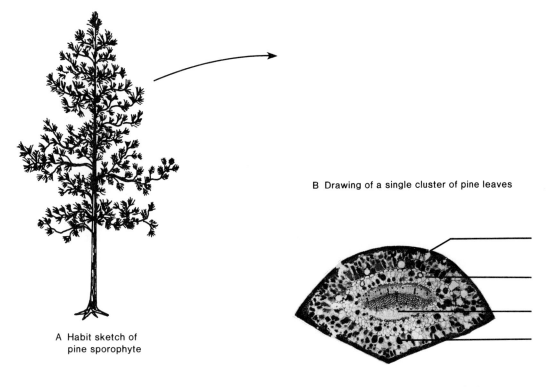

A Habit sketch of
   pine sporophyte

B Drawing of a single cluster of pine leaves

C Cross section of a single pine leaf

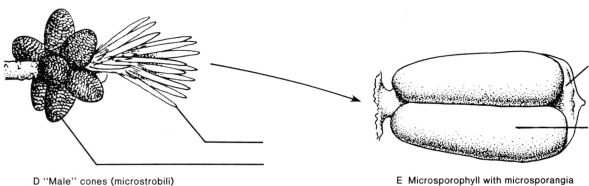

D "Male" cones (microstrobili)

E Microsporophyll with microsporangia

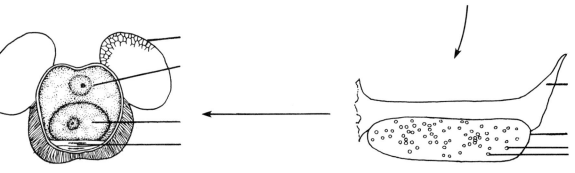

G Pollen grain section

F Longitudinal section of microsporophyll
   with microsporangium and microspores (pollen grains)

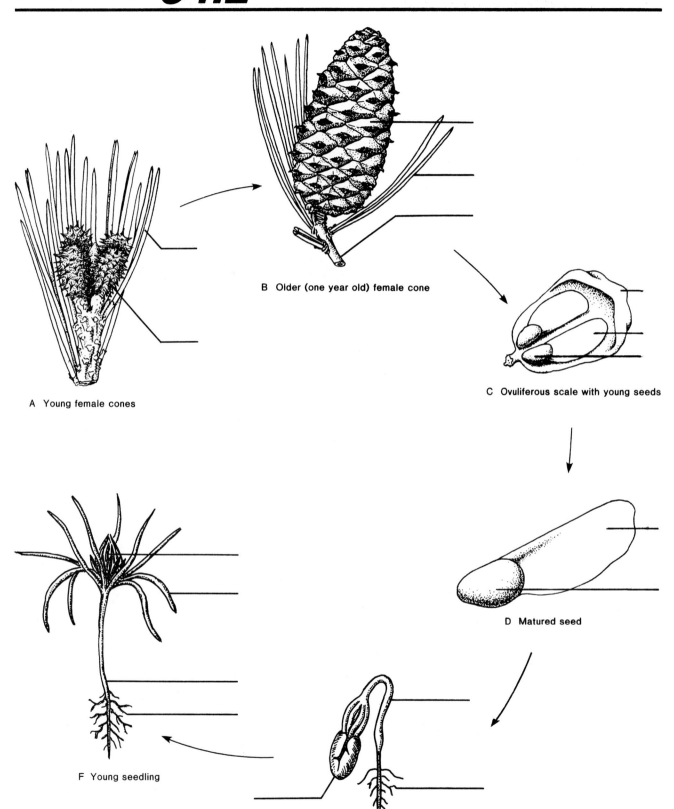

A Young female cones

B Older (one year old) female cone

C Ovuliferous scale with young seeds

D Matured seed

E Germinating seed

F Young seedling

35 Plant Ecology

Introduction

Briefly defined, plant ecology is the study of living plants in relation to their surroundings (environment). Ecology is essentially a field study and necessitates outdoor work under the varying conditions of swamps, rivers, mountains, deserts, and prairies. A knowledge of taxonomy is necessary in order to name the plants. In addition, a background of geology, geography, soil science, statistics, plant anatomy, and especially of plant physiology is required for the proper understanding of modern plant ecology. Plant ecology is thus one of the most inclusive and complicated fields of biological study.

Factors that affect the growth and distribution of plants may be briefly classified under (1) *climatic* (temperature, light, wind, humidity); (2) *edaphic,* or soil characteristics (available water, acidity); and (3) *biotic,* or the effects of living organisms (soil organisms such as bacteria, fungi, nematodes; insects; grazing animals; interference by humans; and competition among plants).

A *plant community* is a group of plants that can thrive together and adjust themselves to the same set of environmental conditions. As environmental conditions change, a new group of plants invade or occupy the region and form a different kind of plant community in the same area. This dynamic process may occur repeatedly in the same area over a long period of time. Each stage that is established prepares the way for the next ensuing stage. This forward progression is called *plant succession. Plant invasion* is the tendency of plants to invade or occupy new areas. The first plants to become established in a new area are termed pioneer plants, and they form a *pioneer community.* Later, such a community may be followed by *intermediate* communities, and finally by the *climax community.* The species that have reached the level of equilibrium with the stable environment of a region constitute the predominant plants of the climax community. The climax community is able to maintain itself continuously as long as the stable environment exists. The climax community is the kind best suited to the stable environment; it represents the highest type of vegetation the area can support and is the culmination of the succession. The type of climax community varies with climate and soil, which are not the same for every locality. *Dominant plants* are those most abundant in a given region, and which, by their growth, control or dominate the vegetation of the area.

Field Study

The instructor will conduct field trips to selected areas. Several ecological situations may be studied, but special attention will be given to the following successions:

1. *Hydrosere.* Plant successions beginning in ponds, lakes, swamps, and marshes are called hydrarch, and the series of different stages of this development is termed a hydrosere. Trace the development from the various hydrophytic plants to the climax community. The climax community in the Midwest may be either grassland (the prairie) or the oak-hickory forest. In other localities the forest climax may be beech-maple-hemlock.
2. *Xerosere.* Plant successions beginning in places of extreme water deficiency are called xerarch, and the series of different stages of this development is termed a xerosere. Trace the development from the various xerophytic plants of bare rock to the climax communities of either prairie, oak-hickory, or other forest associations.

Other successions may be studied as time and local conditions permit. A study may be made of the typical associations and successions of flood plains, forest edge, dunes, cliffs, overgrazed pastures, vacant lots, burned areas, and flooded places.

In the aforementioned studies make complete notes of all factors that can be recognized as affecting plant growth and distribution. List the important plants in each succession, the invaders, relicts, or others as pointed out by your instructor. After all field notes, diagrams, and maps have been made, you are required to write a brief, connected account of the plant successions of each situation studied. Keep all events in the proper order of development. Samples of water plants, xerophytic, and mesophytic forms should be collected and brought into the laboratory for a study of their ecological anatomy. Sketches, diagrams, and notes accumulated from the anatomical study of these plants are to be included in your final report.

Ecological Plant Anatomy

Water is probably the single most important factor affecting the growth and development of plants. Plants may be roughly classified according to their structural and physiological adaptations in respect to the water supply.

1. *Xerophytes* are plants that grow habitually in arid or semiarid regions and have developed structural and physiological features to enable them to withstand excessive dryness.
2. *Hydrophytes* are plants that grow habitually in water or very wet soil. They may be floating, submerged, or amphibious.
3. *Mesophytes* are plants that habitually grow in regions of moderate water supply; they are the common plants of forest, prairie, and meadow. Due to the variation of light received, they are differentiated into sun and shade forms.
4. *Halophytes* are plants that habitually grow in soils or wet places having a very high salt content; they absorb water with difficulty because of this high-solute concentration and may be said to live under conditions of physiological drought. They may resemble xerophytes in structure. Why? Intermediate forms are found between each of the types above, and all degrees of intermediate structural adaptations occur.

In the anatomical study of these forms, attention should be given to the following features: epidermis and cutin, stomata, character and thickness of the cortex and stele, type of central vascular cylinder, structure of leaves, water storage tissues, mucilage cells, structure and branching of roots, and the types of trichomes and spines. Make a table showing these features as they occur in the plants studied. Take brief notes, and make quick, diagrammatic drawings of the parts to include in the final report.

A. Xerophytes

Examine plants of *Aloe, Gasteria, Opuntia,* various cacti, sagebrush, *Verbascum,* Russian thistle, or any xerophytic plants you may have collected during field trips.

Make freehand sketches of sections of the stem of *Opuntia,* and of the leaves of the other forms, and examine microscopically. Tabulate the xerophytic structures brought out in this way, noting especially cutin, epidermis, and other protective outer coverings; water storage, mucilage cells; and the position and structure of stomata.

Draw in outline the anatomical features characteristic of these xerophytic plants. Include bristles of *Opuntia* and hairs of *Verbascum* among the structures studied in this way.

B. Hydrophytes

Elodea. Examine living *Elodea* plants. Lift a plant out of the water. What happens? What does this suggest as to the mechanical tissue? Is there a definite base of the stem to which the roots are attached? Are there any roots? If so, where do they arise? What can you suggest as to their function?

Make a water mount of a cross section of the stem, and examine microscopically. Is there any suggestion of an epidermis? a vascular-cylinder? If so, to what extent is it developed? Where does photosynthesis take place? What is the function of the large air spaces? Compare this section of the stem with a prepared slide of the same. What are the advantages of each? What is aerenchyma?

Make a diagrammatic drawing of a cross section of the *Elodea* stem, labeling fully.

Vallisneria. How does *Vallisneria* compare with *Elodea* as to the leaves, stem, and roots? How does this plant spread? What differences as to habit of growth would you deduce from a comparative study of these two forms?

Make sections of the leaves, rhizomes, and roots. How does the plant compare with *Elodea* as to structure?

Typha. Make sections of the leaves, rhizomes, and roots. Note the large air chambers and prominent diaphragms in the leaf, the aerenchyma of the rhizome and root. How does this plant compare in structural details with *Elodea?*

Make diagrammatic sketches of the cross section of a leaf, a rhizome, and a root of cattail. Label fully.

Study other forms provided, and make brief notes and quick sketches as directed by your instructor. Note the free-floating forms: duckweed, water hyacinth, *Salvinia,* and *Azolla.* How are these plants adapted to an aquatic habitat?

C. Mesophytes

Mesophytes typically occur in areas where the water supply is intermediate between that of xerophytic (extremely arid) or hydrophytic (extremely or always wet) habitats. This water supply may fluctuate greatly during the year from severe drought conditions to severe flooding, but usually enough water is present at the right time to maintain plants during their growing season.

Typical mesophytes have extensive and functional root systems; produce an abundance of large, thin leaves with thin cuticles; and have numerous stomata.

Examples of herbaceous mesophytic plants include bean, *Coleus,* geranium, tobacco, sunflower, castor bean, and most crop and flower-garden plants. Examples of woody mesophytes include nonconiferous trees and shrubs such as lilac, privet, maple, basswood, redbud, hackberry, ash, *Catalpa,* beech, hickory, and most fruit trees.

Study freehand sections or prepared slides of mesophytic leaves in cross section noting the character of the epidermal regions, the thickness of cuticle, and the character of the mesophyll tissues as compared with similar features in cross sections of xerophytic and hydrophytic leaves.

Draw a group of cells from the upper epidermal region of a mesophytic, a hydrophytic, and a xerophytic leaf, indicating accurately the thickness of the cuticle on each leaf. Include any water storage tissues. Be prepared to discuss the anatomical similarities and differences of these plants.

D. Halophytes

Study prepared slides showing cross sections of the stem of *Salicornia,* a salt marsh plant. Do its characteristics most resemble those of the xerophytes or the hydrophytes you have studied? Suggest probable functions of the structures found in *Salicornia.*

Make an outline drawing of a cross section of the stem of *Salicornia* noting significant details of its structure. Label fully.

List several other halophytic plants, and give the localities in which they grow. What features enable halophytes to grow in salt marshes and near salt lakes and seashores?

E. Ecology Seminars for the Classroom

When it is impossible to conduct field studies in ecology, a teacher may profitably substitute one or more classroom seminars on ecology, using as source material any one or all of the selected references that follow. Even when field studies can be made, such seminars should greatly broaden a student's understanding of ecology.

The following references represent special and serious efforts by their publishers to inform everyone about the vital and enormously complex problems involving modern ecology:

Acid Rain: Scourge From the Skies. Robert Collins. *Reader's Digest,* January 1981.
Acid Rain: The Bitter Dilemma. Jennifer Angyal, *Carolina Tips,* September 1980. Burlington, North Carolina: Carolina Biological Supply Co.
Ecology and Environmental Readings (18 articles). From *The Scientific American,* 1980. San Francisco, Calif.: W. H. Freeman and Co.
Ecology, Evolution and Population Biology. Readings from Scientific American. Introduced by Edward O. Wilson. 1974. San Francisco, Calif.: W. H. Freeman & Company.
Environment: Readings for Teachers. Edited by J. W. George Ivany. Contains various readings which will assist the teacher in exploring various stands on the environmental issue. 1972. Reading, Mass.: Addison-Wesley Publishing Co.
Foundations for Today. A joint publishing venture between Wm. C. Brown Company Publishers, Dubuque, Iowa, and Bioscience magazine containing a total of 58 articles selected from those previously published in Bioscience. All books edited by Robert S. Leisner and Edward J. Kormondy.

Volume I—*Population and Food.* Contains 14 articles dealing with the biggest problems in our everyday culture—ecology and evolution, 1971.
Volume II—*Pollution.* Contains 23 articles dealing with the problem of pollution in our ecosystem, 1971.
Volume III—*Ecology.* Contains 21 articles dealing with the human behavior that has precipitated our recent ecology problems, 1971.
Global Ecology: Readings Toward a Rational Strategy for Man. Edited by John P. Holdren and Paul R. Ehrlich. Contains 31 papers reprinted from various sources. 1971. New York: Harcourt Brace Jovanovich.
Man and His Environment series. A series of brief, nontechnical books providing indepth coverage of selected topics relating to man and his environment. Editors: John Bardach, Marston Bates, and Stanley Cain. New York: Harper & Row.
Man and His Environment: Food by Lester R. Brown and Gail Finsterbusch, 1972.
Man and His Environment: Climate by David M. Gates, 1972.
Man and His Environment: Waste by Wesley Marx, 1971.
Man and His Environment: Law by Earl Finbar Murphy, 1971.
Man and the Ecosphere: Readings from Scientific American. Edited by Paul R. Ehrlich, John P. Holdren, and Richard W. Holm. Contains reprints of outstanding articles published in the Scientific American during the past 15 years. 1971. San Francisco, Calif.: W. H. Freeman & Company.
Man's Impact on Environment. Edited by Thomas R. Detwyler. Contains articles selected from a variety of published sources. 1971. New York: McGraw-Hill.
Science Compendium series. Available from American Association for the Advancement of Science, Washington, D.C. Edited by Philip H. Abelson.
Energy: Use, Conservation and Supply, 1974. *Food: Politics, Economics, Nutrition and Research,* 1975.
Population: Dynamics, Ethics and Policy by Priscilla Reining and Irene Tinker, 1975.
Materials: Renewable and Nonrenewable Resources by Philip H. Abelson and Allen Hammond, 1976.
The Survival Equation: Man, Resources and His Environment. Edited by Roger Revelle, Ashok Khosla, and Maris Vinovskis. Contains 38 articles reprinted from various sources. 1971. Boston, Mass.: Houghton Mifflin.

F. Ecology Projects for Class or Individual Study

Because ecology is such a broad and comprehensive subject, one should be able to study at least some aspect of it, however small, practically anywhere. Users of this manual may be in widely scattered locations and in widely varying ecological situations. The following projects may aid in selecting topics from almost any area in the temperate zone. A teacher should survey his own locality and select the best possible ecological sites for class study. If field work must be restricted or is impossible, then one or more classroom seminars in ecology (see part E) as well as suitable motion pictures or lantern slide reviews are strongly recommended.

Acid fog, causes and effects
Acid rain, causes and effects
Aquarium (an ecosystem)
Beach and sand-flat ecology
Bioecology: relationship of insects (pollination), birds, rodents, reptiles, cattle, sheep, and other animals to the plants of various ecological situations
Canals and irrigation ditches
Cleared (treeless) areas
Cliff and rock bluffs ecology
Coral reefs
Cracks in cement walks; spaces between bricks
Dandelions (Why are they so widespread and persistent?)
Deserts
Dry-stream beds and sand bars
Ecological situations in a greenhouse
Ecology at different mountain elevations
Ecology of crop rotation
Ecology of prairies
Endangered species
Environmental-impact statements
Fallen trees (ecology of fungi, mosses, and ferns)
Farm and irrigation ponds
Farm lots and barnyards
Find suitable locations in your vicinity to study the bioecology of one square yard (or larger) areas (quadrats) of ecological situations such as grazed pasture vs. ungrazed or idle pasture; forest floor vs. adjoining grassland; sandy soil vs. black loam; undisturbed grassland vs. nearby area with a much used pathway (make the pathway go through the center of the quadrat)
Flood plains
Forest-floor litter
Grasslands
Gravel pits (a long time unused)
Hay infusion as an ecosystem (adding small amounts of dried livestock manure or commercial fertilizer in an attempt to produce eutrophication)
Invasion of plants into burned areas
Invasion of weeds into neglected meadows, lawns, grasslands, crop lands (corn, wheat, oats, hay fields, etc.), newly disturbed land, fence rows, road sides, etc.
Lake shores with weed beds
Lawn (well cared for vs. neglected or poor lawns)
Litter on vacant lots
Neglected lots and fields
North-facing slope vs. south-facing slope
Overgrazed pasture vs. ungrazed pasture
Peat bogs
Pine barrens
River and stream shores
Roadsides (frequently trimmed vs. seldom or never trimmed)
Salt marsh and brackish water
Sand flats near and away from streams
Swamps and marshy land
Terrarium (an ecosystem)
Timberline ecology
Waterbloom and other water pollution: The quickest and most accurate way to evaluate the degree of pollution in streams, lakes, and ponds is to study the growth responses of individual algae and other plankton organisms found in them. In addition to microscopic examination, chemical tests should be made for dissolved oxygen, nitrates, phosphates, potassium compounds, and other organic or inorganic materials that may be present. Test kits for this are available from all of the supply houses listed in Appendix E.
Weathering stone

Questions

1. What is plant ecology?
2. What is plant succession? Upon what factors does it depend?
3. What is plant recession?
4. How may plants migrate from one area to another?
5. What is competition among plants?
6. What is a pioneer plant? an invader? a relict?
7. How may plant growth fill a pond or lake, eventually resulting in a forest covering the area once occupied by water?
8. List plants according to their adaptations to water supply.
9. What anatomical features are characteristic of each of the plant groups just named?
10. Is plant succession a static or dynamic process? Explain your answer.
11. What is unusual about the osmotic pressure of halophytes? Explain why this osmotic pressure is necessary.
12. Comment briefly on the practical applications of plant ecology.
13. What is aerenchyma?
14. What concentrations of salt (sodium chloride) are halophytic plants able to endure?
15. Comment briefly on the interrelation of plant and animal ecology. What is the practical importance of bioecology?

Exercise 36 — Inheritance in Plants

Plant Materials

Materials needed include ears of corn showing the results of monohybrid and dihybrid crosses, as well as seeds of tobacco, corn, sorghum, and tomato. Ears of corn showing the results of monohybrid and dihybrid crosses, as well as seeds to produce the seedling populations to be counted, may be obtained from botanical and biological suppliers listed in appendix E.

Equipment

Flats with soil for growing seeds, handlens, colored pencils.

Introduction

The basic mechanism of inheritance was first discovered in plants. Gregor Mendel, an Austrian monk, carefully analysed the pattern of the inheritance of several traits in garden peas and reported on his findings in 1866. He succeeded where others failed because he identified readily observed, contrasting traits (phenotypes) and followed each trait by itself through several generations. A look at one of his experiments will illustrate his logic and define the terms needed to understand classical genetics.

Mendel took pure lines of yellow-seeded peas and crossed them with a pure line of green-seeded peas (P_1 = parental generation). The offspring (F_1 = first filial generation) were all yellow seeded. When the F_1 plants were crossed (bred) with each other the second generation (F_2) had both yellow (6,022) and green (2,001) seeds. To explain these results, Mendel derived a set of natural laws. The law of unit characters, as stated by Mendel, said that the factors of inheritance (now called **genes**) occur in pairs. His law of segregation states that only one of the pair is passed on to the next generation by means of a gamete or spore. The law of dominance states that there are alternate forms of the factor (**allele** = alternate form) and one form may mask the expression of the other. In Mendel's experiment, yellow peas were caused by the **dominant** factor while the green peas were the expression of the **recessive** factor. What takes place can be illustrated as follows:

P_1	Yellow seeds (GG) $\times$ green seeds (gg)	
gametes	(G) or (G)	(g) or (g)
F_1	All are Yellow seeded (Gg)	

Notice that the genetic makeup of the yellow-seeded plants in the parent generation (GG) is different from that of the F_1 (Gg). While both have the yellow *phenotype*, they are of different *genotypes*. The pure-line yellow of the parent generation is *homozygous* because both alleles are identical. The hybrid, yellow-seeded plants of the F_1 are *heterozygous* since their alleles are different. What would you call the genotype of the green-seeded plants? The recessive phenotype is only expressed when both recessive genes are present or when there is no dominant gene to mask it. It is for this reason that most genes are identified by a symbol, usually a letter (as g) or a string of letters (as wx for waxy; su for sugary or sweet) that stands for the recessive phenotype. Although geneticists often use the plus ($+$) sign to stand for the dominant gene, we will always use the capital letter (as G). Since this experiment involved only a single pair of alleles it is called a *monohybrid cross*. To understand what happens in the F_1 cross, study the following model. The laws of chance tell us that if there are two forms of the gene, we can expect to encounter either one about 50% of the time and that each of these four possible combinations are equally likely to be found.

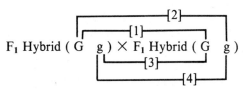

F₁ Hybrid (G   g) × F₁ Hybrid (G   g)

F_2 progeny [1] (GG), [2] (Gg), [3] (gG), [4] (gg)

The model predicts that 3/4 of the offspring will show the dominant phenotype. Mendel's data of 6,022 yellow to 2,001 green (3.01:1) supports the correctness of the model. Mendel's total F_2 data, for all seven traits examined, show 14,949 dominant phenotypes and 5,010 recessive phenotypes; a 2.984:1 ratio close to the 3:1 ratio predicted.

In peas, red (or purple) flowers are dominant and white are recessive. For each of the following crosses, give the genotypes and the percentage of each phenotype. Complete the following information:

Parental Genotypes	Offspring Genotypes	Phenotypes
red (WW) × red (WW)	WW, WW, WW, WW	All four red
red (WW) × red (Ww)		
red (WW) × white (ww)		
red (Ww) × red (Ww)		
red (Ww) × white (ww)		
white (ww) × white (ww)		

All the possible combinations in classical Mendelian genetics are represented in the preceding table. If you learn these crosses, you should be able to solve any classical genetics problem.

A. Monohybrid Cross: Complete Dominance

1. Examine the trays of plants of F_2 populations. Count the number of plants of each phenotype in each tray. Calculate the ratio to determine the F_1 parental genotypes. For example, if in a tray of 50 corn seedlings 26 were green and 24 were white in color, the ratio would be 1:1 (26:24). A glance at the six sample crosses completed earlier shows that only if the parents are of the genotypes Aa × aa will a 1:1 ratio be obtained. Possible traits to observe might include the following:

   sorghum: red/green, green/white
   tomato: cut leaf/broad (potato) leaf, normal/
      hairless

2. Examine seed traits in corn. A strain of corn-producing pure (homozygous) red kernels (CC) is crossed with a strain producing pure white kernels (cc). Red is dominant, and the resulting F_1 ears all bear red heterozygous kernels (Cc). When the F_1 is self-pollinated, the resulting F_2 ears bear both red and white kernels.

   Working in pairs, count the number of red and white kernels on one F_2 ear without removing the kernels. How many red are there? How many white? What is the ratio of red to white? Tabulate the numbers obtained by each pair of students and add these figures to get a grand total for the class. What ratio of red-to-white kernels is now obtained? Why is the ratio derived from larger numbers of kernels more reliable than the ratio from a single ear? Enter the tabulations and totals in your notes.

   Similar ratios are obtained when a strain of corn producing homozygous starchy kernels (SuSu) is crossed with a pure strain producing sweet (susu) kernels.

3. Complete worksheet 36.1 by placing the letters of a correct genotype beside the drawing of each flower. You may show the correct phenotype by shading each drawing with a felt pen or a colored pencil or by writing the name of the color next to each flower.

B. Monohybrid Cross: Incomplete Dominance

It was found that some plants when crossed did not follow Mendel's laws, or so it seemed. Red four-o'clocks (*Mirabilis Jalapa L.*), when crossed with white-flowered plants, did not yield red flowers in the F_1 generation but instead all were pink. What is the genotype of the F_1 plants? Manufacture of the red pigment is controlled by the dominant gene (C). The white plants (cc) have no dominant genes and so make no pigment. The heterozygous F_1 plants (Cc) have half the number of dominant genes that the red (CC) flowered plants have; therefore, less pigment is manufactured and the flowers appear pink.

1. Complete worksheet 36.3 by placing the letters of the correct genotype next to each flower. You may show the correct phenotype by coloring the drawing or by writing the name of the color next to the flower.

2. Examine trays of tomato or soybean seedlings with the phenotypes green, yellow-green, and yellow. Count the seedlings of each type and calculate the phenotype ratio. What is the genotype of each?

C. Dihybrid Cross: Unrelated Traits

When Mendel crossed yellow round-seeded peas with green wrinkled peas, the F_1 offspring were all yellow and round seeded. When these were selfed (crossed with each other), two new phenotypes appeared in the F_2 generation. The results were 315 with round, yellow seeds; 101 with wrinkled, yellow seeds; 108 with round, green seeds; and 32 had wrinkled, green seeds. This is close to a 9:3:3:1 ratio. Analysis of these data led Mendel to formulate his law of independent assortment, which states that the factors (genes) for any unrelated traits will segregate independently of each other into gametes or spores and will be recombined randomly in the formation of a zygote. The biologist William S. Sutton in 1902, after reading Mendel, stated that Mendel's factors (genes) behave exactly the way chromosomes do in meiosis and fertilization. Where then must the genes be located?

Finding two genes in the same zygote is the result of two chance events; (1) the splitting of the gene pair in the parent with one of the two going to a gamete and (2) the meeting of two different gametes in fertilization. The laws of probability tell us that the chance of a number of independent events occurring together is equal to the product of the chances of each event occurring separately. Analysis of Mendel's peas illustrates how this works. Since the F_1 is a hybrid and has yellow, round seeds, it follows that the yellow, round, pure-line parent carried two pairs of dominant genes (GGWW) and the purebred, green-wrinkled parent carried the recessive genes (ggww). The F_1 plants (GgWw) are heterozygous for both pairs of genes. If we treat this as the product of two individual crosses, we can calculate the probable phenotypes. The seed-color cross ($Gg \times Gg$) yields 3/4 yellow ($G-$) and 1/4 green (gg). The shape cross produces ($Ww \times Ww$) 3/4 round ($W-$) and 1/4 wrinkled (ww). There are four possible combinations of these traits. The expected number of yellow-round will be $3/4 \times 3/4 = 9/16$. Yellow-wrinkled will be $3/4 \times 1/4 = 3/16$. Green-round will be $1/4 \times 3/4 = 3/16$. While green-wrinkled will be $1/4 \times 1/4 = 1/16$. This gives us a 9:3:3:1 ratio for this type of cross which matches the experimental data.

A trihybrid cross can be found by calculating the product of each of the three, monohybrid crosses involved. This method can be extended to calculate the probabilities for any number of genes.

1. Examine the trays with F_2 dihybrid populations. Count the number of plants of each phenotype in each tray. Determine the phenotype ratios. Traits to observe might include the following: corn—tall/dwarf, green/albino, or green/albino (yellow and white), which would give a 9:3:4 ratio. Consult a genetics book to find out why.

2. Seed traits in corn. A pure strain of corn producing purple-starchy kernels (RRSuSu) is crossed with a pure strain producing white-sweet kernels (rrsusu). Purple and starchy are dominant, and the resulting F_1 ears all bear purple-starchy, heterozygous kernels (RrSusu). When the F_1 is self-pollinated, the resulting F_2 generation contains the 16 genotypic combinations characteristic of dihybrids. How many phenotypes are there?

   Working in pairs, carefully count the number of kernels of each phenotype appearing on a single F_2 ear. What new combinations are found? Why is it possible to get combinations of characters different from either parent plant? What phenotypic ratio is obtained in a dihybrid cross of this type? Tabulate the results obtained by each pair of students, and add them to secure a grand total. What ratio is represented by this total? Is this ratio characteristic of a simple dominant-recessive type of dihybrid cross? Enter the tabulations and totals in your notebook.

Examine any other ears of corn provided. From the phenotype ratio, determine the genotypes of the F_1 parents that produced each ear examined.

Sometimes several pairs of genes interact to modify a single phenotype such as the weight of a fruit. Such a trait is called a *polygenic trait*. Most continually variable traits like fruit size are polygenic. Remember, dihybrid ratios hold true only when the genes are located on separate chromosomes. Genes located on the same chromosomes are said to be linked and will segregate together.

D. Linked Genes: Crossing-Over and Maps

One of the first examples of genes that did not sort independently was provided by William Bateson and R. C. Punnett in 1906. When they crossed sweet peas having purple flowers and long pollen with ones having red flowers and round pollen, the F_1 were all purple and long. The F_2 did not give a 9:3:3:1 ratio; and when the F_1 was crossed with the homozygous, recessive, red-round peas instead of obtaining a 4:4:4:4 ratio, they found 7 purple long (BbLl), 1 purple round (Bbll), 1 red long (bbLl), 7 red round (bbll). The explanation that this was caused by the two genes being located on the same chromosome and therefore linked was provided by T. H. Morgan who had obtained similar results with fruit flies.

If the color and the pollen-shape genes were perfectly linked, there should be only two phenotypes as a result of the test cross. What would they be? How could the BbLl parent produce Bl and bL gametes? The puzzle was solved when it was found that the chromosomes, when they paired in meiosis, actually exchanged parts. Cytological evidence for this crossing-over was provided by Creighton and McClintock in plants using a mutant variety of corn. (fig. 36.1)

If breakage and crossing-over are equally probable at any place along a chromosome, then it will follow that the greater the distance between two genes, the greater the frequency of crossing-over will occur. Crossover frequency can then be used to map gene distance on a chromosome. If gene A crosses over with gene B 20% of the time, the genes are said to be 20 units apart. If gene C is 30 units from A but only 10 units from B, then the order of genes on this chromosome would have to be either CBA or ABC. The order of genes could not be CAB or BCA. With the aid of a diagram show why this is so. To understand how a gene works, or fails to work, its location on a chromosome must be known. Radioactive tracer molecules are now used to help locate genes.

E. Molecular Genetics

Each gene controls one primary function in an organism by the synthesis of a protein or a polypeptide chain that is a part of it. The sequence of amino acids in the polypeptide is specified by an exact sequence of nucleotides on the DNA molecule located at a particular place on the

Figure 36.1 Demonstration of the cytological basis for crossing over given by Creighton and McLintock in 1931

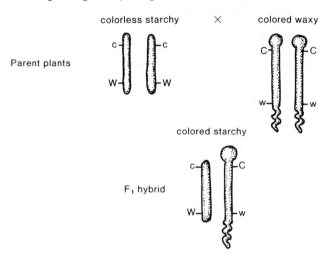

colorless starchy   ×   colored waxy

Parent plants

colored starchy

F_1 hybrid

Hybrid was test crossed with the homozygous recessive

colorless waxy

The test cross results yielded not only the expected parental types but two new recombinant types as well

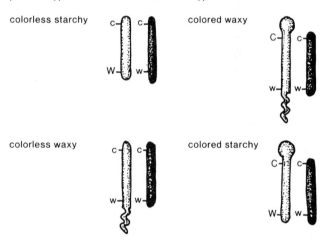

colorless starchy   colored waxy

colorless waxy   colored starchy

Each recombinant type had its own unique chromosome, which proved that an actual physical exchange had taken place.

chromosome. See figure 36.2 (DNA). Discussion of the mechanism of gene action can be found in your textbook. Laboratory investigations in molecular genetics are usually a part of advanced courses in genetics or biochemistry.

F. Genetics Problems

1. When Mendel crossed pure-line, round and wrinkled, seeded peas, the F_1 were all round. The F_2 crosses yielded 5,474 round and 1,850 wrinkled. Give the genotype for each of the phenotypes described.
2. In peas, tall plants are dominant over short plants. Give the genotypes and phenotypes expected in a cross of a heterozygous tall plant with a short plant.
3. In tomatoes, a purple stem (A) is dominant over a green stem (a). If two green-stemmed tomatoes were crossed, would any of the offspring have purple stems? Explain your answer.
4. In soybeans, a gene was found that changed the color of the leaves. The F_1 plants all had leaves that were a light green. When these were crossed with each other, three different phenotypes appeared: dark green, light green, and yellow leaves. Use Y to represent the leaf-color genes. Show the genotypes for each of the individuals involved. Predict the phenotype ratio in the F_2.
5. When some red flowered snapdragons were crossed with some ivory flowered ones, all the offspring were pink flowered. If these pink flowered plants were self-crossed, what percent of the offspring would have red flowers? If the genotype of the ivory plants is (ii) what would be the genotype of the red and pink flowers?
6. In tomatoes, red fruit is dominant to yellow and cut (normal) leaf dominant to potato (entire) leaf. If a yellow-fruited, cut-leaf plant is crossed with a red-fruited, potato leaf plant, what will be the phenotypes and phenotipic ratios of the offspring?
7. Yellow, sphere-shaped squash are homozygous recessive (wwss). A white, disc-shaped squash is crossed with a yellow sphere squash. The offspring produced are 12 white disc, 13 white sphere, 11 yellow disk, and 10 yellow sphere. Give the genotypes of each phenotype, and show how this particular ratio was obtained.

Figure 36.2 DNA molecule from a single cell (Courtesy of
H. L. Dean)

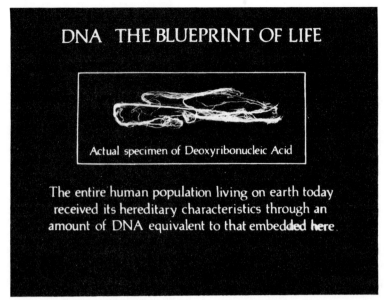

DNA THE BLUEPRINT OF LIFE

Actual specimen of Deoxyribonucleic Acid

The entire human population living on earth today
received its hereditary characteristics through an
amount of DNA equivalent to that embedded here.

8. A long, green-fruited watermelon was crossed with a short, stripe-fruited watermelon. When the F_1 were self-crossed, the F_2 yielded 19 short green, 6 short striped, 5 long green, and 2 long striped watermelons. Identify the dominant and recessive genes, and give the genotypes of the parents and the F_1 plants.

9. In radishes, a round-shaped, white radish was crossed with a long-shaped, red variety. The F_1 were all oval and purple. The F_2 yielded 8 round white, 15 round purple, 9 round red, 16 oval white, 7 long white, 32 oval purple, 16 oval red, 14 long purple, and 9 long red radishes. Give the genotypes for each of the phenotypes found.

10. In squash, a plant that produces a four-pound fruit has the genotype (mmnn) while a plant that produces a six-pound fruit has the genotype (MMNN). A cross of the two produces a squash with a five-pound fruit. If you cross two squashes with five-pound fruits, what phenotypes would you expect to find and how many would there be of each type? Give a genotype for each different fruit.

11. In tomatoes, a homozygous tall plant with smooth-skinned fruit (DDPP) was crossed with a homozygous dwarf plant with peach (hairy) fruit (ddpp). The tall smooth F_1 plant was test crossed to a dwarf peach plant. The test cross results were 94 tall and smooth, 6 tall and peach, 5 dwarf and smooth, and 95 dwarf and peach. Are these genes linked? If they are, what percentage of the plants are crossovers?

12. The following genes are located on chromosome 6 in corn: yellow endosperm (Y), purple plants (Pl), and salmon silk (sm). The Y gene is located 13 units from one end of the chromosome, and its crossover frequency is 42% with sm and 31% with Pl. The crossover frequency between sm and Pl is 10%, or 10 crossover units. Draw a map of corn chromosome 6 to show the location of these three genes.

Dominant-Recessive Type of Inheritance in Garden Pea Flower Color

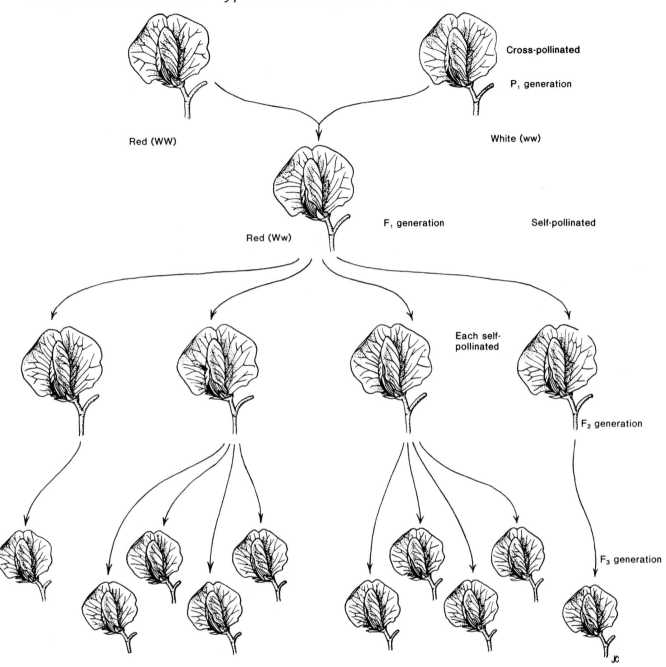

Show the phenotype of each flower in the F₂ and F₃ generations
by shading a pink or red color as necessary with a red pencil.
Indicate the genotype by placing the proper letters beside each
flower of the F₂ and the F₃ generations.

Worksheet 36.2

Name _____

Incomplete Dominance (Blending) Inheritance Four O'Clock Flower Color

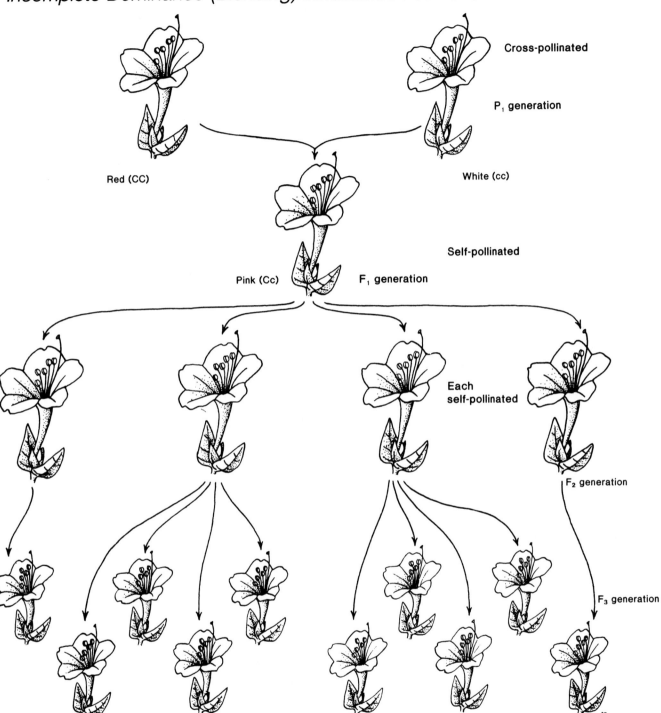

Cross-pollinated

P_1 generation

Red (CC)

White (cc)

Self-pollinated

Pink (Cc) F_1 generation

Each self-pollinated

F_2 generation

F_3 generation

Show the phenotype of each flower in the F_2 and F_3 generations
by shading or coloring as necessary with a red pencil. Indicate
the genotype by placing the proper letters beside each flower
of the F_2 and the F_3 generations.

263

A Appendix
Chemicals, Reagents, and Special Materials

Acetic acid (45%). Add 45-ml glacial acetic acid to 55-ml distilled water.

Acetone.

Ammonium hydroxide, concentrated.

Bacto agar.

Baryta water. Dissolve 3 grams of barium chloride and 21 grams of barium hydroxide in 1 liter of water. Filter and store in a tightly stoppered bottle.

Benedict's solution for sugar test.
A. Dissolve 173 grams of sodium citrate and 100 grams of anhydrous sodium carbonate in 600 ml of hot distilled water. Filter.
B. Then dissolve 17.3 grams cupric sulfate in 150 ml distilled water and slowly add to "A" above with constant stirring. Dilute this to 1 liter.

Chloroform.

Chlorophyll. A strong alcoholic (80% or stronger) solution.

Clove oil.

Cornmeal agar.

Cupric acetate (10%). Dissolve 10 grams cupric acetate in 100-ml water.

Eosin solution (1%). Dissolve 1 gram eosin in 100-ml water.

Ethanol (grain alcohol), various dilutions from 50% to 100%.

Ether.

F.A.A.:
Ethyl alcohol (95%) .... 50 ml
Glacial acetic acid .... 5 ml
Formaldehyde (37–40%) .... 10 ml
Water .... 35 ml

Ferrous sulphate.

Glycerine (10%). Mix 10-ml glycerine with 90-ml water.

Hydrochloric acid, concentrated.

India ink.

Iodine potassium iodide solution (I_2KI). Dissolve 8 grams potassium iodide in 500-ml water, then add 3 grams iodine crystals, and stir until dissolved. Store in a brown bottle.

Karo syrup, white.

Knop's agar:
$Ca(NO_3)_2 \cdot 4H_2O$ .... 0.8 g
KNO_3 .... 0.2 g
KH_2PO_4 .... 0.2 g
$MgSO_4 \cdot 7H_2O$ .... 0.2 g
$FeSO_4$ or $FePO_4$ .... trace
Bacto agar .... 20 g
Distilled water .... 1 liter

Litmus paper.

Nail polish.

Neutral red (0.1%). Dissolve 0.1 gram neutral red in 100-ml water. Filter.

Norit (charcoal).

Oil of peppermint, citronella.

Orcein.

Petroleum ether.

Phenolphthalein.

Phenol red (.04%).

Phloxine (1%). Dissolve 1 gram phloxine in 100-ml water.

Potassium ferricyanide.

Potassium hydroxide solution, (30%). Add 30 grams of KOH pellets to 100 ml of water.

Potassium permanganate crystals.

Pyrogallic acid.

Red food coloring.

Silver nitrate.

Sodium chloride (10%). Dissolve 10 grams sodium chloride in 100-ml water.

Sodium hydroxide solution (5%). Add 5 grams NaOH pellets to 100-ml water.

Strong (10–20%) solutions of phenol, silver nitrate, mercuric chloride, potassium permanganate, and hexachlorophene; full strength Lavoris, Cepacol, Bactine, Sucrets gargle, Listerine, and Micrin; hydrogen peroxide (30% solution).

Sucrose (cane sugar) crystals.

Sudan III.

Sudan IV.

Ten percent solutions of glucose, sucrose, fructose, lactose, galactose, maltose, dextrin, and starch. Add 10 grams of each carbohydrate to 100-ml water.

Tetrazolium chloride (0.5% solution). Dissolve 0.5 grams tetrazolium chloride in 100-ml water.

Vaseline.

B Appendix
Prepared Slides Used in this Manual

Crossed silk fibers.

Evergreen privet leaf, cross sections and paradermal.

Oleandor leaf, cross sections.

Ficus elastica leaf, cross sections.

Castalia leaf, cross sections.

Waterlily leaf, cross sections.

Sunflower stem, cross sections.

Coleus stem tip, longitudinal and cross sections.

Three-year-old basswood stem, cross sections,
or
Liriodendron stem, cross sections.

Pine twigs, 3–5 years old, cross sections.

Pinewood; cross, radial, and tangential sections.

3-year-old oak stem, cross sections.

Oak wood; cross, radial, and tangential sections.

3-year-old maple stem, cross sections.

Maple wood; cross, radial, and tangential sections.

Corn leaf, cross section.

Corn root, cross sections.

Corn stem, cross and longitudinal sections.

Ranunculus root, cross sections.

Onion root tips, longitudinal sections.

Lateral Root origin, root cross section: lupine or willow.

Lily stamens, cross sections.

Lily ovaries, cross sections.

Lily flower buds, cross sections.

Germinating pollen.

Lily anthors, to show meiosis.

Lily ovary, to show meiosis.

Flattened styles and stigmas with pollen tubes.

Capsella embryos.

Ulothrix.

Oedogonium.

Spirogyra.

Fucus receptacles, cross sections.

Polysiphonia combination.

Bacteria: bacillus, coccus, and spirillum.

Bacterial spores: pathological forms.

Root nodules in legume root, cross sections.

Rhizopus zygospores.

Yeast ascospores.

Whole mounts, *Penicillium* and *Aspergillus.*

Peziza apothecium.

Lichen thallus, cross sections with apothecium.

Whole mount, corn smut spores.

Wheat stems to show uredospore and teliospores.

Barberry leaves to show pycnia and aecia.

Mushroom gills, cross sections.

Sections of *Marchantia* thallus, cupules, antheridiophores, archegoniophores, and sporophytes.

Moss protonema.

Anthoceros sporophyte longitudinal section.

Moss capsule, cross and longitudinal sections.

Pteridium rhizome, cross sections.

Fern sorus, longitudinal sections.

Fern prothallia, cross sections with antheridia and archegonia.

Pine leaves (needles), cross sections.

Pine staminate cone, longitudinal sections.

Pine ovulate cone, longitudinal sections.

Pine pollen.

C Appendix
A Guide for Growing Plants Used in this Manual

The suggestions given are for growing plants under standard greenhouse conditions, and it is expected that they will receive regular greenhouse care. Seeds are to be planted 7 mm deep in flats of wet sand or vermiculite unless otherwise indicated. A glass plate (on wooden blocks) placed over a flat will retard water loss. Growth will be slower during winter months and faster during summer months.

Listed below are various growth stages of plants used in this manual as they should appear when grown in a greenhouse during October, November, and December at a temperature of 75° F (24° C).

Plant	Growth stages	Time in days to attain growth stages
Squash	Sprouting	6
	1¼ inch (32 mm)	12
	4 inches (10.2 cm)	19
	5–8 inches (12.7–20.2 cm)	26
Peas	Sprouting	6
	2½ inches (6.4 cm)	12
	4 inches (10.3 cm)	19
	5 inches (12.7 cm)	26
Beans	Sprouting	6
	2 inches (50 mm)	12
	5 inches (12.7 cm)	19
	7 inches (17.5 cm)	26
Corn	Sprouting	6
	2 inches (50 mm)	12
	5–6 inches (12.7–15.2 cm)	19
	8–10 inches (20.2–25.4 cm)	26
Onion. In sandy soil, seeds barely covered	Sprouting	7
	1½ inch (38 mm)	12
	2½ inches (6.4 cm)	19
	4 inches (10.3 cm)	26
	7–8 inches (17.5–20.2 cm)	45
Peanut (Spanish). In sandy soil	Sprouting	12
	3 leaves and cotyledons showing	40
Sunflower	Sprouting	5–6
	8 inches (20.2 cm)	31
	10–14 inches (25.4–35.8 cm)	42

Plants Needing Different Treatment

Beans, Exercise 1

Flowers and small beans are usually present at the same time on a plant 28–35 days after sprouting. Bean plants 50–60 days old seldom have flowers, but the pods are large and well formed.

Buckwheat, Exercise 1

Plant the buckwheat seedlings 7 mm deep in vermiculite; and 7–9 days later transplant the seedlings, one each into a 7.6-cm pot of good soil. They will flower 35–40 days after sprouting and should have both flowers and young fruit in another 15–20 days.

Note: Buckwheat flowers must be pollinated by hand or by bees, or fruit will not develop. To prevent older plants from falling over and breaking, it will be necessary to tie them loosely to bamboo stakes pushed into the soil of a pot.

Wheat or Oats, Exercise 7

Soak wheat or oat seeds overnight in water. Solidly pack the bottom of wooden flats or trays with wet sphagnum moss to a depth of 2.5 cm. Cover them with wet paper towels (5 layers). Pour in soaked seeds to a depth of 18 mm, and cover with 5 layers of wet paper towels. Gently stir or agitate daily to aerate. Keep towels wet. Ready for use in 3–4 days.

Wheat for Guttation, Exercise 8

Plant wheat seeds directly 7 mm deep in 6.4-cm pots of good soil. They will be ready for use in 7–10 days.

Radish Seedlings for Root hairs, Exercise 15

Scatter radish seeds on five layers of wet-paper toweling in a petri dish and cover. They will be ready for use in 48 hours.

Redtop Seedlings for Root Hairs, Exercise 15

Sprinkle redtop (or other grass) seeds on the surface of water filling a 10.3-cm glass bowl. They will be ready for use in 4–6 days.

Adventitious Roots on Cuttings, Exercise 15

Insert cuttings in vermiculite and keep in the shade. They will be ready as follows:

Coleus in 14 days.
Geranium in 30 days.
Tomato in 20 days.

Acknowledgment: Adapted from the University of Iowa Greenhouse Staff Records.

The metric system now used in most countries of the world has been standardized and is known as "Le Systeme International d'Unites," or often referred to simply as SI. It is a decimal system based on units of ten. Only some of the metric units used in biological work will be noted here. The units are as follows:

1. Meter (m) = base unit of length.
2. Liter (1 or ℓ) = base unit of volume.
3. Kilogram (kg) = base units of mass (weight).
4. Degrees Celsius (°C) = unit of temperature replacing both Centigrade degrees (°C) and degrees Fahrenheit (°F).

Some Metric Units and Their Symbols

Unit	Symbol
Micrometer	(μm)
Millimeter	(mm)
Meter	(m)
Kilometer	(km)
Gram	(g)
Kilogram	(kg)
Milliliter	(ml)
Liter	(1 or ℓ)
Degree Celsius	(°C or C)

Prefixes placed before a metric base unit (liter, meter, gram) give a numerical value to that unit equal to that of the prefix added. For example, kilo (k) plus liter (l) becomes kiloliter (kl) and means that a kiloliter is 1,000 times more than 1 liter. Hence a kiloliter = 1,000 liters.

Similarly, deci (d) plus meter (m) becomes decimeter (dm), and means that a decimeter is equal to 0.1 of a meter (or 10 cm).

Note: Micrometer (μm) replaces micron (μ). Milliliter (ml) replaces cubic centimeter (cc). Degrees Celsius (°C) replaces degrees Centigrade (°C).

The symbols designated earlier, and those for other metric units, are just symbols and not abbreviations, so they are written without a period following them (i.e., m—NOT m.). There are no plurals and no capital letters (C for Celsius is an exception).

Numbers with five or more digits are not separated by a comma (i.e., 25,400), but the comma is represented by a space (i.e., 25 400). In addition, any decimal fraction will always have a zero (0) to the left of the decimal point. For example, 0.125—NOT .125.

The spelling *litre* and *metre* is used in SI metrics throughout the world. (The U.S. spelling *liter* and *meter* may also be used.)

Metric Prefixes

	Prefix	Symbol	Meaning
From	Kilo	(k)	1 000 times a metric base unit
Greek	Hecto	(h)	100 times a metric base unit
	Deka	(da)	10 times a metric base unit
From	Deci	(d)	0.1 of a metric base unit
Latin	Centi	(c)	0.01 of a metric base unit
	Milli	(m)	0.001 of a metric base unit

Units of Length

The meter (m) is the base unit of linear measure.

Kilometer (km)	=	1 000 m
Hectometer (hm)	=	100 m
Dekameter (dam)	=	10 m
Meter (m)		
Decimeter (dm)	=	10 cm
Centimeter (cm)	=	10 mm
Millimeter (mm)	=	1 000 μm
Micrometer (μm)	=	1 000 nm
Nanometer (nm)	=	10 A°
Angstrom (A°)	=	10 000 Å = 1 μm

Units of Mass (weight)

The kilogram (kg) is the base unit of mass.

Kilogram (kg)	=	1 000 g
Hectogram (hg)	=	100 g
Dekagram (dag)	=	10 g
Gram (g)		
Gram	=	10 Decigrams (dg)
Gram	=	100 Centigrams (cg)
Gram	=	1 000 Milligrams (mg)
Decigram (dg)	=	0.1 g
Centigram (cg)	=	0.01 g
Milligram (mg)	=	0.001 g

Units of Volume

The liter (l or ℓ) * is the base unit of volume.

Kiloliter (kl)	=	1 000
Hectoliter (hl)	=	100
Dekaliter (dal)	=	10
Liter (l or ℓ) *		
Deciliter (dl)	=	0.1 ℓ
Centiliter (cl)	=	0.01 ℓ
Milliliter (ml)	=	0.001 ℓ

Cubic Measurements

kl³ Cubic kiloliter. For large volumes of fluids. Found in dams, lakes, reservoirs, oil storage tanks.

m³ Cubic meter. Volume of a barn, fieldhouse, astrodome, auditoriums; truckloads of sand, gravel, coal.

l³ Cubic liter. Liquid volumes of l³ liter or more. Gasoline, paints, bottled drinks, volume of grocery products.

ml³ Cubic milliliter. Liquid volumes less than l³. For making up solutions in laboratory work, medical doses, small cans of paint, oils, vegetables, cooking recipes.

μm³ Cubic micrometer. For microscopic volumes. Plant cells, nuclei, volume of tissues, root hairs, trichomes, glands, and similar structures.

Area Measurements

km² Square kilometer. For large areas, such as counties, lakes, states, and oceans.

m² Square meter. For areas of farm and home lots, ponds, farms, estates, rooms in houses and other buildings.

cm² Square centimeter. For areas smaller than 1 m². Size of a paper sheet in this manual, dollar bill, tags and shipping labels, small books, leaf areas.

mm² Square millimeter. For areas larger than 1 mm². Size of small insect wings, insect eyes, area of plant cells in section, a fingernail.

μm² Square micrometer. For microscopic areas. Area of a cell wall, tissue masses, embryonic cells, and bacteria.

Temperature

The Celsius scale, which is used to measure most biological temperatures, is identical to the Centigrade scale. The term *Centigrade* in some countries has other meanings, so the name Celsius (after Ander Cellsius, a Swedish scientist) was adopted to avoid confusion. Study the following comparisons between common readings on the Fahrenheit and the Celsius scales.

To convert from Celsius to Fahrenheit:

$$°F = \frac{9}{5} \text{ (C degrees)} + 32 \text{ to get Celsius degrees}$$

To convert from Fahrenheit to Celsius:

$$°C = \frac{5}{9} \text{ (F degrees)} - 32 \text{ to get Fahrenheit degrees.}$$

Comparisons between Fahrenheit and Celsius temperature scales

212° F	Water boils	100° C
104° F	Hot summer day	40° C
98.6° F	Body temperature	37° C
86° F	Warm summer day	30° C
68° F	Room temperature	20° C
50° F	Cool day	10° C
32° F	Water freezes	0° C
−4° F	Cold winter day	−20° C
−40° F	Only point where readings are identical	−40° C

---

*The script (ℓ) is used instead of the printed (l) whenever the printed (l) might cause confusion. Like when llll is supposed to mean lllℓ (lll liters) and not the number 1 111.

Below is the conversion of selected U.S. Measures to (SI) metric system equivalents. Common measurements in this manual are included here.

U.S. measure		Metric equivalent
1/16 inch	=	1.6 mm
1/8 inch	=	3.2 mm
1/4 inch	=	6.4 mm
5/16 inch	=	7.9 mm
1/2 inch	=	12.7 mm
3/4 inch	=	19.1 mm
1 inch	=	2.5 cm
1¼ inches	=	3.2 cm
1½ inches	=	3.8 cm
2 inches	=	5.0 cm = 50 mm
2½ inches	=	6.4 cm
3 inches	=	7.6 cm
3½ inches	=	9.0 cm = 90 mm
4 inches	=	10.1 cm
5 inches	=	12.7 cm
6 inches	=	15.2 cm
7 inches	=	17.7 cm
8 inches	=	20.3 cm
10 inches	=	25.4 cm
12 inches	=	30.4 cm
15 inches	=	38.1 cm
20 inches	=	50.8 cm
25 inches	=	63.5 cm
30 inches	=	76.2 cm
36 inches (1 yard)	=	91.4 cm
39.37 inches (1 meter)	=	100 cm

Note: To convert from inches to centimeters:
Inches $\times$ 2.5 = cm
To convert from centimeters to inches:
Centimeters $\times$ 0.4 = inches

Botanical and Biological Supplies

Carolina Biological Supply Company
Burlington, North Carolina 27215
or
Gladstone, Oregon 97027

Parco Scientific Company
316 Youngstown Kingsville Road
P.O. Box 595
Vienna, Ohio 44473

Ward's Natural Science Establishment, Inc.
5100 West Henrietta Road
P.O. Box 92912
Rochester, New York 14692
or
11850 East Florence Avenue
Santa Fe Springs (L.A.)
California 90670

Marine Organisms

Marine Biological Laboratory (Supply Department)
Woods Hole, Massachusetts 02543

Gulf Specimen Company
P.O. Box 237
Panacea, Florida 32346

Laboratory Equipment and Chemicals

Central Scientific Company
11222 Melrose Avenue
Franklin Park, Illinois 60131–1332

Clay-Adams Company (dissecting instruments only)
141 East 25th Street
New York, New York 10010

Cole-Parmer
7425 North Oak Park Avenue
Chicago, Illinois 60648

Fisher Scientific Company
(28 regional sales and distribution centers—see catalog)
711 Forbes Avenue
Pittsburgh, Pennsylvania 15219–4729

Matheson Scientific
11 Regional offices in U.S., 3 in Canada—consult catalog for nearest branch

Sargent-Welch Scientific Company
7300 North Linder Avenue
P.O. Box 1026
Skokie, Illinois 60077

Arthur H. Thomas Company
99 High Hill Road at I-295
P.O. Box 99
Swedesboro, New Jersey 08085

Biochemicals

ICN Nutritional Biochemicals
P.O. Box 28050
Cleveland, Ohio 44128

Matheson Scientific
11 Regional offices in U.S., 3 in Canada—consult catalog for nearest branch

Microscopes and Other Instruments

American Optical Company
Instrument Division
Eggert and Sugar Roads
Buffalo, New York 14215

Bausch & Lomb Optical Company
625 St. Paul Street
Rochester, New York 14602

E. Leitz, Inc.
Rockleigh, New Jersey 07647

Nikon Instrument Division
Ehrenreich Photo-Optical Industries
623 Stewart Avenue
Garden City, New York 11530

Swift Instruments, Inc.
P.O. Box 562
San Jose, California 95106

Unitron Instrument Company
66 Needham Street
Newton Highlands, Massachusetts 02161

Carl Zeiss, Inc.
444 5th Avenue
New York, New York 10018

Special Equipment

Edmund Scientific Company
101 E. Gloucester Pike
Barrington, New Jersey 08007

Algae, Bacteria, and Fungi

American Type Culture Collection
12301 Parklawn Drive
Rockville, Maryland 20853

The Culture Collection of Algae
Department of Botany
Indiana University
Bloomington, Indiana 47401

Fungal Genetics Stock Center
Department of Biological Sciences
Dartmouth College
Hanover, New Hampshire 03755

Biological and Ecology Test Kits

Carolina Biological Supply Company
Burlington, North Carolina 27215
or
Gladstone, Oregon 97027

Hach Chemical Company, Sales Dept.
P.O. Box 389
Loveland, Colorado 80539
or
Divisional Office
P.O. Box 907
Ames, Iowa 50010

LaMotte Chemical Products Company
P.O. Box 329
Chestertown, Maryland 21620

Ward's Natural Science Establishment, Inc.
5100 West Henrietta Road
P.O. Box 92912
Rochester, New York 14692
or
11850 East Florence Avenue
Santa Fe Springs, California 90670

Bacteriological and other Media

Difco Laboratories, Inc.
P.O. Box 1058A
Detroit, Michigan 48232

Microscope Slides (Botanical)

Triarch Incorporated
P.O. Box 98
Ripon, Wisconsin 54971

Microscope Slides (Botanical and General)

Carolina Biological Supply Company
Burlington, North Carolina 27215
or
Gladstone, Oregon 97027

Turtox, Inc.
P.O. Box 266
Palos Heights, Illinois 60463

Ripon Microslides, Inc.
Box 262
Ripon, Wisconsin 54971

Seeds

W. Atlee Burpee Company
Philadelphia, Pennsylvania 19132

Vaughans Seed Company
5300 Katrine Avenue
Downers Grove, Illinois 60515

Testing Equipment

Drink-O-Meter Tubes
Luckey Laboratories, Inc.
7252 Osbun Road
San Bernardino, California 92404

Glossary

Abscission separation of fruit, leaf, or other part from plant

Abscission layer a zone of cells in the petiole or other plant structure whose cells separate, and thereby bring about leaf fall, fruit drop, etc.

Absorption intake of substances from the outside

Achene (akene) a dry, indehiscent, one-seeded fruit in which the seed coat is attached to the pericarp at one point only

Adsorption the concentration of molecules or ions on the surfaces of colloidal particles or solid bodies

Adventitious organs arising in unusual positions, as buds from roots, and roots from stems

Agar a gelatinous substance extracted from certain red algae (Rhodophyta), and used as a solidifying agent in the preparation of nutrient media for microorganisms

Aggregate fruit fruit formed from a group of ovaries produced on a single flower

Allele alternate forms of a gene producing contrasting characteristics

Alternate leaves a leaf arrangement with only one leaf at each node

Alternation of generations the alternation of a gamete-producing phase with a spore-producing phase in the life cycle of a plant

Amino acids organic acids, each with a NH_2 group, which combine to form proteins

Amylase an enzyme which digests starch converting it to sugar

Anabolism processes which build complex organic substances from simple materials

Anaerobic respiration respiration in the absence of free oxygen

Anaphase the stage in mitosis or meiosis when the chromosomes are moving toward the poles

Angiosperm one of the flowering plants (the seeds are enclosed in fruits)

Annual a plant which lives only one year

Annual ring the ring of secondary xylem (wood) produced in one year

Annulus a ringlike structure, such as the ring around the mushroom stalk or a fern sporangium

Anther the pollen-bearing part of a stamen

Antheridium a structure in which sperms are produced

Antipodal cells the cells (generally three) in the embryo sac located at the end opposite to the egg

Apetalous a flower without petals

Apical meristem tissue at the tip of a root or stem where cell division occurs

Apothecium a cup-shaped structure lined with asci containing ascospores

Archegonium a flask-shaped, multicellular egg-producing structure

Ascogonium a one-celled structure containing a female gamete in Ascomycetes

Ascomycetes a group of true fungi whose sexually produced spores are formed in sacs called asci

Ascospore a fungus spore formed inside an ascus

Ascus a sac characteristic of Ascomycetes in which ascospores are produced after nuclear fusion and meiosis

Asepalous a flower lacking sepals

Asexual reproduction reproduction which does not involve the fusion of gametes

Axillary bud a bud borne in the upper angle formed by the leaf and the stem; this angle is known as an axil

Bacillus a rod-shaped bacterium

Bacteria the common name for one-celled plants in the division Schizophyta

Bark the tissues of a woody stem or root outside the xylem including vascular cambium, phloem and cork

Basidiomycota (club fungi) true fungi whose sexually produced spores are formed on a basidium

Basidiocarp the multicellular spore bearing structure; the part of a mushroom usually seen

Basidiospore a spore produced on a basidium after meiosis

Basidium a spore-bearing structure in Basidiomycetes; the spores are borne externally, and generally on points called sterigmata

Berry a fleshy fruit, such as tomato and grape, formed from a single pistil; the entire pericarp is fleshy

Biennial a plant requiring two years to complete its life cycle, usually flowering and fruiting the second year only, and then dying

Binomial the generic name and the specific name taken together

Biotic pertaining to life

Blade the expanded part of a leaf

Bract a modified or reduced leaf subtending a flower or inflorescence

Bryophyte any of the mosses or liverworts

Bud an undeveloped branch protected by leaves, scales or bracts

Bud scale a modified leaf enveloping the more tender part of a bud

Bulb an underground stem with fleshy, food-storing, scale leaves; essentially a below-ground bud, for example, onion

Bundle scars small scars within a leaf scar that represent the ends of bundles that entered the leaf

Bundle sheath a cell layer which surrounds the conducting tissues of a vein

Calyptra a cap upon the apex of a moss capsule derived from the archegonium

Calyx the outermost whorl of a complete flower; a collective term for the sepals

Cambium (vascular) a layer of dividing cells located between the xylem and phloem, and which produces secondary xylem and phloem

Capsule the spore case of a moss or liverwort, or a dehiscent dry fruit composed of two or more united carpels (a compound ovary)

Carbohydrate a class of foods composed of carbon, hydrogen, and oxygen, the ratio of elements being 1:2:1

Carotene an orange pigment occurring in certain plastids

Carpel a floral part which bears ovules; a pistil is composed of one or more carpels; the ovary wall

Caryopsis a one-seeded, dry indehiscent fruit in which the seed coat and pericarp are united, for example, a corn grain

Catabolism metabolic processes in which complex materials are changed into simpler compounds, for example, digestion and respiration

Catalyst a substance which influences the rate of a chemical reaction without being consumed in the reaction

Catkin an inflorescence bearing apetalous staminate or pistillate flowers, as in willow

Cell the structural and physiological unit of plants and animals, generally consisting of cytoplasm and nucleus, and also, in plant cells surrounded by a cell wall

Cell sap the solution in a vacuole

Cellulase an enzyme which digests cellulose

Cellulose a carbohydrate formed from glucose, and which is a major constituent of cell walls

Centromere that portion of a chromosome to which a spindle fiber is attached and connects sister chromatids

Chambered pith soft pith interrupted by hard diaphragms arranged crosswise, forming small cavities

Chemotropism a growth movement in response to a chemical

Chlorenchyma parenchyma cells containing chloroplasts

Chlorophylls the green pigments of plants which absorb light used in photosynthesis

Chloroplast a cellular structure (plastid) made up of protoplasm and containing the green pigment chlorophyll

Chromatin a nuclear substance which stains deeply with certain dyes, and from which the chromosomes form during mitosis and meiosis

Chromoplast a colored plastid also containing pigments other than chlorophyll; they are often yellowish or red in color

Chromosome one of the rodlike structures formed from chromatin during mitosis and meiosis; the chromosomes bear genes

Class a taxonomic group of related orders

Climax the terminal community of a succession, and one which maintains itself indefinitely provided no marked environmental changes occur

Coccus a spherical bacterial cell

Coenocytic multinucleate and lacking cross walls; non septate

Coleoptile a sheath around the epicotyl of a grass embryo

Coleorhiza a sheath around the radicle of a grass embryo

Collenchyma living cells whose walls are thickened in the corners

Colony a group of similar organisms living in close association, usually microorganisms as bacteria or protists

Columella the central part of a sporangium or capsule, it does not produce spores

Community a group of organisms of several species living together

Companion cell a long, narrow, nucleated cell associated with a sieve tube in the phloem of flowering plants

Complete flower a flower having sepals, petals, stamens, and a pistil or pistils

Compound leaf a leaf whose blade consists of two or more leaflets

Compound pistil a pistil comprised of two or more united carpels

Conceptacle a cavity containing antheridia or oogonia, or both, in certain brown algae, as in *Fucus*

Conidiophore a hypha which produces conidia

Conidium an asexual fungus spore cut off from the tip of a conidiophore

Conjugation union of like gametes (isogametes) by connecting cells

Conjugation tube a tube connecting one cell with another, and through which a gamete moves

Cork a protective layer of cells (having suberized walls) on stem, root, and certain other surfaces; the outer bark of a woody plant

Cork cambium a layer of dividing cells which forms cork externally; also known as phellogen

Corm an erect, thickened, underground stem lacking fleshy scale leaves, as in gladiolus

Corolla the petals taken collectively; the floral parts just within the calyx, and usually of a bright color

Cortex the primary tissue of a root or stem between the epidermis and the vascular tissue

Cotyledon a seed leaf

Cross-pollination the transfer of pollen from the anther of one plant to the stigma of a flower on another plant

Cuticle a waxy layer secreted by epidermal cells on their outer surface

Cuticular transpiration loss of water vapor through the cuticle

Cutin a waxy, somewhat waterproof substance

Cutting a severed plant part used for propagation

Cyme a flat or convex flower cluster, the innermost flowers of which are the oldest

Cytokinesis the partitioning of one cell into two

Cytology the science of cell structure

Cytoplasm the protoplasm in a cell exclusive of the nucleus, plastids, and other protoplasmic structures of rather definite form

Deciduous refers to plants which shed their leaves at the end of the growing season, and which are bare for part of the year

Dehiscent splitting open in a characteristic manner at maturity

Denitrification the changing of nitrogen compounds into gaseous nitrogen by denitrifying bacteria

Deoxyribose nucleic acid (DNA) the nucleic acid found in the chromosome, combined with a protein as a nucleoprotein; involved in the transmission of hereditary characteristics; site of the genes

Dextrinase an enzyme which digests dextrins

Diastase a group of enzymes which digest starch into glucose

Dicotyledonous plant a flowering plant having two cotyledons or seed leaves in the embryo

Differentially permeable membrane a membrane which permits some substances to pass through, but which stops or restricts the passage of others

Diffusion the movement of molecules from regions of high to regions of low concentration

Digestion the conversion of complex foods, generally insoluble, to simpler substances which are soluble in water

Dihybrid cross a cross between parents differing in two characters

Diploid having two sets of chromosomes, one set coming from one gamete, the second set from the other gamete

Dominant character in heredity, a character which masks the expression of a recessive character

Dormancy a period of reduced activity in seeds, bulbs, buds, etc., during which growth does not occur

Double fertilization in angiosperms where one sperm fuses with the egg, and the second sperm fuses with the polar nuclei to produce zygote and endosperm

Drupe a fleshy fruit in which the pericarp (ripened ovary wall) is differentiated into a stony endocarp surrounding the seed, a fleshy mesocarp, and a thin external exocarp

Early wood the more porus wood formed at the beginning of a growing season; spring wood

Ecology the study of communities of living things and the relationships among organisms and with their environment

Edaphic factors soil factors

Egg female gamete or sex cell

Elater a hygroscopic elongated structure that aids in spore dispersal; seen in *Marchantia* and *Equisetum*

Embryo a young plant developed from a zygote (fertilized egg)

Embryo sac a sac characteristically containing an egg, two synergids, two polar nuclei, and three antipodal cells; it is the female gametophyte in flowering plants, and develops from a megaspore

Endocarp the inner pericarp layer, often stony, as in a drupe

Endodermis the innermost cortex layer, clearly evident in roots

Endoplasmic reticulum the interconnected network of membranes that constitute a part of the submicroscopic structure of the protoplasm

Endosperm in angiosperms usually a triploid nutritive tissue surrounding the developing embryo which, depending on the species, may or may not be present in the mature seed; in gymnosperms the endosperm is replaced by female gametophyte tissue

Enzyme an organic catalyst containing protein and which speeds up a specific reaction

Epicotyl the part of the embryo above where the cotyledons are attached; it consists of a stem tip and several minute embryonic leaves; it is also known as the plumule

Epidermis the outermost cell layer on leaves, roots, and stems before cork is formed

Epigynous flower a flower in which the floral parts appear to arise from the top of the ovary

Evolution changes in the genetic composition of a population with the passage of each generation

Exocarp the outer layer of the pericarp

F₁ in genetics the first generation offspring following a cross; F_2 denotes the second generation

Family in classification, a category below an order; it includes one or more related genera

Fat a food composed of carbon, hydrogen, and oxygen, with the latter being proportionately less than in carbohydrates

Fertilization the fusion of two gametes to form a zygote

Fiber a long, thick-walled cell serving to strengthen the tissue

Fibrous root system a root system in which all roots have about the same diameter with many the same length

Filament of stamen the stalk of a stamen supporting the anther

Fission a simple form of asexual reproduction occurring in unicellular organisms whereby one cell divides to form two organisms

Flagellum a whiplike, cytoplasmic extension of certain unicellular organisms, zoospores, etc., which propels the cells

Floral tube a tube resulting from the fusion of the basal parts of sepals, petals, stamens, and a pistil

Flower the reproductive structure of angiosperms, often consisting of sepals, petals, stamens, and a pistil

Flower buds buds containing undeveloped flowers

Follicle a dehiscent dry fruit of one carpel, splitting when ripe along one side only as in milkweed

Food chain a sequence of oganisms feeding on each other to acquire energy and organic building blocks

Foot an absorbing organ of the sporophyte of bryophytes, ferns, and certain other vascular plants; the foot is anchored in the gametophyte, from which nourishment is secured

Frond a fern leaf

Fruit the ripened ovary, or group of ovaries, together with other adhering parts of the flower

Fucoxanthin a pigment of brown algae

Funiculus the stalk connecting an ovule to the placenta in an ovary

Gamete a sex cell which, after union with another, develops into a new individual

Gametophyte the haploid plant generation which produces gametes

Gemma a small, budlike structure, formed by certain liverworts, which develops into a new plant

Gene the hereditary unit; most genes are located on chromosomes, but a few are in the cytoplasm; a part of a DNA molecule that codes for a protein that governs one primary function

Genetics the science of hereditary and variation

Genotype The gene complex of an organism: genetic makeup

Genus a group of related species; in the technical name of an organism, the genus is the first of the two names (Binomial)

Geotropism a growth movement, a bending in response to gravity; roots are positively geotropic, shoots negatively

Germination the resumption of growth by a seed, spore, zygote, or other reproductive structure after dormancy

Gills the spore-bearing plates on the undersurface of a mushroom cap (pileus)

Glucose a simple sugar ($C_6H_{12}O_6$), also known as dextrose

Glume an outer bract of a grass spikelet

Grafting the joining of a bud or twig of one plant to the body of another plant

Grain an indehiscent simple fruit of a grass, in which the seed coat is united with the pericarp; a caryopsis

Granum one of the disklike bodies containing chorophyll which is present in a chloroplast

Growth rings a ring of secondary xylem produced in a growing season; annual ring

Guard cell one of two epidermal cells which enclose a stoma

Guttation the loss of liquid water from plants

Gymnosperm a seed plant in which the seeds are not enclosed in ovaries; pine, fir, spruce, and other conifers are examples

Halophyte a plant that grows in brackish coastal water, or other saline or alkaline conditions

Haploid having one whole set of chromosomes (n), as in gametes

Head a dense cluster of flowers on a receptacle, as in sunflower and other composites

Heartwood the darker colored nonconducting wood in a tree trunk which is surrounded on the outside by the lighter colored conducting sapwood

Herb a soft-stemmed plant lacking a persistent stem above ground

Heredity the sum total of characteristics which are transmissible from parents to offspring; traits transmitted

Heterocyst a large colorless cell in the filaments of certain blue-green algae such as *Nostoc* and *Anabaena;* thought to function in nitrogen fixation

Heterogamous producing two kinds of gametes (sperm and egg)

Heterosis hybrid vigor

Heterosporous producing two or more different kinds of spores

Heterozygous having two unlike members of a gene pair, two different alleles

Hilum the scar on a seed coat where the funiculus (stalk) was attached; also the bright center of a starch grain

Holdfast the basal portion of an algal thallus which anchors it to a solid object

Homosporous producing only one kind of spore

Homozygous descriptive of organisms in which both members of a gene pair are identical; hence pure breeding for the trait governed by the gene pair having identical alleles

Hormogonium a fragment of a filament of blue-green algae that serves as a means of asexual reproduction

Hybrid a term applied to progeny whose parents differ from each other in one or more traits

Hybridization the crossing (breeding) of individuals that differ in one or more traits

Hybrid vigor the enhanced vigor of progeny resulting from the crossing of two different inbred plants

Hydathode a pore, generally at the tip of a vein, capable of exuding liquid water

Hydrophyte a plant adapted for growth in water, or in very wet places

Hydrotropism the growth movement in response to unequal distribution of water, as when roots curve toward moist soil

Hypha a filament of the body (mycelium) of a fungus

Hypocotyl the part (stem) of an embryo or seedling that is between the attachment of the cotyledons and the radicle

Hypogynous flower a flower in which the sepals, petals, and stamens originate from the receptacle below the ovary

Imbibition the uptake of a liquid with swelling by a substance such as cellulose, agar, or gelatin, and the release of heat

Imperfect flower a flower lacking either stamens or a pistil

Inbreeding the breeding of closely related organisms; self fertilized flowers

Incomplete flower a flower lacking one or more whorls of floral parts; for example, petals may be absent

Indehiscent refers to a fruit which does not split open at maturity

Indusium a covering over fern sporangia

Inferior ovary an ovary which is below the other floral parts; an inferior ovary results when the floral tube is fused with the ovary

Inflorescence a flower cluster

Inheritance the transmission of characteristics from parents to offspring

Integument the outer layers of an ovule which develops into the seed coat

Interfascicular cambium the vascular cambrium between the vascular bundles

Internode the region of a stem between two successive nodes

Irregular corolla a corolla whose petals are unlike in size and form, as in orchids

Isogamete a gamete that is similar in form and size to the cell with which it unites

Isogamy sexual reproduction involving a fusion of isogametes

Karyolymph nuclear sap

Knot the base of a branch which is embedded in wood of the stem

Lamina a leaf blade

Lateral attached to a side

Lateral bud an axillary bud, that is, a bud in the leaf axil

Late wood the denser wood formed toward the close of a growing season; Summer wood

Leaf a green, thin, expanded organ (blade) attached to a petiole (stalk), and sometimes with stipules (often leaf like) where the petiole joins the stem at the node; has many modifications; the primary function of a leaf is photosynthesis

Leaf bud a bud which develops into a stem bearing leaves

Leaflet one of the parts making up the blade in the compound leaf of a rose and Virginia creeper, for example

Leaf primordium a protuberance, formed at a stem tip, which grows into a leaf

Leaf scar a scar on a stem where a leaf was previously attached

Legume a dry, dehiscent, one-carpelled fruit that splits along two sides; also a member of the pea family (Leguminosae)

Lenticel an opening in the cork of roots and stems through which the exchange of gases occurs

Leucoplast a colorless plastid in which starch is frequently formed

Lignin an organic chemical which occurs in the walls of cells, especially wood cells

Lipase an enzyme which digests fats into fatty acids and glycerol

Maltase an enzyme which hydrolyzes maltose to glucose

Maltose a crystalline sugar with a formula of $C_{12}H_{22}O_{11}$

Megasporangium a spore case producing megaspores

Megaspore the larger spore of the two kinds formed by seed plants and certain other vascular plants produces a female gametophyte

Megasporophyll a modified leaf bearing megasporangia

Meiosis the two divisions which halve the number of chromosomes; the chromosomal number is reduced from the diploid to the haploid number

Meristem a tissue whose cells divide

Mesocarp the middle layer of the pericarp; middle ovary wall

Mesophyll the leaf tissues which contains chlorenchyma, and which are located between the upper and lower epidermis

Mesophyte a plant that grows in moderately moist habitats, neither dry nor extremely wet

Metabolism the sum total of the chemical processes occurring in an organism

Metaphase the stage in mitosis or meiosis when the chromosomes are at the equator

Micropyle a small pore in the integuments and later in the seed coat

Microsporangium a spore case producing microspores

Microspore the smaller of the two kinds of spores formed by seed plants and certain other vascular plants germinating to form male gametophytes

Microsporophyll a modified leaf which bears microsporangia

Middle lamella a layer, usually of calcium pectate, which cements adjacent cell walls together

Mitochondrion an extremely small granular or rod-shaped cytoplasmic body which is the site of enzymes of respiration

Mitosis the division of a nucleus involving the longitudinal splitting of the chromosomes and the regular distribution of chromosome halves to two daughter nuclei; mitosis insures that each of the two resulting nuclei will be exactly like the parent nucleus

Mixed bud a bud that contains both flowers and leaves in an undeveloped condition

Monocotyledon a member of the large group of flowering plants characterized by embryos having one cotyledon

Monohybrid cross a cross between parents which differ in one character

Multiple fruit a fruit formed from many flowers which ripen together; for example, fig and pineapple

Mycelium the mass of filaments (hyphae) which forms the body of a fungus

Naked bud a bud which lacks bud scales

Nectary a glandular structure secreting nectar usually on a flower

Net venation a pattern of leaf veining in which the veins form a network

Nitrification the oxidation by certain bacteria of ammonia and ammonium compounds to nitrates, with nitrites as intermediate substances

Nitrogen fixation the changing of nitrogen gas into compounds of nitrogen which can be used by higher plants

Node the region of the stem where one or more leaves are attached

Nodule enlargements on the roots of certain plants within which are found masses of nitrogen-fixing bacteria

Nucellus the part of an ovule inside the integuments within which the megaspore forms and develops into the female gametophyte

Nucleic acids the structural units of DNA and RNA

Nucleolus the small, spherical, deeply staining body located in the nucleus; a center of RNA synthesis

Nucleoprotein a substance formed by the combination of protein and nucleic acid

Nucleus the more or less spherical protoplasmic structure that contains the chromosomes; it also governs the activities of the cell

Oogamous producing a large, nonmotile egg and a small sperm

Oogonium a one-celled structure in which one or more eggs are produced

Operculum in mosses, the lid or cover of the capsule (sporangium)

Order a taxonomic group including one or more families ranking below a class

Organic compound a compound containing carbon

Osmosis the net movement of water through a differentially permeable membrane from a region of high diffusion pressure to a region of lower diffusion pressure of water

Osmotic concentration the total concentration of solutes

Osmotic pressure the maximum pressure which may develop in a solution separated from pure water by a rigid membrane permeable to water only

Ovary the enlarged, basal portion of a pistil in which ovules develop

Ovule in seed plants, a megasporangium surrounded by one or more integuments; it develops into a seed

Oxidation a loss of electrons; in biology, an energy-yielding process usually resulting from a loss of hydrogens or the addition of oxygen to a compound

Palisade mesophyll a leaf tissue composed of cylindrical cells containing chloroplasts

Palmately compound leaf the leaflets are all attached at the top of the petiole

Palmate venation a type of net venation in which several main veins originate at the base of the leaf blade and radiate outwardly

Paradermal a section of a plant organ such as a leaf cut parallel to the epidermis

Parallel evolution organisms acquire similar characteristics independently of one another though they stem from related ancestral stocks

Parallel venation a type of venation in which the main veins of a leaf are parallel or nearly so

Parenchyma cells which are thin-walled and basically isodiametric; it forms typically a storage tissue like cortex which retains meristemic capabilities

Parthenocarpy the development of fruit without fertilization

Parthenogenesis the development of an embryo from an egg without fertilization

Pathogen a disease-producing organism

Pedicel the stalk of one flower in a cluster

Peduncle the main stalk of a flower cluster or the stalk of an individual flower

Penicillin an antibiotic produced by certain species of *Penicillium,* an Ascomycete

Perennial a plant which lives for more than two years; it usually flowers annually after a period of vegetative growth

Perfect flower a flower having both stamens and a pistil

Perianth collectively the calyx and the corolla

Pericarp the wall of a fruit formed from the ovary wall; the ripened ovary wall

Pericycle the outer layer of the stele located between the endodermis and the phloem; often meristematic

Periderm the outer layer covering an older root and stem, consisting of cork, cork cambium (phellogen), and phelloderm (secondary cortex)

Perigynous a flower whose stamens, sepals, and petals arise from a floral tube which surrounds the ovary

Peristome hygroscopic, bristlelike or toothlike structures around the mouth of a moss capsule

Petal one of the floral leaves of the corolla

Petiole the stalk of a leaf

Phellogen the cork cambium

Phenotype the external appearance of an organism; visible characteristics

Phloem the specialized plant tissue which conducts sugars and other dissolved foods

Phloem ray that portion of the vascular ray which extends through the secondary phloem

Photosynthesis the synthesis of carbohydrates and formation of oxygen from carbon dioxide and water in the presence of chlorophyll, with light being the energy source

Phototropism a growth curvature resulting from unequal light intensities on different sides of a plant organ

Phycology the study of algae

Phylum (division) the major subdivision of the animal kingdom

Pileus the gill-bearing cap of a mushroom

Pinnately compound leaf a compound leaf having leaflets arranged at intervals on each side of a common rachis or central stalk

Pinnate venation a vein arrangement characterized by secondary veins originating at different intervals along a common midvein

Pistil the central part of a flower, composed of one or more carpels, and consisting of a stigma, style, and an ovary which contains ovules

Pistillate flower a flower having a pistil but lacking stamens

Pit a thin area in the cell wall

Pith the tissue composed of parenchyma cells in the center of a stem; also present in certain roots

Pith Ray parenchyma cells extending from the pith between the vascular bundles of stems serving for lateral conduction

Placenta the part of the ovary wall which bears an ovule or ovules

Plankton the floating or free-swimming organisms, usually of microscopic size, of lakes, oceans, and other aquatic habitats

Plant pathology the study of plant diseases

Plasma membrane the outermost layer of cytoplasm which is differentially permeable

Plasmodesmata thin protoplasmic strands extending from cell to cell

Plasmodium the multinucleate, naked mass of protoplasm of a slime mold

Plasmolysis the osmotic loss of water from a cell with a resultant shrinkage of the protoplast from the cell wall

Plastid a specialized protoplasmic body suspended in the cytoplasm

Plumule another name for the epicotyl of an embryo

Polar nuclei the two nuclei in the center of the embryo sac, which unite with a sperm to form a usually triploid endosperm nucleus that develops into the endosperm tissue of the seed

Pollen grains the developing male gametophytes of seed plants

Pollen tube the tubular outgrowth of a pollen grain which carries the sperm to the egg

Pollination in angiosperms, the transfer of pollen from an anther to a stigma, or in gymnosperms, from a microsporangium to an ovule

Polyploid a cell with more than two whole sets of chromosomes

Pome a fleshy, apple-like fruit which develops from an epigynous flower in which the floral tube is fused with the ovary

Pore an opening in the end wall of a xylem vessel or seive tube element

Primary phloem the first-formed phloem, differentiated from cells formed by an apical meristem

Primary xylem the first-formed xylem, differentiated from cells formed by an apical meristem

Procambium a strand of immature cells, derived from the apical meristem, which differentiates into primary xylem and phloem

Propagation increasing plant numbers by cuttings, bulbs, tubers, and other parts without using seeds

Prophase the first stage of mitosis or meiosis; during the prophase of mitosis the chromosomes become fully formed with two chromatids and then move to the equator

Protease an enzyme which digests proteins

Protein a class of foods composed of carbon, hydrogen, oxygen, nitrogen, and often sulfur and phosporus; proteins are formed from amino acids

Prothallus the gametophyte of ferns and similar plants

Protonema a branched filament which develops from a spore in mosses; buds formed on the protonema develop into leafy gametophytes

Protoplasm the living matter in plant and animal cells

Protoplast the cell, exclusive of the cell wall

Pyrenoid a starch-forming proteinaceous body on chloroplasts of certain algae

Raceme an indeterminate inflorescence having a main stalk (peduncle) bearing unbranched pedicels, each of which is terminated by a flower

Rachis the extension of the petiole which bears the leaflets

Radial section a longitudinal section of a root or stem cut along a radius

Radicle the lower part of the embryo axis which develops into the root when the seed germinates

Receptacle the top of a floral axis from which the floral parts arise

Recessive gene a gene whose expression is masked when a dominant gene is also present

Reduction division also known as meiosis; cells produced by reduction division have just one set of chromosomes

Regular corolla a corolla whose petals are alike in size and shape

Respiration the release of energy from foods through a complex series of biological reactions; in aerobic respiration, glucose and oxygen are used, and carbon dioxide and water are formed

Rhizoid a hairlike absorbing and anchoring structure on a gametophyte of moss, liverwort, fern, or similar plant

Rhizome a horizontal stem at or below ground level from which shoots grow upward, and roots grow into the soil

Ribose nucleic acid (RNA) the nucleic acid found in the nucleolus and cytoplasm; it carries genetic information to the ribosomes where it becomes involved in protein synthesis

Ribosome submicroscopic granules located in the endoplasmic reticulum; they contain RNA, and are the main site for protein synthesis

Root cap a thimblelike, protective mass of cells over the root apex; it develops from the apical meristem

Root hair a tubular outgrowth from a root epidermal cell which increases the absorbing area of the root

Runner a slender horizontal stem growing over or above the soil surface, and which frequently develops roots and upright shoots at the nodes

Samara an indehiscent, dry, winged fruit as a maple

Sapwood the outermost wood of a tree, generally light in color, which conducts water and minerals

Sclerenchyma heavy-walled cells, usually either fibers or stone cells

Secondary cell wall the wall formed inside the primary cell wall found in sclerenchyma cells

Secondary tissue tissue produced by the vascular cambium or cork cambium; xylem formed by the cambium is secondary xylem, and phloem so formed is secondary phloem

Seed the characteristic reproductive structure of seed plants which consists of an embryo, a seed coat, and a supply of food that in some species is stored in the endosperm; a seed develops from an ovule

Seed coat the outermost layer of the seed which develops from the integuments of the ovule

Sepal one of the modified leaves of the calyx, which, in a complete flower, is the outermost whorl of floral parts, and is generally green in color

Sessile lacking a stalk

Seta the stalk that supports the capsule of a moss sporophyte

Sexual reproduction reproduction resulting from the fusion of gametes (sex cells)

Shoot a collective term for a stem and its leaves

Sieve tube a food-conducting tube of the phloem consisting of sieve tube cells arranged end-to-end

Sieve tube element an elongated phloem cell having perforated end walls (sieve plates)

Simple fruit a fruit formed from one ovary

Simple leaf a leaf with an undivided blade

Softwood wood lacking vessels, as in wood of conifers

Solute a substance dissolved in a solvent

Solvent a liquid in which other substances are dissolved

Soredium a lichen reproductive structure consisting of fungal hyphae enclosing some algal cells

Sorus a cluster of sporangia on the lower surface of a fern leaf

Species a unit of classification consisting of a group of closely related individuals resembling one another in most characters; the members of a species interbreed freely and share a common origin

Sperm the male gamete

Spike an inflorescence with sessile (lacking a stalk) flowers upon an elongated axis

Spindle a fibrous structure appearing during nuclear division which brings about the regular distribution of the chromosomes to the poles

Spirillum a spiral or corkscrew-shaped bacterial cell

Spongy mesophyll cells more or less rounded, green leaf cells, usually located below the palisade cells

Sporangiophore the stalk which bears a sporangium

Sporangium a case in which spores are produced

Spore an asexual, microscopic, reproductive structure made up of one cell

Spore mother cell a diploid cell which undergoes meiosis to form four haploid spores

Sporophore a spore-bearing structure of a fungus

Sporophyll a leaf which bears sporangia containing spores

Sporophyte the diploid, spore-producing generation of a plant

Spring wood the more porous wood of an annual ring which is formed early in the growing season; Early wood

Stamen the pollen-producing organ of a flower, made up of an anther and a filament

Staminate cone a gymnosperm cone which produces pollen grains

Staminate flower a flower having stamens but no pistil

Starch a complex, insoluble carbohydrate built up from many molecules of glucose, principal plant storage product

Stele the portion of a root or stem in which the conducting tissues are located; included in the stele are the pericycle, vascular tissue, and, when present, pith

Sterigma a narrow, pointed stalk located on a basidium bearing a spore

Stigma the upper part of a pistil which receives pollen

Stipe the stalk that supports a mushroom cap; also the stalk in larger brown algae, and the petiole of a fern frond

Stipule an appendage located near the base of a petiole

Stolon a trailing above ground stem, or a hypha which gives rise to erect branches

Stoma a pore in the epidermis of a leaf or young stem which is surrounded by two guard cells

Streptococcus coccus cells that divide in one plane and adhere to form chains that are sometimes curved; many are pathogenic

Strobilus a number of sporophylls or ovule-bearing scales grouped terminally on a stem to form a cone

Style the part of a pistil between the stigma and the ovary

Suberin a waxy substance deposited in cell walls of cork

Succession an orderly sequence of different plant communities in an area; one community replaces another until the climax is reached

Sucrase an enzyme which changes sucrose to glucose and fructose

Summer wood the harder, less porous wood of an annual ring which was formed during the late season; late wood

Superior ovary an ovary located above where the other floral parts originate

Suspensor a row of cells forming an elongated structure to which an embryo is attached; or a hyphal branch connecting the zygote to the mycelium

Symbiosis an intimate association of two or more species resulting in mutual benefit

Sympetalous flower a flower having united petals

Synergid one of the two cells situated on each side of the egg in an embryo sac

Tangenital section a longitudinal section of a stem or root cut at right angles to a radius

Tap-root system a root system characterized by a large primary root which penetrates deeply into the soil, and which bears distinctly smaller branch roots

Taxonomy the science of naming and classifying organisms

Telophase the last stage in mitosis during which two new nuclei become reorganized

Tendril a slender structure which coils around an object and aids in supporting the stem; a tendril may be a modified stem, leaf, leaflet, or stipule

Testa the seed coat, a structure which develops from the integument or integuments of an ovule

Tetraploid a plant with four whole sets of chromosomes (4n)

Thallus a simple plant body which is not differentiated into true roots, stems, and leaves; for example, the bodies of algae and fungi

Thigmotropism a bending growth movement in response to contact

Thorn a pointed, hard, modified branch

Thylakoid one of the membranes in chloroplasts

Tissue a group of cells having a similar origin and function, and usually a similar structure

Trachea a vessel cell whose end walls have pores

Tracheid a water-conducting and strengthening cell in the xylem; a tracheid is a long, thick-walled cell with tapering ends

Translocation the movement of materials from one part of a plant to another

Transpiration the loss of water vapor from plant parts chiefly through stomata and lenticels

Transverse section a section of a plant organ cut at right angles to the long axis; a cross section

Tree a woody plant with one main stem (trunk) rising from the ground

Triploid an organism with three whole sets of chromosomes (3n)

Tropism a bending growth induced by a unilateral stimulus such as light or gravity

Tube nucleus the nucleus in a pollen tube which directs the growth of the tube

Tuber a swollen, underground, food-storing stem bearing buds; for example, a potato tuber

Tundra a treeless area in high latitudes or high altitudes which has permanently frozen subsoil; the plants of the tundra are dwarfed

Turgid applied to a cell or tissue which is plump because of the internal pressure resulting from the osmotic uptake of water

Turgor pressure the outward pressure on the cell walls as a consequence of osmotic uptake of water

Umbel an indeterminate inflorescence having the pedicels of the flowers radiating from about the same place at the top of the main axis

Unicellular refers to an organism which consists of a single cell

Unisexual either male or female, not hermaphroditic

Vacuolar membrane the cytoplasmic membrane bordering a vacuole; Tonoplast

Vacuole a space in the cytoplasm, usually filled with cell sap

Variation a deviation from the norm in the anatomical, physiological, or genetic charcteristics of an organism

Vascular bundle a strand of xylem and phloem with or without a cambium

Vascular ray an aggregation of cells extending radially through the xylem and phloem, and serving for lateral conduction

Vascular tissue conducting tissue

Vegetative not concerned with sexual reproduction

Vegetative organs organs concerned chiefly with the development of the individual, instead of with reproduction

Vegetative propagation plant reproduction using vegetative organs

Vein a vascular bundle in a leaf, petal, or other expanded organ

Venation the arrangement of veins in a leaf

Venter the swollen basal part of an archegonium containing an egg

Vessel a tubelike structure in the xylem for water conduction that is formed from a vertical series of cells whose end walls are partially or completely dissolved to form pores

Vessel element one of the cells in a vessel; it's a somewhat elongated, pitted, thick-walled sclerenchyma cell in which the end walls are gone

Volva a cuplike structure at the base of the stipe or stalk of some mushrooms such as the *Amanita* species

Whorled leaf arrangement an arrangement in which three or more leaves occur at each node

Wilt   a limp or flaccid condition resulting from a deficiency of water and a low turgor pressure within cells

Wood   technically, wood is xylem, which is the principal water-conducting tissue in plants

Woody   a plant or plant organ that has considerable secondary xylem, and lives for more than one year

Xanthophyllis   yellow or orange carotenoid pigments associated with chlorophyll in chloroplasts; also present in certain chromoplasts

Xerophyte   a plant with structural and physiological features which permit it to grow in a dry habitat

Xylem   the woody portion of the conducting tissue which is specialized for the conduction of water and mineral salts

Xylem ray   the part of a vascular ray located in the xylem; the xylem ray conducts water, minerals, and foods across the xylem

Zoosporangium   a spore case in which zoospores are produced

Zoospore   a swimming spore

Zygospore   a thick-walled resistant spore developed from a zygote as a result of the fusion of gametes

Zygote   a diploid cell produced by the fusion of two gametes; a fertilized egg

Index

Bold-faced type indicates an illustration